SECOND EDITION

HUMAN EVOLUTION

READINGS IN PHYSICAL ANTHROPOLOGY

Edited by

NOEL KORN
Los Angeles Valley College

and

FRED W. THOMPSON
San Fernando Valley State College

HOLT, RINEHART AND WINSTON, INC.

New York • Chicago • San Francisco • Atlanta • Dallas • Montreal
Toronto • London

Dedicated to
HARRY REECE SMITH
1906-1962

PREFACE

This collection of readings will acquaint the beginning student in physical anthropology with the different lines of evidence that provide a unified view of the processes and results of human evolution. Studies in genetics, ecology, and archeology, field studies of primate behavior, descriptions and interpretations of the fossil record, experimental studies in human adaptation, and descriptions of population differences all form the subject matter of modern evolutionary research by anthropologists, and in this volume we have tried to include examples of all of these studies.

Scientists establish generalizations concerning the relationships among phenomena by use of the experimental method. Indeed, it can be said that each of the sciences has been successful in generating theories and in finding facts to the extent that it has relied on experiments. At first, it might be thought that physical anthropologists cannot utilize the experimental method in the study of human evolution. Fossils must be recovered, and conclusions drawn about their significance. This process would seem to obviate the use of experiment.

However, this is not really true at all: at least it is not true for modern studies of human evolution. The processes of evolution—the "how" of evolution—*can* be studied in the laboratory. In fact, the synthesis of knowledge about evolutionary processes—mutation, recombination, selection, drift, and hybridization—which has been gained largely through laboratory studies and the descriptive studies of fossils, has proved to be very fruitful in providing our present picture of human evolution and in integrating the study of human culture and human evolutionary biology into a single discipline, anthropology.

In this collection, Part One: The Scope and Aims of Physical Anthropology consists of an article giving an overview of the interests and methods that characterize contemporary anthropological research in human evolution based on the synthesis of knowledge about the processes of evolution.

It used to be thought that if only there were enough fossils, the course of human evolution would become clear. Thus for a long time, anthropologists relied primarily on fossil-collecting and the comparison of fossils with living forms of man and his closest relatives, the apes. Yet it is now evident that the fossil record itself is simply not enough; recovering fossils is very important, but the fossil record must be interpreted according to rules and principles that are not at all apparent in the study of the fossils themselves. This is the rationale for selection of the articles in Part Two: Evolution, Genetics, and Natural Selection. Here we can obtain some insight into the principles and agencies of biological evolution as geneticists and other evolutionary biologists have been able to establish them.

Defined biologically, man is what he is, not simply in terms of the body structures that differentiate him from other forms, but also in terms of his behavior. "Man is a cultural animal" sums it up, but the evolutionary anthropologist is interested in tracing the ways in which particular populations of animals came, in the course of time, to be arrays of human bodies behaving in human ways. The dynamics of human evolution, the part that the capacity for culture has played in human evolution, are discussed by the authors of the articles in Part Three: The Dynamics of Hominid Evolution.

The interest of anthropologists in the evolution of behavior has led to a need to know more about the behavior of monkeys, apes, and other nonhuman primates. Reconstructing the origins of human behavior depends upon an understanding of the nature of the prehuman behavioral base from which behavior must have evolved. The articles in Part Four: Studies of Primates are field-study reports of primates and interpretations of the relation of infrahuman primate behavior studies to the evolution of man.

In Part Five: Interpreting Fossil Man, the student can become acquainted with some of the problems of describing and interpreting the fossil record of human evolution. Natural selection as the prime evolutionary force in the evolution of human form is the major principle enabling paleontologists and archeologists to make sense out of the welter of bone fragments and broken artifacts that makes up their respective raw data.

In the same way, natural selection is the clarifying principle in understanding differences among modern human populations or races. It used to be thought that the small-scale changes differentiating populations developed through the operation of one set of rules, while the large-scale changes that differentiated man from other animals operated according to another. Here again, the synthesis of genetic evolutionary research with the traditional interest of physical anthropologists in racial differences has produced a new understanding of how populations within the species have come to differ from one another. We may also be able to assess more clearly the significance of these differences. In Part Six: Race and Raciation, the articles reflect this approach to race differences. Moreover, in anthropology, no less than in other disciplines, techniques of research are very important. Accordingly, we have included an article by Paul T. Baker as an example of technique and methodology in the study of human adaptive differences.

Evolution is a continuous process, and natural selection did not simply "occur" in the past as a series of bio-historical events. The concluding section of the book, Part Seven: Is Man Still Evolving? consists of two articles that provide a basis for identifying some of the possible directions of present and future human evolution.

The task of editing a collection of articles such as this for the use of beginning students is as much a question of what not to include as it is one of what to choose. In looking over the possibilities among the publications of the last decade or so, we were surprised at how many papers, originally written for scientific audiences, lent themselves to reprinting for elementary students in physical anthropology. Other editors might easily have chosen the same number of other equally useful selections.

We have had to treat the problem of bibliography more harshly than we would have liked. Regretfully, but firmly, we have eliminated all bibliographic references in each article. Advanced students will wish to consult the original publications; elementary students will find the suggested readings at the end of each part adequate for their needs in pursuing the ideas developed by the authors in that part.

The editors wish to express their gratitude to the anthropologists and teachers who have made helpful suggestions and comments: Sherwood L. Washburn, Jane Lancaster, Gabriel W. Lasker, Joseph B. Birdsell, Mildred Wissler, Merle I. Kuhner, and C. Loring Brace. Appreciation is expressed to Jacqueline Hetrick for her excellent drawings and charts which have contributed much to this volume. The editors also wish to thank their wives, June Korn and Phyllis Thompson, who provided endless help and encouragement in the preparation of the manuscript.

And, lastly, we again should like to thank all our students whose enthusiasm in our anthropology classes stimulated us to believe that there might be room for another volume on the science of man.

N. K.
F. W. T.

NORTHRIDGE, CALIFORNIA
APRIL 1967

CONTENTS

PART ONE

THE SCOPE
AND AIMS
OF PHYSICAL
ANTHROPOLOGY

The greater part of this collection of readings is devoted to articles that illustrate the ways in which physical anthropologists deal with human biology and human evolution. Like other social and life sciences, anthropology has undergone remarkable changes in the last few decades. As a matter of fact, it is only recently that physical anthropologists have actually begun to define their field of research and the problems that they are investigating.

Of course, physical anthropologists have traditionally been interested in the human fossil record and the differences and similarities among living humans. This interest was supported by detailed descriptions—chiefly of bones—and by the construction of theories of fossil man as well as of the "races" of men that bore very little resemblance to the kind of theory-building that was going on in the other life sciences, which were aided by discoveries in genetics and evolutionary process.

Today the study of human evolution is proceeding along lines that reflect a synthesis of the newer biochemical, genetic, and ecological approaches with the traditional concerns of physical anthropology. For instance, contemporary anthropological research in the human blood groups, the hemoglobins, and the haptoglobins requires an understanding of genetics and biochemistry, whereas the roots of anatomical anthropology stretch back to the nineteenth century. The addition of new methods of studying man has broadened the field of anthropology tremendously and opened the way to the treatment of new problems.

The first article in this collection deals with the interests of physical anthropologists as viewed by the eminent researcher Gabriel W. Lasker. In this selection, ''The 'New' Physical Anthropology Seen in Retrospect and Prospect,'' the reader will find a description of the various kinds of physical anthropological research. He will learn what anthropologists do and with what problems of human evolution and human differences they have concerned themselves.

1

THE "NEW"
PHYSICAL ANTHROPOLOGY
SEEN IN RETROSPECT
AND PROSPECT

Gabriel W. Lasker

Gabriel W. Lasker is editor of Human Biology *and Professor
of Anatomy in the College of Medicine at Wayne State
University in Detroit, Michigan. In the following article,
he surveys the different interests within the subdivisions of
physical anthropology and describes the kinds of research underway in each specialty. Such a general description is perhaps as
close as we are able to come to a definition of physical anthropology.*

I

"The New Physical Anthropology" is a term coined by S. L. Washburn in 1951 to refer to the study of the mechanism of human evolution:
the experimental study of adaptive functions and the application of
population genetics to an understanding of their evolution. The concept
was controversial from the start; no one wants his research to be excluded
from the main stream and labeled as "old hat." Furthermore, others
have since staked claim to the "newest" physical anthropology. It is
probably time for an inclusive definition of physical anthropology, and
an attempt to chart current trends.

Physical anthropology is a way of looking at problems in human
biology.

Some regard physical anthropology merely as whatever physical an-

(From *The Centennial Review of Arts and Sciences*. Michigan State University, 1964, pages 348–366. By permission of the author and the publisher.)

thropologists study, but that leaves one with the antecedent question: what is a physical anthropologist? By any definition some persons trained as physical anthropologists are practicing other professions whereas many persons trained in biology, medicine, or general anthropology are practicing physical anthropologists. The boundaries of the subject can not be defined in this way.

Another suggested definition is that physical anthropology is a species-limited branch of zoology limited to a single taxon (like ornithology, lepidoptery, or icthyology). But this is both too broad and too narrow a view: there are many anatomists, geneticists, pathologists, and others whose work is limited to man, but who are not concerned with anthropology. Likewise, there are significant concerns with problems far from the human species which are part of physical anthropology. Thus, the functional anatomy of locomotion in non-human mammals, the dating of climatic changes during the Pleistocene Epoch, and the distribution of malaria and mosquitoes that carry it can be vital questions for physical anthropology.

No single problem holds the field together, although a case can be made that the concept of organic evolution is usually not far from sight. Thus the interest in laboratory tests of locomotion in non-human mammals may be aimed at understanding which anatomical adaptations would have to be lost and which gained to transform a quadruped into a functional bipedal form. Climatic changes during the Pleistocene Epoch would relate to emergence of particular types of fossil man and their survival, migrations, and intermating. And the interest in malaria and its vector, the mosquito, lies in the fact that man has evolved a number of adaptations to this disease (the adaptations are apparently different for different types of malaria).

Historically, human evolution, past and potential, has been a central problem of physical anthropology, but I do not think it is an essential aspect.

Human biology is the zoology that treats of man—especially of man in the mass, causes and correlates of the similarities and differences between groups of different age, sex, origin, or way of life. And the specifically anthropological contribution to these studies is a method: the open-ended method by which meaningful influences are sought in the widest possible frames of reference. Physical anthropology's contribution lies especially in investigating the effects on human biology of those very diverse and peculiarly human modes of learned behavior which we call *culture*. The question of the use of hand tools is thus part of the story of anatomical transformations from quadrupedal to two-footed human bipedalism. Types of clothing, shelter, and the keeping of fires by different types of hominoids of the Pleistocene Epoch no doubt helped determine who survived what climates.

In the more restricted field of the human biology of the living, it is physical anthropology which asks, even when it can not answer, such questions as: why do certain peoples beat drums to induce a trance during magical practice of spirit possession? Does the fast drum beat itself help induce the physiological state? How small and isolated would human groups have to be for them to diverge significantly in their genetic endowments merely through the chance of certain genetic predispositions happening to occur more often in offspring of one group, less often in offspring of another? How can one explain the tendency for inhabitants of cold localities to be heavier relative to their height than denizens of deserts and tropics? Is it due to the need, in cold regions, for a relatively small surface area which will radiate less heat? Where this relationship of body build to climate fails to hold, such as in the mountainous zones of Central and South America, does it depend on chronic food deprivation there?

The old, purely descriptive and speculative methods of physical anthropology are giving way to an emphasis on problems and tests. It would be a mistake, however, to give the impression that old-fashioned physical anthropology, the description and measurement of human beings and their remains, has completely given place to a new dynamic functional anthropology. Even aside from the problems of ancient man and fossil hominoids, the methods of anthroposcopy and anthropometry (man viewing and man measurement) are still of interest and have a continuing methodological validity. Indeed, it is impossible to draw a sharp line of distinction between old-fashioned methods and newfangled concepts. The former often supply the very data needed to test the latter. Nevertheless, of nine topics into which physical anthropology of the living can arbitrarily be divided, the first five seem closer to the descriptive facts than the other four. These older interests include the majority of works in five fields: (1) the form of bones and teeth; (2) determination of age, race, and sex from bones and teeth; (3) human growth; (4) body composition; and (5) body build and applications to human engineering of knowledge of the spaces occupied by the human form.

The number of "dynamic" topics is much more indefinite, the number depending on what one includes and on how one divides them up. These are sometimes referred to as the new or the newest physical anthropology, the newness depending on how superficially one studies their history and how cavalierly one dismisses the forerunners of these lines of thought. For the most part, they bear intellectual kinship to the "new synthesis," the marriage of evolutionary theory and the concepts of genetics. They encompass: (6) blood group studies; (7) biochemical human genetics, especially of so-called polymorphisms; (8) analysis of evolutionary factors such as, (a) mutation, (b) continuing natural selection, (c) random genetic drift, and (d) gene flow; and (9) studies of living non-human primates, notably in respect to blood groups, genetics, and local evolutionary factors, but also in respect to the behavior of monkeys and apes and its relevance for evolutionary problems.

II

(1) *Bones and teeth.* The anthropologists' special stake in studies of these structures stems initially from the fact that they are the hardest tissues in the body (one can strike sparks with steel on dental enamel). They are, therefore, the only parts usually fossilized. But studies of these tissues have other advantages: the density of bones means that they cast clear X-ray shadows and can be studied on the living as well as the dead. Erupted teeth of the living are even easier to compare with those of the dead. The relative rigidity of bone (despite the active metabolism of this tissue) makes it form a sort of permanent imprint of the biological experience of the individual. Childhood diseases are reflected in radiologically dense lines in the parts of the shafts of long bones which were at the growth plane at the time of the disease. Evidences of hypoplasia of the enamel of teeth occupy similar sites where growth was active at the time of the disease. The practice of many peoples of the world of deliberately binding an infant's head, or even the practices of swaddling and cradling which may require him to sleep in a fixed position, cause changes in shape and proportion of the skull which last throughout life. But perhaps the most remarkable imprinting on the bones and teeth is that of inheritance. There are resemblances between parents and offspring in details of form in the skull and other bones. Monozygous (single egg) twins are very similar to each other in these respects so we know that the traits are largely inherited even though they are often difficult to define precisely and their modes of inheritance are still poorly known. In the case of teeth, the evidence is a little better: absence of particular teeth, such as the lateral incisors, is inherited directly from parents to children with few skipped generations. Some other less drastic modifications of teeth and jaws, such as protrusions of teeth (extra cusps, enamel pearls) or bones (so-called tori of palate and mandible), also have a genetic component.

The members of the populations of the main land masses of the earth, the major racial groups, also tend to differ in respect to bony characters: prognathic protruding front teeth in Africa south of the Sahara, Japan, much of India, and parts of China; flat facial bones with little protrusion of the center of the facial skeleton throughout the Far East; prominent nasal bones in Europe, the Near East, and North Africa. Studies of disinterred skeletons show that these and similar traits have persisted from ancient times in these peoples. Physical anthropologists continue to study the extent to which the traits have a genetic basis and the light they cast on the biological origins of man in one area of the world's surface or another.

(2) *Determination of age, sex, and race.* Age, sex, and (as already noted) racial origin leave their imprint on bones. Since almost all biological variables in man show some correlation with these three factors, anthropologists have always found it necessary to specify their material in terms of these (or in terms of two of these if the third constituted the unknown factor under study). Surprisingly, an occasional investigation in medicine omits adequately to take into account possible influences of this kind (such as a difference in response to particular drugs which correlates with geographical origins). But in general these factors are universally introduced into studies of human biology. In anthropological studies of skeletons retrieved from excavations, the ascription of age, sex, and race is a matter of interpretation. The search for the skeletal hallmarks of age, sex, and race, and the careful study of their correlation with other biological processes such as maturational phenomena and disease, so necessary in historical anthropology, also have their applications in forensic (legal) medicine. The identification of a skull unearthed by a bulldozer as that of an ancient American Indian has more than once permitted the authorities to rule out the likelihood that they were dealing with a case of foul play—at least of foul play still requiring apprehension of the perpetrator. Age changes in the skeleton and their relationship to chronological age have important theoretical and clinical implications. The progressively younger age at which maturation takes place in the Western World represents a reversal in evolutionary terms since man is the slowest maturing of the mammals. The earlier age of onset of degenerative changes in the vertebral column of Eskimos, for instance, leads to the exploration of the Eskimo way of squatting and working as well as to Eskimo diet and inheritance in the search for the etiology of these particular ailments of the back.

(3) *Human growth.* A special and well developed discipline, embryology, concerns itself with early developmental phenomena, but the late fetal and postnatal changes, for the most part quantitative rather than, as in the case of the earliest stages, qualitative, have been left to a small group of physical anthropologists and other scholars to unravel.

Time trends are a type of statistical analysis requiring complex procedures and, in the case of human growth, sequential studies of the same individuals over an extended period of time. All too often, after many years of work, it turns out that some of the critical factors have been omitted from the study. Such considerations have led to the development of a strategy based on a continuing periodic study of individuals in a stable non-migratory population. Such a study usually includes a fixed schedule of bodily measurements, X-rays, and photographs of various segments of the body, records of eruption of teeth, age of menarche, etc. But the key to accomplishment in this type of study has been a super-imposed fluidity of problem. Biochemical, physiological, dietary, endo-crinological, psychological, and other aspects of development are attacked as the researchers recognize the problems. Garn and Shamir, in describing their experiences at the Fels Research Institute, evaluate this strategy, that incorporates a rigid backbone of basic data and more ''loosely jointed'' members, by a research staff who will seize on new research leads as they arise.

(4) *Body composition.* Like the study of growth, that of body composition is one in which anthropologists are usually associated with an interdisciplinary team. The body contains fat, bone, metabolizing tissues, water, etc., and the ratios of some of these, such as body fat and electrolytic balance, have direct relevance to state of health. The methods used in these studies have recently been reviewed by Brožek and Henschal. They include radiographic estimation of subcutaneous fatty tissue, skin-fold thickness and other body measurements, dissection and weighing of parts of cadavers, underwater weighing, gas displacement, tracer elements, and statistical analysis of the interrelationship of measurements made by these diverse methods.

(5) *Body build.* Aside from body composition, the distribution of tissues on the human form clearly has significance for bodily performance and health. Unfortunately these factors have so far proven refractory to satisfactory observation and analysis. Certain relatively subjective methods such as constitutional typing have been refined and somewhat objectified by the use of standardized nude photographs and measurements. But the resultant observations are difficult to standardize, and so little is known of the cause and course of body form (except to some extent in respect to superficial fat) that data are hard to group, and correlations hard to interpret. The integration of these studies with those of human composition provides some promise for advance. In addition, form in its external aspect is of increasing practical significance. In a space craft the man space is a critical element. Not only static displacement, but work space—what a man can reach to work—are primary considerations of capsule design. In this applied field of anthropology and anatomy the traditional anthropometer soon gives way to the mock-up and the model.

III

(6) *Blood groups.* Blood group anthropology is almost synonymous with genetic anthropology. Aside from rare variants, a dozen distinct blood-group systems are known. These are: ABO, Rh, Lutheran, Duffy, Kidd, Kell, MNSs, P, Diego, Sutter, Lewis, and the sex-linked Xg. These systems consist of allelic or, according to one view, very closely linked genes. All sorts of anthropological principles are exemplified by these blood group systems. They are polymorphisms. That is, the alternatives to the most frequently found blood group in each of these systems occur, at least in some populations, at frequencies too great to be accounted for by repeated mutations alone. So far only three genetic linkages in man that are carried on chromosomes other than the sex chromosomes are definitely known: all involve blood groups. The blood groups and other genetic traits that are regularly penetrant, i.e., expressed in all individuals who have certain genetic constitutions, have a special value in determining genetic relationships. Since genetic relationship implies similarity in the genetic code, characteristics such as blood groups which, because of high penetrance, directly reflect the code and represent many symbols in the code, give the most valid measure of relationships. Of course it need not follow that the more blood group genes two people share, the more recent their common origins. But it is true that similarities of populations in respect to the frequencies of the genes for various blood groups constitute a very fundamental measure of likeness.

Blood groups are not simply meaningless markers on the code, significant merely in the tracing of racial types. The independence of the various systems permits a multidimensional analysis. One can project frequencies of blood group genes in such "mixed" peoples as Brazilians, Puerto Ricans, Dominicans, Black Caribs, American Negroes, Cherokee Indians, etc., against the frequencies for Europeans, Africans, and putatively unmixed American Indians, of the groups most similar to the probable ancestors. Several formulae have been devised for the calculation of the percentages of contribution of each ancestral group on the basis of such data. When the frequencies of a number of different genes are examined in this way, the findings are sometimes quite dissimilar for different blood group systems. Thus the proportion of African ancestry might be calculated at one figure on the basis of the gene for blood group Rh° and at another on that for U or Hunter or Henshaw. One explanation may lie in the fact that although the present populations may be large enough to yield adequately large samples for statistical purposes, the first contact generation or the intervening generations may have seen sharp drops in population size (often as a result of introduction of new diseases or exploitative political and economic policies which so often marked the contacts of Europeans with members of other groups). In such periods of population constriction, the sampling variance of gene frequencies would be great and chance deviations from expected results might constitute large divergences in different directions in different blood group systems.

Besides random divergences, however, it may be that the very diseases and deaths in contact situations of which we have spoken may not occur at random in individuals of different blood groups. It is well known that certain genotypes may be selected for survival, for instance through the maternal-fetal incompatibility that occurs when Rh-negative women mate with Rh-positive men. Furthermore, although the evidence is less certain, there may well be differences, depending on blood groups, in disease-specific morbidity and moribundity. It should be noted that the differences in these respects are so small that legitimate doubts have been expressed concerning the validity of the statistics, but it should also be mentioned that a very small selective advantage, quite possibly too small to demonstrate statistically, might well lead to modification of gene frequencies in a dozen generations or so (the approximate span of time involved in most of the mixed peoples of the New World).

From the foregoing it should be clear that besides being widely used to unravel the relationships between peoples, blood group studies are even more significantly, as we shall consider again later, being applied to the study of the dynamics by which the diversity of mankind has been achieved, maintained, and modified. In the last two years somewhat over 15 per cent of the contents of the *American Journal of Physical Anthropology* have been devoted to blood group anthropology. Although a major fraction, this represents a decrease from the previous few years, since purely descriptive and methodological articles on this subject are now more often published elsewhere, and most of the recent reports on blood groups in the *American Journal of Physical Anthropology* deal with wider anthropological considerations.

(7) *Biochemical human genetics.* Biochemical human genetics is nearly as old as modern genetics. A number of diseases exist in which the dysfunction results from the lack of a genetically determined enzyme. What is perhaps of more anthropological interest is the discovery of balanced polymorphic systems. One genetic type does not tend to displace all others as classic Darwinian theory would suggest. Instead, a high frequency of variants probably results from the fact that individuals who are heterozygous have some advantage in fertility or resistance to disease. Thus, those who inherit different genetic capacities from their mother than from their father are in some ways better endowed to survive and reproduce. Unlike the deliberate breeding to produce hybrid corn,

human beings breed more or less at random in respect to genetic endowment. The advantageous heterozygotes are therefore always in a minority if only two alternatives are possible. Because of the evolutionary imperative, balanced polymorphisms must therefore tend to develop into multi-allelic systems, and also must tend to be replaced by genes which can do the same work in homozygous condition in all members of the population. The balance of a balanced polymorphism may itself be in flux, giving way to simple dominants while new polymorphisms develop.

The best-known case of balanced polymorphism involves human hemoglobins. Many aberrant hemoglobins are now known. Chemically, they differ in very small respects, the substitution of a different amino acid in a specific peptide of one of the polypeptide chains of which the hemoglobin molecule is composed; these specific changes are controlled by genes—presumably a very limited and specific segment of the nucleic acid of the genetic code. When an individual is homozygous and inherits from both parents the same gene for one of the aberrant hemoglobins, the individual has a severe anemia. Thus, for instance, persons homozygous for hemoglobin S, the one that causes sickle-shaped red blood cells, are diseased and usually die at a young age. But if the individual is heterozygous, the usual adult type (A), hemoglobin is synthesized in adequate amounts to maintain ordinary red cell function (the transport of oxygen from the lung to the tissues of the body). Furthermore, the heterozygous SA individuals have a greater resistance to malaria. The S hemoglobin in this combination apparently provides an unfavorable environment for the plasmodium organism of falciparum malaria. In certain regions of the tropics where man has cut down the forests and planted crops and provided conditions for malaria-carrying by mosquitoes, large proportions of the population carry the gene for hemoglobin S. Apparently deaths from homozygous SS anemic individuals born to AS X AS matings are balanced by deaths of AA individuals from malaria, so the relatively high frequency of the S gene is maintained. The same situation probably holds for hemoglobin C, and for thalassemia (the Mediterranean anemia).

An even more complicated case, also possibly involving resistance to malaria to judge from the world distribution of the gene, is that of glucose-6-phosphate dehydrogenase deficiency, called G-6-PD, or simply enzyme deficiency. This particular deficiency depends on a sex-linked gene which affects males who carry it on their X-chromosome, females who carry it on both of their X-chromosomes and, to a variable extent, some females who have the gene in a single dose on one X-chromosome. The deficiency was first discovered when it was noticed that about 10 per cent of American Negro soldiers developed severe anemia following administration of an antimalarial drug called Primaquine. Many other drugs have the same effect and so does one common food, the broad bean or fava bean. The enzyme deficiency may not be a single entity in the genetic sense and there is even some doubt about its role in respect to malaria, but again the most plausible explanation of the different frequencies of the trait in different places is a balanced polymorphism dependent on exposure to malaria and the presence of food plants which cause destruction of blood in affected individuals.

Besides some of the genetic traits previously mentioned, a few polymorphisms, such as the ability to secrete blood group substance in saliva and the ability to taste phenylthiourea, have been known for some years. In the last few years many other polymorphisms have been discovered in blood serum constituents in man. These include haptoglobins, transferrins, gamma globulin groups, and beta-lipoproteins. All these seem to follow simple genetic patterns and manifest differences in frequencies between different populations. Convincing evidence, however, bearing on the selective pressures which may maintain these polymorphisms has not yet been adduced.

IV

(8) *Evolutionary factors.* The existence and increased knowledge of such allelic systems in man as the blood groups, hemoglobins, and serum proteins have permitted studies of the evolutionary forces acting in the populations of man in the world today. The sum total of change may well be small over a single generation or so (as we would judge to be the case from examination of the fossil record). But the fact is that evolutionary forces act in contradictory ways and those favoring man's adaptation must run for the species merely to stand still.

(a) *Mutation.* If we assume that the type of biological being we are is, for the most part, good for the kind of lives we live, then it follows that accidental and random changes in what we are would usually be for the worse. That is, if the genetic code which is transmitted from generation to generation carries the message: "Make another person like me," errors in the code will make for diseases. Such errors are called mutations and are constantly occurring but in a rare, sporadic, and unpredictable manner. Naturally occurring mutation rates in man have been counted or calculated by indirect methods. They are usually of the order of one in ten thousand to one in a hundred thousand. Since the number of genes in man is roughly of the same order, a high proportion of conceptions involve one or more mutations. Some of these are lethal genes which cause prenatal death and thus eliminate themselves, others affect health or fertility and are eliminated in the first generation. And a few are probably neutral (producing no ill effects) or actually cause advantageous biological modifications.

(b) *Natural selection.* Natural selection, as we have already noted in respect to balanced polymorphism, is merely another way of saying that those who are diseased or infertile leave fewer progeny. It need have no simple relationship to survival of types we would value as good or desirable. It may tend to select heterozygotes as in the sickle-cell trait but there will be an even stronger inherent tendency to select favorable dominant mutations. Natural selection in varying environments such as those in which men live will serve to maintain diversity in the species. Natural selection in the long run will select whole systems—such as a mutable genetic code itself (for an immutable one could not modify itself for changed modes of life), and the bisexual mode of reproduction which permits constant reshuffling of the genetic constituents and consequent appearance of more different combinations of parts of the code). Natural selection can work only if there are differences between which the selection takes place. The major adaptations of the animal and plant world are thus easily viewed as the product of a long series of selective steps. It need not follow, however, that all the minor individual or racial differences are adaptive: quite the contrary, for them to be maintained in such similar beings they would have to be nearly neutral. Natural selection merely implies that at the lowest level there must be differences within the group which are ordinarily randomly varied but on which natural selection can work when one or the other form becomes adaptively advantageous.

(c) *Random genetic drift.* It has been clear in theory, and substantiating facts are now accumulating, that mere accidents of sampling cause human populations to diverge from each other. If such groups are relatively but not completely reproductively isolated from each other, the experiments of natural selection go on separately in many places. The chance changes that can take place in small populations tend to maintain the genetic diversity necessary for these natural experiments. Sewall Wright, to whom we owe the concept of random genetic drift, has likened the favorable ways of life to a system of valleys, the deepest valleys being the most lush and fertile. And man could be viewed as so many round beans. Natural selection could only roll them downhill into the nearest valley. But random genetic drift, the chance selection of any combination of genes, would keep the beans in motion like Mexican jumping beans and some would pop over the higher ridges and down into deeper valleys —never to stay at the bottom, of course, but constantly to seek lower ground. Wright has shown that the extent of random genetic drift is a function of the effective size of the breeding population. The smaller the population and the more variable the number of progeny per parent, the greater will be the chance of drift. Anthropologists have recently found evidence of random genetic drift, in the form of divergent frequencies of specific genes, in small populations of religious groups who mate among themselves, in isolated remnants of hunting and gathering tribes, and on constricted islands. Thus, the aborigines of the Wellesley Islands in the Gulf of Carpentaria, Australia, have virtually completely sealed themselves off from outside contacts. With the primitive rafts used in these parts, inter-island travel is rare and hazardous. In one group of islands, there is appreciable blood-group A but no B. On another island, there is more B than in any other known group of Australian aborigines, and no A. At some time, perhaps when the populations were especially tiny because of water shortages, famine, or accidents at sea, no individual with blood-group B survived in the first group of islands and no person with blood-group A in the second. There is no reason to assume any meaningful relationship between these blood groups and their chance of survival (natural selection) so the causes are treated as statistical and described as "random selection."

(d) *Gene flow.* Mating between different groups of peoples seems always to be possible and usually to occur at least occasionally. Thus even peasant communities and primitive tribes receive some 5 to 35 per cent immigrants per generation. Some Australian aborigines have been in effective contact with whites for such a short time that they can recall precontact marriages. Fifteen per cent of these were intertribal. It is true, of course, that migration of a single individual, like a single mutation, is unlikely to have much genetic effect. Only repeated migrations like repeated mutations should affect gene frequencies appreciably. In man, such marked influences are possible. The migrants may have techniques or attitudes which swamp the local groups—as in the replacement of Indians by Europeans in North America, or aborigines by Chinese in Formosa. At a more local level, intermarriage between nearby villages counteracts the effects of random genetic drift by enlarging the effective size of the breeding population.

The forces of continuing human evolution must be seen as all part of the same matrix, pulling in different degrees and ways: mutation, natural selection, random genetic drift, and gene flow can be seen and measured as vectors producing the patterns of polymorphism which characterize the racial distinctions of man. The anthropologist today investigates the history, blood groups, biochemistry, population structure, and environmental situations of the peoples he studies to get at this matrix of forces.

(9) *Non-human primates.* One difficulty with studies of modern peoples is that we can not automatically project the findings back to beings on an Australopithecine level of development for instance. Even the population dynamics of ancient man are difficult to estimate. For this

reason, studies of non-human primates have often been used to help set the limits within which our thoughts about early hominoids must be confined. Primatological studies have recently been encouraged because of the applicability of results to medicine and to explorations of outer space. These comparative studies of non-human primates tend to fall into two classes: first, investigations of the basic biochemistry and genetics of the primates; and, secondly, observations of sizes of groups, breeding habits, subsistence, defense against predators, territory inhabited, and other aspects of behavior—especially social behavior—and the influences of environment and adaption on behavior.

At the basic biological genetic level, it is now clear that polymorphisms highly similar to the human ones occur in other primates. Blood-group substances occur widely in the animal world, and those found in the great apes are essentially the ones known in man. A variety of serum proteins is found among the mammals. Thus, the transferrins are polymorphic in monkeys and in apes as well as in man; serum albumin is found in all mammals and that of the chimpanzee and the gorilla is indistinguishable from that of man by the immunological tests used to make such comparisons. Since specificities of proteins reflect the genetic code more directly than physical features, studies of this kind are the best measures of degrees of genetic relationship, although they may not exactly measure the relative recency of last common ancestors. Naturally, the degree to which the same biochemical syntheses are followed in man and another primate determines the likelihood that susceptibility to microorganisms, reactions to to environmental stresses, and responses to drugs will be similar. Several species of primates, above all in importance the gorilla, are near extinction, and it is of the utmost practical importance that these species be preserved. Even the common varieties of monkey are needed in such numbers for testing polio vaccines and the like that there is a real threat of depopulation. Some non-human primates may become as useful to man as domestic cattle have been, since they can synthesize substances similar to man's, just as the cow synthesizes a milk which can substitute for human milk, and the maintenance of herds of these animals is an urgent necessity.

The story of behavioral studies of non-human primates is an old one. The very meaning of the verb "ape" indicates appreciation of the man-like aspects of this behavior. Nevertheless, in step with the researches at the biological level, psychological studies of these animals have been on the increase. And this pointed to a need for further naturalistic studies of social behavior in the wild. Since Professor Sherwood L. Washburn of the University of California became actively interested and threw his very considerable talents into further studies of this kind, a plethora of first rate studies—many of them by his students—have been conducted.

The whole gamut of primatological studies is now on firmer ground than ever before. Like human biology, primatology is a multidisciplinary subject. It is held together by the broad interrelationships of anatomical, physiological, psychological, and evolutionary aspects, and it is to a considerable extent primatologists trained in anthropology, as was Washburn, who have stimulated these integrative studies.

V

It is a mistake, however, to think that higher levels of analysis involving integration of interdisciplinary studies in human biology will automatically make for progress or put anthropology in the key position in this field of science. As in all sciences, progress in human biology depends on the specific relationships hypothesized and tested. If these hypotheses are meaningful and susceptible to validation and if the practitioners of the science have the technical skills and facilities, progress will continue to be made. But it is also clear that so many different skills and understandings are called for in human development, human evolution, human genetics, human behavior, human culture, and even comparative studies of non-human animals, that the expert anthropologist is an unobtainable myth. Specialization, as in other sciences, is unavoidable. But in the physical anthropology of the living, as in anthropology in general, over-specialization poses a grave threat to understanding, and students of anthropology, however specialized, will need a very broad base of knowledge in other subjects—the relation of which to their own can not always be perceived in advance. Becoming such a scholar, therefore, predicates a long period of training—not to acquire the skills and attitudes of the profession, which can be achieved in relatively brief periods of apprenticeship—but to build up a wide knowledge in cultural anthropology and in biological science. Training as an anthropologist in respect to the distinctive functions visualized in this essay will therefore have to continue to require years of graduate study. Only those who have given considerable time and attention to the study will be able to put the pieces of knowledge together meaningfully.

Because professional training in physical anthropology is likely to remain a long course of study, much of the contribution of this field will be through the increased understanding of individuals specializing in other disciplines such as anatomy, biochemistry, demography, ethology, genetics, immunology, orthodontia, orthopedics, pathology, and even sociology and psychology. When they deal with man in the mass, and man as a biological species, students of these subjects may well contribute to, as well as learn from, the science most concerned with the aspect of man which he shares with other forms and those in which he is unique, physical anthropology.

SELECTED READINGS

Birdsell, J. B., 1957, "On Methods of Evolutionary Biology and Anthropology," *American Scientist*, 45:393–400.

Harrison, G. A., J. S. Weiner, J. M. Tanner, and N. A. Barnicot, 1964, *Human Biology: An Introduction to Human Evolution, Variation and Growth*. New York: Oxford University Press.

Weiner, J. S., 1957, "Physical Anthropology . . . an Appraisal," *American Scientist*, 45:79–87.

PART TWO

EVOLUTION, GENETICS, AND NATURAL SELECTION

Our present-day understanding of evolution has developed from many different kinds of research in the biological sciences. Advances both in theory and in the accumulation of information have made clearer the nature of the processes by which changes in hereditary material are distributed and redistributed within populations and by which new kinds of populations can come into being. Close study of the fossil record by paleontologists has been enlarged by insights from the field of ecology: the study of evolution has benefited from understanding how animal and plant populations are related to one another in space.

What principles may be said to be the product of contemporary research into evolution? There are several, and they all have implications for the study of human evolution, implications that are now being pursued and tested. First is the realization that *evolution is what happens to populations*. The meaningful unit of study in evolutionary biology is the population, the naturally interbreeding group of organisms more or less isolated reproductively from other similar groups.

Second, the study of evolution is the study of *dynamics* or of *processes*. Evolutionary anthropology has swung away from research as "sorting out the results of evolution," in Washburn's felicitous phrase, toward attempts to understand the nature of the relationships of populations to each other and to the environment over spans of time. Paleontology also has been vastly enriched by this shift in emphasis.

Furthermore, evolutionary processes did not simply occur in the past but operate continuously within the mechanisms of heredity. Natural selection, for example, which is the major agency of evolutionary change, does not merely act to redistribute genetic material in the gene pools of populations as a response to alterations in their ecological niches; it acts to maintain an equilibrium between the genetic potential of a population and its conditions of life. There are probably no such things as structures that are "evolutionarily neutral." The hereditary characteristics of populations and their distribution *at any given time* are expressions of the ecological relation between the population and its ecological niche at that time. (In the face of this realization, we might question the validity of the interpretation of modern "racial differences" as being adaptations to conditions of 700 generations ago, that is, the late Pleistocene.)

We are, moreover, becoming increasingly aware that the human fossil record itself is comprehensible in evolutionary terms only if we try to understand the changes in behavior that correspond to the changes in structure of the hominids through the last two million years.

In the selections that follow, the major cornerstones of the modern synthetic theory of evolution are interpreted. Wallace and Dobzhansky specify exactly what geneticists and evolutionary biologists mean by their use of the term "population." Stebbins reviews the principal agencies of evolutionary change and discusses the evidence on which our understanding of them is based. Kettlewell describes the experimental evidence supporting the reality of the role of natural selection in evolution.

2

GENES IN MENDELIAN POPULATIONS

Bruce Wallace and Theodosius Dobzhansky

The word "population" has a different meaning for a statistician, a demographer, or a zoologist. What does "population" mean in the biological sense? How does the geneticist describe a population? How can such a genetic description aid in the study of evolution? These are the questions that are taken up by Bruce Wallace and Theodosius Dobzhansky in the following extract from their book, Radiation, Genes, and Man.

Bruce Wallace is Professor of Genetics at Cornell University. Theodosius Dobzhansky, born in Russia in 1900, is Research Professor at Rockefeller Institute in New York City. Over the past forty years he has made a distinguished contribution to our understanding of evolutionary processes. In recent years, he has brought his knowledge of evolutionary dynamics to the questions of human raciation and human evolution.

WHAT IS A POPULATION?

Up to this point we have considered heredity as it manifests itself in individuals and in families. We have discussed the laws, discovered by Mendel, which govern the segregation and recombination of genes in the progeny of heterozygous parents; the interactions of heredity and environment; the origin of mutations, their frequency, their effects on the welfare of their carriers, and their induction by high-energy radiation. But people live in groups, in communities, from the members of which individuals usually select their mates and membership in which parents bequeath to their children. Such communities—tribes, castes, social classes, nations, races—bound together by a network of marriages and of common descent, are Mendelian populations. We must now consider the phenomena of heredity in such populations. Genetics takes on an added dimension when it encompasses populations as units.

We speak of "Mendelian populations" because the word *population* has a variety of meanings both in everyday language and in biology. Thus, one may speak of a "population" of trees composing a forest, or of a bird "population" which inhabits this forest. The population of the world is estimated to be close to 2,700,000,000 people; that of the United States consists of some 170,000,000; that of Cleveland, Ohio, is somewhat less than 1,000,000; while that of McKean, Pennsylvania, is about 300. These are the numbers of persons who live in a given territory at a given time. A geneticist is interested in organisms that reproduce sexually and in populations as reproductive communities—in short, in Mendelian populations.

Mendelian populations have a temporal continuity; they exist through time. The starlings in the United States, for example, comprise a population that has existed since 1890, the year these birds were introduced from Europe. In man and many other species, individuals representing several generations—children, parents, grandparents, and great-grandparents—may be living at the same time, and the successive generations need not be discrete. In insect populations children may mate with their parents. On the other hand, many organisms have but one generation per year, and the preceding generation is dead before the succeeding one reaches adulthood.

In man, population structure reaches its greatest complexity. Mankind —the human species, *Homo sapiens*—is the most inclusive Mendelian population, one which inhabits nearly the whole globe. Its genetic unity is attested by the existence of English, German, Japanese and other war brides, the convergence of immigrants from many countries on Israel, the world-wide dispersal of Russian refugees, etc. But even before modern means of transportation made these extensive migrations possible, there were people who wandered around as soldiers, traders, slaves, or simple vagrants; and when people travel they are likely to leave some of their genes along the way. However, this does not mean that people intermarry in a random manner with respect to the place where they were born. A girl from Dallas is much more likely to marry a Texan than a Californian, a German, or a Chinese. Mankind is, therefore, split up into geographic Mendelian populations whose boundaries are usually not sharply defined and which need not coincide even approximately with political units such as countries or states. Nor are marriages contracted at random even between inhabitants of the same state, city, or village. Differences of language, religion, economic status, educational background, and profession erect numerous, although usually not sharply delineated, communities of Mendelian populations. Mankind is, thus, divided and subdivided into smaller and smaller population units; the smaller the unit, the closer the approach to "random" mating between its members.

THE GENE POOL OF A POPULATION

Suppose that we examine the population of some Middletown which is reasonably uniform in social, economic, and religious respects, and find that about 49 percent of the persons in this community have blue eyes and 51 percent have brown eyes. Assume that the difference between blue and brown is due to a single gene and that blue is recessive (this is not strictly correct, since shades of eye color are determined by several genes, and a person with greenish-blue eyes may actually carry the gene for brown). Will the proportion of blue- and brown-eyed persons remain the same generation after generation? What proportion of brown-eyed parents will have some blue-eyed children? And should, for some reason, all blue-eyed persons leave Middletown before reaching adolescence, how many blue-eyed persons will there be produced in succeeding generations? These are examples of elementary problems with which population genetics has to deal.

With problems of this sort, it is convenient to focus our attention not on individuals but on their gametes and the genes which these gametes contain. Assume that every individual member of a Mendelian population contributes to the *gene pool* (*pool* used in this sense is analogous to its use in "motor pool" or "pooled resources," not to a "pool of water") of this population equal numbers of functioning sex cells; and assume that these sex cells combine at random in fertilization. These assumptions are not as unrealistic as they may seem to be. We know that some persons have more children than others; however, we are assuming here merely that brown-eyed and blue-eyed people have, on the average, the same number of children. Nor is it too farfetched to assume that people with eyes of a given color will not select their mates preferentially according to the eye color of the latter.

Suppose now that in the gene pool of the Middletown population 70 percent, or the fraction 0.70, of the total number of sex cells carry the gene *a* for blue eyes, and the remainder—that is, 30 percent or 0.30 of the total, carry the gene *A* for brown eyes (0.70 happens to be the square root of 0.49, which is the frequency of blue-eyed persons in our Middletown population; why we have chosen just these figures will appear shortly). Since the sex cells of this population combine at random, the sperm carrying the gene A will have 7 chances out of 10 of fertilizing an egg cell with the gene a, and 3 chances out of 10 of uniting with an egg cell carrying A. Similarly, the sperm with a will have a 7-in-10 and a 3-in-10 chance of uniting with a and with A eggs respectively. The results of the union of these sex cells will, accordingly, be as follows:

EGG CELLS		SPERM		CHILDREN	
Gene	Frequency	Gene	Frequency	Gene	Frequency
A	0.30	A	0.30	AA	0.09
A	0.30	a	0.70	Aa	0.21
a	0.70	A	0.30	Aa	0.21
a	0.70	a	0.70	aa	0.49

In other words, 0.09, or 9 percent of the population, will have brown eyes and will be homozygous for the gene A (AA); 0.42, or 42 percent, will have brown eyes and will be heterozygous for A and a (Aa); and 0.49, or 49 percent, will have blue eyes and will be homozygous for a (aa). Since the homozygous (AA) and heterozygous (Aa) browns have eyes of about the same color, the frequency of brown-eyed and blue-eyed persons will be 0.51 and 0.49 respectively.

The fundamental problem concerning us is what the next generation will be like: Will the proportion of blue-eyed and brown-eyed persons change, or will it remain the same? To solve this problem, remember that the homozygotes AA and aa will contribute to the gene pool of the next generation only A or a gametes respectively, while the heterozygotes, Aa, will produce, according to Mendel's law of segregation, gametes A and a in equal numbers. As shown above, the three genotypes AA, Aa, and aa occur in the proportions 0.09, 0.42, and 0.49. Therefore, the proportion of A and a in the gene pool will be as follows:

$$A = 0.09 + 0.21 = 0.30$$
$$a = 0.21 + 0.49 = 0.70$$

The proportion of the genes A and a in the gene pool remains the same as in the previous generation. The incidence of blue- and brown-eyed persons in the population will remain constant generation after generation. Neither the dominant nor the recessive gene will increase or decrease in frequency. Do not make the error which beginning students of genetics are prone to make: The dominant gene does not necessarily tend to displace the recessive, nor are dominant genes or dominant traits necessarily more frequent than recessive ones.

THE HARDY-WEINBERG THEOREM

The conclusion we have reached is valid regardless of the actual frequencies of the genes in the population. Consider a population in which the gene A has a frequency p and the gene a the frequency q, such that $p + q = 1.00$. Proceeding as before we have:

EGG CELLS		SPERM		CHILDREN	
Gene	Frequency	Gene	Frequency	Gene	Frequency
A	p	A	p	AA	p^2
A	p	a	q	Aa	pq
a	q	A	p	Aa	pq
a	q	a	q	aa	q^2

The composition of the population will, therefore, be p^2 of AA homozygotes, $2pq$ of Aa heterozygotes, and q^2 of aa homozygotes. The frequency of the genes A and a in the gene pool of the next generation will be:

$$A = p^2 + pq = p(p + q) = p$$
$$a = pq + q^2 = q(p + q) = q$$

This demonstration of the constancy of the gene frequency in the gene pool of a population was first given independently in 1908 by G. H. Hardy and W. Weinberg. It is the basic theorem of population genetics (see Figure 2–1).

RANDOM MATING

The assumption we have made above is that marriages and the union of gametes occur at random. The validity of this assumption may now be examined. "Random mating" obviously does not mean promiscuity; it simply means, as already explained above, that in the choice of mates for marriage there is neither preference for nor aversion to the union of persons similar or dissimilar *with respect to a given trait or gene.* Not all gentlemen prefer either blondes or brunettes. Since so few people know what their blood type is, it is even safer to say that the chances of mates being similar or dissimilar in blood type are determined simply by the incidence of these blood types in a given Mendelian population.

In addition to the A-B-O and the Rh blood group systems, there is another set of blood types called M, MN, and N, which is independent of the foregoing ones. The interest of these latter types is that the heterozygotes in this case are easily distinguishable. Group M persons are homozygous for a gene which we may call M; these are MM persons.

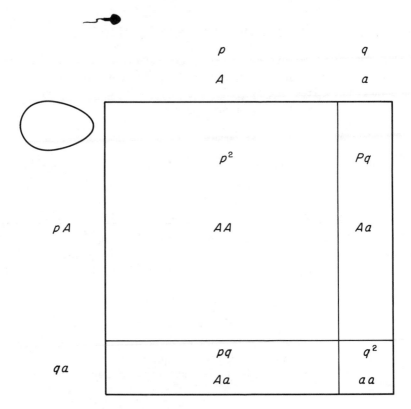

FIGURE 2–1—This "checkerboard" diagram shows the relationship one expects to find between the frequency of two genes in a population and the frequency of individuals of the three possible genotypes. . . . Gene frequencies in a population need not be limited, as are those of individuals, to the three values—100, 50, and 0 percent—but can assume any value; and, therefore, the dividing lines within the square have been displaced off center by an arbitrary distance. (From Wallace and Dobzhansky, *Radiation, Genes and Man*.)

Group N persons are homozygous for a gene which we may call M^N. And finally, group MN persons are the heterozygotes, MM^N. Neither gene is dominant to the other.

A study of 6,129 white persons of the United States population showed that 29.16 percent had M blood, 49.58 percent MN, and 21.26 percent had N blood. What is the composition of the gene pool of this population? Remember that persons of blood type M produce gametes with the gene M; N persons, gametes with the gene M^N, and MN persons produce sex cells with M and with M^N in equal numbers. Therefore, the frequencies of the two genes in the gene pool are:

$$M = 0.2916 + 0.2479 = 0.5395 = p$$
$$M^N = 0.2479 + 0.2126 = 0.4605 = q$$

Now, if marriages in this population are at random with respect to these blood types, then, according to the Hardy-Weinberg equation, the proportion of the three blood groups in the population should be:

$$M = p^2 = 0.54^2 = 0.2916$$
$$MN = 2pq = 2 \times 0.54 \times 0.46 = 0.4968$$
$$N = q^2 = 0.46^2 = 0.2116$$

The predicted incidence of the three blood types coincides almost exactly with the observed incidence. There is obviously random mating in the population of the United States with respect to these blood types.

Gene frequencies are not constant from race to race. In fact, races can be understood and defined best as Mendelian populations differing in the frequencies of various genes. Although within each race matings may occur at random with respect to certain traits, matings between races are less frequent than would be expected by chance. Indeed, if random mating prevailed between races, these races would fuse in a single Mendelian population. Although individuals in such a population would show a great deal of genetic variability, the races would no longer exist as distinct entities. Now, in a group of American Indians the incidence of blood types was found to be $M = 60.00$ percent, MN $= 35.12$ percent, and $N = 4.88$ percent. The frequencies of the genes M and M^N in the gene pool can be calculated, as in the example above, to be $M = 0.776$ and $M^N = 0.224$. If mating were at random, the incidence of the three blood types should be M $= 60.15$ percent, MN $= 34.81$ percent, $N = 5.04$ percent. The agreement between the observed and the calculated values is again extremely close. But note that the gene pool of American whites has a composition different from that of American Indians.

CHANGING GENE FREQUENCIES BY
MUTATION AND SELECTION

The Hardy-Weinberg theorem shows that gene frequencies in a Mendelian population tend to remain constant from generation to generation. This is, however, correct only if (1) genes do not change by mutation; (2) the carriers of different genes are adaptively equivalent and leave, on the average, the same number of surviving offspring; (3) there is no immigration to or emigration from the population that would bring in or remove one gene in preference to the other; and (4) the population is large enough so that accidental fluctuations of gene frequencies may be ignored. No population in reality satisfies these conditions completely.

We know that genes do undergo mutation, albeit usually with a low frequency, such as 1 new mutant gene per 100,000 sex cells per generation. Nevertheless, even such a low mutation pressure will eventually be enough to influence the gene frequency in the population. Suppose that the gene *A* is occasionally converted into *a* by mutation. The mutation of *A* to *a* is to the frequency of the gene *a* in a population as the flow of water from a faucet is to the amount of water in a tub; in itself the mutation does not determine the final gene frequency, but without mutation the frequency of the mutant allele would surely be zero.

The final frequency attained by a gene is one representing a dynamic equilibrium; this frequency is constant (or very nearly so) not because life is static and the frequency is frozen at one level but because rates of input and outflow have become equal. Using the tub analogy once more: If the stopper is not placed properly, water will drain out of the tub. It will drain out faster as the water gets deeper and deeper. Eventually the water in the tub may be deep enough to drain out as rapidly as the faucet is running; the amount of water in the tub remains con-

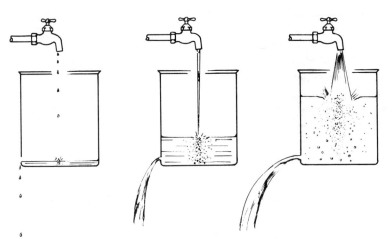

FIGURE 2–2—An analogy to illustrate the idea of genetic equilibrium: the more water flows from the faucet into the vessel, the higher the level of water in the vessel becomes and, consequently, the faster it escapes from the hole in the bottom. Equilibrium is established when the rates at which water enters and leaves the container are equal. In living populations, harmful mutations are constantly produced (water from the faucet); the more frequently mutations arise per generation, the greater the frequency with which they are found in the population (the level of water in the vessel), and the greater the frequency of "genetic death" (water escaping through the hole in the vessel). (From Wallace and Dobzhansky, *Radiation, Genes and Man.*)

stant once this equilibrium is established (see Figure 2–2). The water in the tub is not, however, the same from one minute to the next; it is in dynamic equilibrium. There are two forces which oppose mutation in bringing about an equilibrium of gene frequencies. These are (1) back mutation of a to A and (2) natural selection. Of the two, natural selection is of more importance and of greater interest to us.

GENETIC EQUILIBRIUM

The genetic equilibrium with respect to two variant (allelic) genes in a population is reached when one of these genes enters the population at the same rate by which it leaves. It enters by mutation and leaves by back mutation and by selection. Let us consider some examples of selection. The simplest illustration is probably that of a fatal hereditary disease caused by a recessive lethal gene. Assume that the normal gene A mutates to the lethal a once in every million gametes, and that all aa individuals die before reproducing. Equilibrium is established when one individual in every million born is homozygous aa; elimination of the gene a by the death of aa individuals then balances the origin of new a genes by mutation. We saw above that the frequency of aa individuals equals q^2; therefore, q, the equilibrium frequency of the gene a, equals 0.001, the square root of the mutation rate (see Figure 2–3).

To better visualize this situation, imagine 170 persons in the population of the United States, or one person in a million, dying in each generation (25 to 30 years) from a recessive lethal mutation of this sort— an average of about 6 deaths per year in the whole country. This may seem to be a very rare disease. It is, however, important to realize that although the number of homozygotes dying because of this disease is small, the number of people who are carriers of the recessive lethal gene in heterozygous condition is relatively large. According to the Hardy-Weinberg theorem, the frequency of the heterozygous carriers is $2pq$, or $2 \times 0.001 \times 0.999$, or about 0.002—roughly 1 per 500 persons. In a population as large as that of the United States, the number of such persons, who enjoy normal health themselves but who nevertheless carry the lethal gene, is about 340,000. This is about the same number of persons as the number living in Syracuse, New York.

The great majority of recessive genes for lethal and semi-lethal hereditary diseases are, thus, carried not in the homozygotes who show the effects of these genes but rather in the heterozygotes who do not. This fact raises a tremendous difficulty for any attempt to eradicate a recessive hereditary disease by sterilizing, or otherwise preventing the reproduction of, persons who are afflicted with it. In the example discussed above, only 170 persons show the disease in a population as large as that of the United States, but there are 340,000 heterozygous carriers. Since we have not discovered a method of distinguishing these heterozygotes from normal noncarriers, there is little that can be done to prevent the birth of a new crop of afflicted homozygotes in every generation.

As we have seen in foregoing chapters, not all gene mutations are

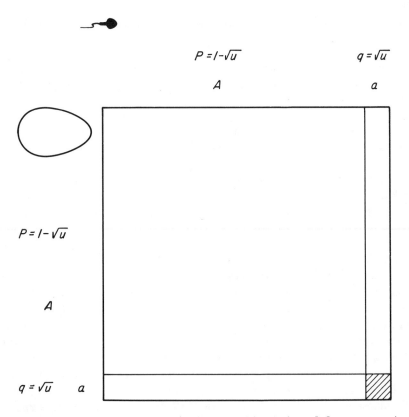

FIGURE 2–3—Another checkerboard, one which is intended to represent the equilibrium that is established between mutation and selection in the case of a recessive lethal gene (a). The rate at which a arises from gene A equals u, usually a small fraction. The shaded portion of the diagram represents aa individuals who die because of the lethal nature of this gene. Each death of an aa individual removes two mutant genes from the population, one from the initial supply of these genes among sperm and the other from the initial supply among eggs. Consequently, equilibrium is reached when the shaded area equals u. Each side of the shaded square corresponds to the frequency, q, of the gene a in the population. Hence q^2 equals u, or q, the gene frequency, equals $\sqrt{u}$. Note that the quantity q^2 is much smaller than q. (From Wallace and Dobzhansky, *Genes, Radiation and Man*.)

completely lethal. Recessive semilethal and subvital mutants cause the death of fewer than 100 percent of their homozygous carriers; in other words, some of the homozygotes manage to survive and even to beget children of their own. In general, if a fraction s of all individuals homozygous for a given gene die before reproducing (or if the number of children born to such individuals is lower than the average number per couple in the population by a fraction s), then an equilibrium is established when sq^2 equals the mutation rate. We can translate sq^2 as the fraction lost per homozygote multiplied by the frequency of these homozygotes in the population. If we denote the mutation rate by u, we have a stable equilibrium when:

$$sq^2 = u$$
$$\text{or, } q^2 = u/s$$
$$\text{or, } q = \sqrt{u/s}$$

If s equals 1—that is, if all homozygotes die or for other reasons leave no children—we have the equilibrium $q = \sqrt{u}$ discussed above.

To illustrate the more general relationship, consider a gene B which mutates to b once in a million sex cells per generation. The effect of the gene b is to reduce the average number of children born to bb parents (either to bb mothers or to bb fathers; what happens when both parents are bb is relatively unimportant because of the rarity of such matings) to 99 percent of the average of the population as a whole. The value of s equals, then, 0.01. The frequency of bb individuals at equilibrium will be, according to the formula above, $q^2 = u/s = 0.000,001/0.01$, or 1 per 10,000 persons in the population. Within the United States there would be some 17,000 homozygous bb persons born in each generation, or some 600 per year. The frequency of the harmful gene b in the gene pool at equilibrium will be $q = \sqrt{u/s} = \sqrt{0.0001} = 0.01$; that is 1 percent of all sex cells will carry this gene. The heterozygous carriers of this gene will amount to almost 2 percent of persons in the population: $2pq = 2 \times 0.01 \times 0.99 = 0.0198$, or a total of 3,400,000 heterozygous carriers in the population of the United States. Gathered into one place, these carriers would form a city large enough to be listed among the ten largest in the world!

GENETIC DEATH

It must be made clear just what is meant by the elimination of mutant genes from a population. The symbol s used above stands for *coefficient of selection*. This is a very important variable, and its meaning demands a fuller explanation. Two rather striking phrases have been used by geneticists in describing the action of selection on human populations: "genetic death" and "genetic murder will out." Genetic "death" encompasses, however, a great deal more than death as we understand it from accounts of automobile accidents and hatchet murders.

First of all, complete or partial sterility is equivalent to complete or partial lethality as far as selection is concerned. To a geneticist, any person who dies childless is counted as genetically "dead": that is, whatever genes he carries are, by virtue of his actions or lack of actions, removed from the population just as surely as if he had been stillborn. It is obvious, however, that the emotional impacts of death and of childlessness are in no way comparable. Second, if the mutant gene is lethal or semilethal, the actual death caused by the action of this gene can occur at any time from conception on. The loss of an individual within the first few weeks after conception is often imperceptible and, hence, causes no emotional trauma. Death at any later time, however, is recognizable as such and is accompanied by at least some degree of sadness and sorrow. We must, nonetheless, guard against rigidly equating the seriousness with which we regard the deaths of individuals and the degree of mourning or sense of loss accompanying these deaths. If there must be deaths, by all means let them occur early in development, so as to be as painless to the individual and to others as possible. But, if deaths are unnecessary, let us not develop the callous attitude that undetected deaths are of no importance. How easily this attitude can spread to encompass even living persons!

Finally, there is a perhaps unexpected property of selection that must be clearly understood. We know that many mutant genes are lethal, and that some of these cause incurable hereditary diseases which result in death only after much illness or agony. On the other hand, a subvital gene opposed by a relatively mild selection, such as we have discussed above ($s = 0.01$), may act simply by lowering the vitality of its carriers to the extent that they leave 99 surviving children where an equal number of nonmutant individuals would have left 100 offspring. At first sight, the lethal gene would seem to cause many more genetic deaths than the subvital gene. But this is not so at all. Provided that the mutation rates, u, which yield the lethal and subvital genes are equal, these genes will cause the same number of genetic deaths in the population at equilibrium.

This fact becomes apparent when we consider the implications of the equation $q^2 = u/s$, used above to describe the equilibrium frequency of mutant homozygotes in the population. It will be recalled that the selection coefficient, s, is equal to the amount by which the chance of surviving or the average number of offspring is reduced in homozygous individuals. The net effect of the mutant gene on the population, is u/s

times s: the frequency of affected persons times the average adverse effect per person. This product equals u, the mutation rate. The conclusion is clear. The effect of a recessive mutant gene on a *population* is a function of its mutation rate, and is independent of the effect, as measured by the selection coefficient, of the mutant on homozygous individuals. This does not imply, however, that the emotional impact of these various types of mutation is at all similar. To watch a child suffer from hemophilia is quite different from realizing—if one could realize such things—that a child's life expectancy is destined to be one or two years less than that of his playmates.

We have considered the genetic equilibrium for mutants with recessive harmful effects. The situation with respect to genetic deaths is analogous for dominant deleterious mutants, but the effect on the population is twice as large. A dominant lethal which produces a fatal disease (such as some inherited forms of muscular dystrophy), or a subvital which produces only a slight handicap for survival or reproduction (such as brachydactyly, short fingers), causes twice as many genetic deaths as there are mutations. If the reader is still baffled by the equivalence of the very "bad" and the only mildly disadvantageous mutations, perhaps the following argument will help. Any harmful mutant, whether its effects are drastic or barely perceptible, will sooner or later have to be removed from the population in which it occurs. Indeed, the genetic equilibrium is a situation obtaining when the number of mutants produced is balanced by the number of mutant genes removed from the population. A harmful gene that comes into a population eventually has to get out.

The facts listed above have an obvious bearing on the problem of genetic damage caused by radiation in human and other populations. . . . This genetic damage cannot be measured adequately by taking into account only grave hereditary diseases. Mutant genes with less deleterious effects result in genetic damage just as surely as the more drastic mutants.

3

THE DYNAMICS
OF EVOLUTIONARY CHANGE

G. Ledyard Stebbins

On the one hand, the processes of heredity make for stability and similarity from generation to generation. On the other hand, built into these same processes are the possibilities for variation and change, possibilities that are exploited by natural selection and other forces of evolution. In this selection, G. Ledyard Stebbins reviews the dynamics of evolution—variation, natural selection, and drift—and discusses their impact on the characteristics of living populations. Stebbins is a Professor of Botany at the University of California, Davis.

Since the time of Charles Darwin, the concept of evolutionary change has permeated the entire field of biology. It is accepted without question by all working biologists, because of the immense body of facts which now demonstrates its existence. Furthermore, change through time is now recognized as one of the guiding principles of the universe, from stellar galaxies to human societies. Biologists of modern times are relatively little concerned with showing that change has taken place. Even the directions which evolutionary changes have taken in particular groups of plants and animals have proven to be a less rewarding field of study than the mechanism of evolutionary change. The challenging question which most modern evolutionists are trying to answer is: ''What forces or processes can bring about the evolution of a population of organisms into a new type, with a different appearance and a changed way of life?''

This was, of course, the main question which Darwin himself was try-

(From *Lectures in Biological Sciences*. The University of Tennessee Press, 1963, pages 37–62. By permission of the author and the publisher. All rights reserved.)

ing to answer. To do this, he developed the theory of natural selection, for which he was able to gather together a body of factual evidence, much of it experimental, which in his day appeared impressive enough to convince most biologists that his views were correct.

But in the period after Darwin's death, and particularly in the early part of the twentieth century, experimental biology made great strides, both in the facts about living things which it uncovered and the techniques of investigation which it developed. The biologists of this time, moreover, were concerned chiefly with the mechanism of life. This mechanism can be understood best by intensive studies of individual organisms, while evolution is best understood by means of the comparative study of populations. Consequently, biological techniques and standards of experimentation far outstripped those which were used by Darwin and which were adequate in his day, without contributing much to our understanding of evolution.

This fact explains in part the low opinion which many biologists of a generation ago held in regard to Darwin's theory of natural selection. In addition, the rediscovery of Mendel's laws of inheritance focused attention upon unit characters, or conspicuous differences between organisms which are inherited as single units. When the origin of such unit characters by genetic mutation was demonstrated in the evening primrose (*Oenothera*) by De Vries and in the fly *Drosophila* by Morgan, this seemed to many biologists to spell the doom of the natural selection theory, based as it was on the accumulation through selection of small differences between individuals.

The past thirty years have seen a great revival of interest in Darwinism, and an added confidence not only in the correctness of the evolutionary theory itself, but also in Darwin's explanation of natural selection. This revival has been brought about by scientists who have applied modern quantitative and experimental methods to the sphere of action in which the evolutionary processes are actually at work. This is the genetics of natural populations. Population genetics has erected three great pillars which can support the edifice of evolutionary theory. First, it has shown that multiple-factor or polygenic inheritance is the way in which most differences between natural populations are inherited. This leads to the corollary that, as Fisher and many others have maintained, mutations with relatively small effects, which contribute to the almost imperceptible differences between individuals upon which Darwin relied, play a larger role in evolution than the conspicuous mutations observed by De Vries and Morgan. Second, population genetics has accumulated a great body of evidence showing that the selective value of any single gene depends partly upon the other genes with which it is associated in any individual. This fact disposes simultaneously of any theories which would make either the individual organism or the gene the basic unit of evolutionary change. Mendelian segregation tells us that the individual is merely the temporary home of a collection of genes which is partly scattered and assembled anew with each successive generation of individuals. The rarity of mutations makes each gene a relatively permanent entity, but as an evolutionary unit its significance is reduced by its changing adaptive values. Because of this fact, Dobzhansky and others have correctly recognized the "Mendelian population" in sexually reproducing organisms as the basic unit of evolutionary change. The third pillar erected by population genetics is the quantitative, experimental approach to the study of selection itself. In the last century, evolutionists tried to establish the validity of natural selection chiefly by showing how a particular characteristic, such as body color, could have a selective advantage in a given environment. They failed to realize that the interactions between an organism and its environment are extremely complex, so that the way in which a characteristic is advantageous is often indirect and very hard to demonstrate conclusively. Population genetics has taught us that the best way to show the action of natural selection is to demonstrate statistically that a given gene, or gene combination, has an adaptive advantage in a known, controlled environment. This demonstration is relatively easy in organisms which are well known genetically, and can sometimes lead to a further study of how selection acts.

Supported by these three pillars, evolutionists have erected a theory of how evolution works which has often been called the "synthetic theory," and sometimes the "Neo-Darwinian theory." Natural selection still serves as its cornerstone, but the mutation theory, Mendelian genetics, and the statistics of population dynamics are almost equally important components of its foundations. The symposia which were held in various parts of the world during the year of the Darwinian centennial, 1959, impressed most of their participants with the degree to which biologists actively working in the field of evolution are agreed on the soundness of this theory. A generation ago, many leading biologists felt that none of the processes which had been invoked to explain evolution was satisfactory and that the true explanation would come with the discovery of some hidden "cause" not then known. Now most biologists agree in believing that the major causes of evolution are known, but that no one of these causes is sufficient in itself. Mutation, genetic recombination, and natural selection are complementary to each other. The task of the future lies chiefly in showing how these processes act in relation to each other and to the changing environments through which the earth has passed and is passing.

SEVEN BASIC POSTULATES

At the Cold Spring Harbor Symposium of 1959, the present writer became so strongly impressed by the solidity and implications of this widespread agreement about the major processes of evolution that he undertook to formulate a series of seven basic postulates which seem to express the extent of the agreement and may serve as solid foundations for future working hypotheses about how the processes of evolution operate. The discussion presented there served as a summary of the symposium, which it concluded, and was therefore illustrated solely with examples taken from that symposium. In the present article, the same postulates will be discussed in a broader fashion, with examples selected from all of the evolutionary literature as most clearly illustrative of the postulate being discussed. One must remember, however, that, in a discussion as brief as the present one must be, only a tiny fraction of the available evidence can be reviewed.

The first basic postulate can serve as a summary of the present introduction, or of the entire discussion. Its validity depends upon that of the other six, so that no particular evidence needs to be cited in its favor. It is stated as follows:

At least in higher animals and plants, evolution proceeds principally as the result of the interaction between four indispensable processes: mutation, gene recombination, natural selection, and isolation.

THE ROLE OF MUTATION AND GENE RECOMBINATION

The next two postulates are stated as follows:

Second, mutation neither directs evolution, as the early evolutionists believed, nor even serves as the immediate source of variability upon which selection may act. It is, rather, a reserve or potential source of variability which serves to replenish the gene pool as it becomes depleted through the action of selection.

Third, the mutations which are most likely to be accepted by selection and so to form the basis of new types of organisms are those which individually have relatively slight effects on the phenotype, and collectively form the basis of polygenic or multiple-factor inheritance.

These two postulates are complementary to each other. Together, they express the conclusion that in sexually reproducing organisms both mutation and genetic recombination are essential contributors to the gene pool. This can be defined as the supply of hereditary variation in a population on which natural selection can act. The existence of a great store of variability in the gene pool is best shown by two types of experimental evidence: first, from experiments with artificial selection and second, from experiments which have uncovered concealed genetic variability by obtaining certain chromosomes or chromosome segments in the homozygous condition.

To understand the meaning of recent experiments with artificial selection, we should first make predictions as to what the limits of selection would be on the basis of two contrasting hypotheses. One hypothesis assumes that the gene pool is very small, so that selection changes populations by increasing the frequency of favorable mutations just as soon as they occur, and cannot be effective unless favorable mutations are constantly occurring at a reasonably high rate. We may call this the hypothesis of *direct selection* of favorable mutations. Either by direct statement or by implication, we can recognize this hypothesis as basic to the thinking of De Vries, Johannsen, Bateson, Morgan, and most geneticists of a generation ago.

The second hypothesis assumes that the gene pool is very large, so that, if a population is placed into a new environment and subjected to selection in a new direction, new gene combinations are sorted out from the supply of genes already present in the gene pool, and selection can be effective for many generations even if no new mutations occur. We can call this the hypothesis of *indirect action,* since it assumes an indirect rather than a direct connection between mutation and selection.

If evolution usually proceeds by direct selection of new mutations, then the limits of selection would be set by the rate of favorable mutations, which is always very low. Selection would change the population for only a very few generations. This assumption was made by De Vries, Bateson, and particularly Johannsen, and was apparently borne out by Johannsen's well-known experiments with the garden bean. On the other hand, if the gene pool of most populations is large and diverse, then selection can be expected to change a population in the same direction for many generations, even if no new mutations occur at all.

Recent selection experiments with corn, *Drosophila,* mice, chickens, and other cross-fertilizing populations of higher plants have consistently shown that such populations are capable of responding to selection for many generations on the basis of the genetic variability stored in them. Two good examples are the Illinois corn experiment and the selection experiments by Mather and his associates for the number of abdominal bristles in *Drosophila.*

The Illinois experiment, described by Woodworth and Jugenheimer, was as follows: In 1895 the agronomists at the University of Illinois decided to find out the number of generations in which they could produce a change in a characteristic by continuous artificial selection, using a cross-fertilizing population of field corn. They selected for four different characteristics—high protein of the kernels, low protein, high oil content of the kernels, and low oil. This experiment was continued for fifty generations; the most recently published results were obtained in 1959 (the experiment was briefly interrupted during the last war). In all four lines the population responded to selection for at least thirty-five generations. In the case of high oil and low protein, a significant change took place in the populations even between the forty-fifth and fiftieth generations. During the experiment, the protein content was more than doubled in the high-protein line and reduced to less than half of the original concentration in the low-protein line. Even greater results were obtained by selecting for high and low oil content. The kernels of the original population contained 4.7 per cent of oil. After fifty generations of selection, the mean oil content in the high line was raised to 15.4 per cent, and in the low line it was lowered to 1.0 per cent.

The facts which we know about mutation rates in corn tell us definitely that the Illinois agronomists must have been sorting out genetic differences which existed in their original population. Since in each line of corn being selected the number of plants raised per generation was between 200 and 300, the total number of plants raised during fifty generations in each line was between 10,000 and 15,000. We do not know the actual rates of mutation for changes in oil or protein content. But the data of Stadler on rates of mutation for other characteristics in corn tell us that for a particular characteristic the occurrence of one mutation in 50,000 plants is a relatively rapid rate. Hence the occurrence of even one mutation in the desired direction during the course of the experiment is rather unlikely. The slow, steady way in which the populations responded to selection shows that many genetic differences were being sorted out. Since these differences could not have arisen by mutation during the course of the experiment, they must have existed in the gene pool of the original, unselected, but cross-fertilizing population.

The experiments of Mather and his associates on selection for high and low number of abdominal bristles in *Drosophila* gave similar results. In these experiments the response to selection was less regular than in corn, and the undesirable secondary effects, particularly the appearance of a high degree of sterility, were more marked. The actual response was in a series of short bursts, lasting five to twenty generations, and separated by intervals of several generations during which no response to selection occurred. Nevertheless, selection was effective even after one hundred generations, and the calculations of Mather and Harrison, like those given above for the corn experiment, show that the response to selection was based upon genetic differences already present in the gene pool of the initial population, rather than mutations occurring during the course of the experiment. Furthermore, Breese and Mather tested six different marked regions of one chromosome for genes affecting the difference between the line selected for high and that for low bristle number. They found such genes in every region, which suggested that the gene pool contained a very large supply of genes affecting bristle number, at many different loci. Indirect evidence leading to the same conclusion was obtained by Clayton and Robertson, who found that an inbred line of *Drosophila,* which would be expected to contain a smaller gene pool than the crossbred population used by Mather and Harrison, responded very slowly to selection for increased bristle number.

The experiments of Goodale and MacArthur on selection for body size in mice, and those of Lerner on shank length in chickens have yielded similar results, indicating that large gene pools for various characteristics are normally present in populations of cross-fertilizing higher organisms. The experiments of King on selection of *Drosophila* for resistance to DDT showed that the gene pool of this fly contains so many genes which affect DDT resistance that, if two lines derived from the same original wild population are kept apart and subjected to simultaneous but independent selection for resistance, they will each acquire a different combination of genes for DDT resistance.

A second type of experiment which has explored the nature of the gene pool is the analysis of hidden variability by artificial inbreeding, usually accompanied by special ways of manipulating the chromosomes so that their role in determining this variability can be understood. Most of these experiments have been conducted on various species of *Drosophila* by Dobzhansky and his associates. They have shown us that natural populations of this fly not only possess a great store of hidden genetic variability, but also that this variability is highly organized. Genetic linkage serves to bind together adaptive combinations of genes on particular chromosome segments. Often the adaptiveness of a particular linked combination depends not entirely upon its own properties but on its interaction with another combination in a different, but homologous, chromosome. Such chromosome segments are said to be co-adapted. A fly containing such pairs of interacting homologous chromosomes has heterosis or hybrid vigor. In many species, the integrity of such combinations is preserved by means of chromosomal rearrangements, particularly inversions of chromosomal segments. The fact that natural selection can increase the frequency of chromosomal rearrangements because of their value in promoting hybrid vigor has been demonstrated experimentally by Dobzhansky and Pavlovsky and Levine. Furthermore, Levene, Pavlovsky, and Dobzhansky have shown that this complexity of the gene pool strongly affects the adaptive value of genes. The adaptive value of a gene can increase or decrease not only through changes in the external environment, including the other living organisms with which the population is associated. Even if these factors remain constant, a gene can change markedly in adaptiveness as it becomes associated with different genes during the continuous process of segregation and recombination which goes on in any cross-fertilizing population.

These facts have led Dobzhansky to the "balance hypothesis" of population structure. According to this hypothesis, adaptiveness is normally maintained through a combination of genes and chromosomal segments kept in the heterozygous condition. Individual genes do not usually respond directly to selection as separate units, but rather their adaptive value depends upon the way in which they contribute to the gene pool. Large numbers of genes are thus kept in the germ plasm because their effects are neutral or actually beneficial in heterozygous combinations with other alleles, when these same genes would be strongly disadvantageous or actually lethal if they were present in the homozygous, or "pure," condition.

The experiments of modern population genetics, therefore, tell us that natural selection acts indirectly upon a spectrum of variability generated largely by genetic recombination which takes place in a very complex fashion. Mutation serves to replenish the store of variability as it becomes depleted through selection. Most of the genes which enable a population to change in response to a new environment are not newcomers which have recently appeared through mutation; they are "old-timers" which presumably originated by mutation many generations ago and have been preserved either as hidden recessives or as contributors to some past adaptive complex.

This principle does not mean that genes with large effects on the appearance of the individual never play an important role in evolution. On the contrary, some of the most striking demonstrations of the action of natural selection which have been made in recent years have involved such genes. The most striking example is industrial melanism. In the industrial areas of Europe, populations of moths have become completely transformed in a few years from light- to dark-colored types through selection of dominant mutations for dark color. The experiments of Kettlewell have shown conclusively that these changes were the result of natural selection and have told us much about how selection has acted. In other examples, resistance of insects to insecticides has been shown to result largely from the selection of single mutations with large effects.

In plants, genetic information recently obtained about the columbine,

Aquilegia, suggests that the distinctive features of its flower were originally acquired through the occurrence and establishment of a single gene with large effects. The columbine differs from all of its relatives in that its petals bear long spurs containing nectar. This serves to attract animal pollinators, which may be bumblebees, hawk moths, or humming-birds, depending upon the species of columbine. The related genera all have white flowers without spurs and are pollinated by various kinds of insects. A single species of *Aquilegia* closely related to the columbine, but without spurs on its petals, is found in eastern Asia. When this species was crossed with the common European columbine, the spur of the latter was found to be determined by a single dominant gene, although many different genes affected its length. We can suppose, therefore, that the new direction of evolution, which started long ago in the columbine genus and evolved species having flowers with a variety of shapes, sizes, colors, and spur lengths, was originally triggered off by the establishment in a population of a single mutation with a conspicuous and highly adaptive effect.

THE POSITIVE EFFECT OF NATURAL SELECTION

The fourth basic postulate is stated as follows:

The role of natural selection is much more than the purely negative one of eliminating unfit types. By greatly increasing the frequency of gene combinations which otherwise have a very low chance of appearing, selection has an essentially creative and progressive effect.

The experiments on the genetic structure of populations which have already been reviewed can themselves be regarded as strong evidence in favor of this postulate. Even more striking evidence has recently been obtained from experimental studies of mimicry in butterflies. The phenomenon of mimicry, or resemblance in outward appearance between a distasteful or harmful species and an unrelated, harmless species, was used even in Darwin's day as evidence for the power of natural selection. Although some biologists in more recent times have been skeptical of the existence of this phenomenon, the recent experiments of Brower have established its validity beyond reasonable doubt. She offered specimens of the distasteful monarch butterfly to jays under carefully controlled conditions and showed that birds "trained" to avoid the monarch butterflies would also refuse to eat its mimic, the viceroy, although this butterfly was shown to be completely palatable to birds.

Sheppard has recently studied the genetic basis of mimicry in African butterflies of the swallowtail genus (*Papilio*) by extensive hybridization between the different mimicking forms which occur in a single species (*P. dardanus*), as well as crosses between mimetic and non-mimetic forms.

These studies have shown clearly that mimetic forms will become more common and their mimicry will become more perfect in regions where the distasteful models are the most frequent. Where models are rare, mimicry is imperfect and variable within the same population, while in regions where the distasteful species is absent, the species consists entirely of non-mimetic forms. Crosses between mimetic and non-mimetic forms show that the general features of the mimetic pattern are determined by a single gene with a large effect, but that perfection of the mimicry is brought about by the action of many modifying genes, each with a small effect. In *Papilio dardanus* of central Africa there exist half a dozen or more different mimetic forms, each of which mimics a different species or subspecies of distasteful butterfly, with three different genera represented among the models. The different mimetic races are all determined by different allelomorphic genes at a single locus, with each of these major or "switch" genes giving the butterfly a superficial resemblance to a particular model. In regions where the model is abundant, the "switch" gene responsible for mimicry of that model has gathered around itself a collection of modifiers at many different loci, which have perfected the resemblance between mimic and model to a remarkable degree. The evolution of mimicry in these butterflies has, therefore, been brought about by natural selection of many different genetic changes, some with large and others with small effects. These have all been brought together into a harmonious combination which adapts the population to a special situation (i.e., the presence of a particular distasteful model). There is good reason to believe that this type of progressive action of natural selection on a number of highly specific genetic changes has been responsible for all of the extraordinary adaptations found in nature, such as the remarkable shapes and color patterns of such flowers as orchids and milkweeds, the unbelievably complex instincts of such animals as spiders and solitary wasps, and the social behavior of bees, ants, and primitive men.

THE ORIGIN OF SPECIES

The fifth and sixth basic postulates of the modern synthetic theory of the causes of evolution concern the problem of the origin of species:

Fifth, the continued separation of new adaptive lines of evolution from related lines with different adaptations requires the origin of barriers of reproductive isolation, preventing or greatly restricting gene flow between them. This separation is essential for maintaining the diversity of adaptations which exists in any one habitat, and so should be regarded as the basis of species formation.

Sixth, the origin of reproductive isolation, like that of new adaptive types, requires the establishment of many new genetic changes, including structural alterations of the chromosomes and cytoplasmic changes as well as gene mutations.

These two postulates place the origin of species on a different level from the origin of different adaptations or races of a single species. Both processes are based upon natural selection of genetic differences, but for the origin of species natural selection must sort out differences of a very special kind. These affect the behavior of a population toward certain specific related populations rather than its adaptation to the environment as a whole.

A recent symposium on the species problem has shown us that the problem of the nature and origin of species is by no means solved and that divergent opinions exist both as to what species are and how they came into being. Nevertheless, a large array of facts obtained from a great variety of experiments tells us that species are distinct from each other chiefly because they are separated by barriers which restrict or prevent gene exchange between populations.

The basic importance of reproductive isolation in maintaining adaptive diversity within a community of organisms is evident from the widespread occurrence of two phenomena which have been much studied in recent years, hybridization and character displacement. If two related populations which have been isolated from each other in different habitats are permitted by environmental changes to come together, then their subsequent evolution will depend upon the degree of reproductive isolation which has developed between them. If they are still able to cross and produce fertile hybrids, the result of their contact will be the production of an intermediate, hybrid swarm, in which the identity of the original populations will become lost to a greater or lesser degree. Numerous examples of this can be cited, particularly in higher plants. On the other hand, if their ability to intercross and produce fertile hybrids is so much reduced that each population can maintain intact its own adaptive properties, then the populations will tend to compete with each other. Since direct competition tends to destroy reproductive capacity, natural selection will favor genotypes of each population which are as differently adapted as possible from the norm of the competing population and so will cause the two populations to diverge from each other. Lack has shown that in the finches of the Galapagos Islands, a race of a particular species, if it is the sole occupant of a particular island, will have a rather wide and generalized range of variation. Another race of the same species, which on a different island is sharing its habitat with a distinct but related species, will have a narrower and more specialized range of variation. This phenomenon, known as character displacement, is also described in ants by Brown and Wilson, who review additional examples in birds.

The diversity and genetic complexity of reproductive isolating barriers are evident from a great wealth of observational and experimental evidence, which is summarized in part by Stebbins, Dobzhansky, and Mayr. If all of the barriers separating two related species are studied, they are found to be of various sorts, and any two species are usually isolated by many different kinds of barriers. Sometimes the species can be easily hybridized artificially, and fertile offspring can be raised under human supervision, but they nevertheless fail to hybridize in nature because of differences in their breeding seasons, mating instincts, or similar factors. The distinctness of various species of pines in California is of this nature, as is also the separation of the mallard from the pintail duck. In other instances, as in the wild rye (*Elymus*) genus of grasses and its relatives, natural hybrids are common, but they are so sterile that they rarely, or never, reproduce. More common, however, are examples in which two related species are separated from each other by a variety of barriers. A classic example is *Drosophila pseudoobscura* and *D. persimilis,* which are separated by different temperature requirements for maximum sexual activity, an instinctive tendency for females to mate with males of their own species, sterility of F_1 hybrids (which is complete in the male sex), and weakness of sterility of backcross progeny from the partly fertile F_1 females.

We can also see how diverse and complex the reproductive isolating barriers between two species can be by crossing two related species many different times, using as parents different races of the same pair of species. Such experiments have been performed in *Drosophila* and various groups of higher plants, such as the tarweeds, *Madiae*; the phlox family, *Polemoniaceae*; and the grasses. In each example, the same kind of result has been obtained. Both the ease of crossing and the fertility of the F_1 hybrid differ greatly depending upon the particular parental strains used. Any widespread species contains a great store of genetic variability, including not only genes which affect the adaptation of the population to its environment, but also those which help or hinder the ability of a species to cross and exchange genes with individuals of another species.

The genetic complexity of reproductive isolating mechanisms is shown by studies of segregation for fertility in later generations of hybrids between partly interfertile species. Two good examples are the hybrid between *Galeopsis getrahit* and *G. bifida,* of the mint family, analyzed by Müntzing, and that between *Drosophila pseudoobscura* and *D. persimilis.* In both examples segregation was very complex, and indicated that many different gene pairs were contributing to the sterility barrier. Less complete data from many other crosses point in the same direction. The inability of two species to cross and form fertile hybrids is not acquired through the appearance of one or two mutations with profound effects. Like other differences between races and species, it is built up gradually through the accumulation of many genetic differences, each one with a small effect.

The ways in which natural selection can build up reproductive-isolating barriers are by no means fully understood, but evidence concerning them is accumulating. For instance, in both frogs and fishes, races of the same species which are adapted to growth under different optimal temperature conditions may produce abnormal embryos when crossed with each other. This is apparently the result of disharmony in interaction between genes controlling different rates and temperature optima of embryonic growth.

In plants, the sterility of interspecific hybrids is often due largely to differences between the parental species in chromosomal structure. Within certain species, such as *Trillium kamschaticum*, special cytological techniques have revealed many differences between both individuals and races in respect to small details of chromosome structure. These differences are partly correlated with both the climatic features of the present environment in northern Japan, where the species is common, and with the geological history of that region. Since chromosomal diversity in this species runs parallel with diversity in morphological characteristics, we can suspect that natural selection has operated in similar ways to bring about both kinds of differences. Although the chromosomal differences between the races of this particular species of *Trillium* are not great enough to cause hybrids between races to be sterile, the related species of *Trillium* differ from *T. kamschaticum* in respect to more numerous chromosomal differences of the same kind. Furthermore, although hybrids between diploid species of *Trillium* are not known, a wealth of evidence from hybrids between species in other plant genera shows that chromosomal differences such as those which exist between the diploid species of *Trillium* can be responsible for hybrid sterility. Furthermore, this sterility can be overcome by doubling the chromosome number. This places together in the same hybrid nucleus duplicate sets of chromosomes, which are consequently able to pair normally and produce viable gametes.

Once reproductive isolating barriers have arisen, they can be strengthened and reinforced by natural selection which favors those individuals of a species having an instinctive tendency to mate with others of their own species. This process has been fully discussed by Dobzhansky.

A final way in which species-separating barriers can be formed is as a secondary result of hybridization between preexisting species. The process of amphiploidy, or the production of fertile, true-breeding species by doubling the chromosome number of sterile hybrids, is now well known to geneticists, and numerous examples have been described, both in the garden and in nature. In addition, more recent experiments have shown that highly sterile, though slightly fertile interspecific hybrids can produce more fertile offspring in later generations without change in chromosome number. Furthermore, some of the fully fertile strains which can be bred from such offspring may form partly sterile hybrids when crossed with either of the original parental species. This is apparently brought about by the effects of genetic recombination, which in rare instances may build up a new harmonious recombination of those genetic differences which were responsible for the original sterility barrier.

Half a century ago, many evolutionists believed that the critical experiment which would demonstrate our understanding of evolutionary processes would be the production under controlled conditions of a new species. This they defined as a population which would breed true and would be reproductively isolated by hybrid inviability or sterility from all other pre-existing populations. Amphiploids, or doubled hybrids, fulfill this qualification in every respect, and the partially isolated segregates with unchanged chromosome number which have been produced in *Elymus, Nicotiana,* and *Delphinium* come close to it. While the former constitute a special type, rare or lacking in the animal kingdom, segregates of the latter type might be expected in all types of organisms. Furthermore, since partial sterility is found in many hybrids between different races of the same animal species, the origin of new species from such hybrids would require the addition of only a few mutations to the extreme segregants which gene recombination can produce in the progeny of such hybrids. The origin of species, one of the most crucial steps in evolution, is well on the way to becoming understood.

THE MAJOR TRENDS OF EVOLUTION

The seventh and final basic postulate about evolutionary processes is as follows: The origin of genera and other higher categories, as well as the longtime trends which have given rise to increasingly complex and highly organized forms of life, results from the continuation into geologic spans of time of the processes responsible for evolution on the racial and species level. The only new element which must be considered is the increasingly evident extinction of populations intermediate between the successful lines.

The first type of evidence in favor of this postulate is the fact that some of the same kinds of differences which in one group of organisms may form the distinction between genera, or even families, can in a related group exist as differences between species of the same genus or even between races of the same species. This has been illustrated elsewhere for the grass family.

Even more convincing evidence has been obtained from careful studies of fossil lineages, particularly in mammals. This evidence is carefully reviewed by Simpson. He has shown that the earliest representatives of lines which led eventually to very different kinds of animals were so much alike that they would unquestionably be placed in the same group if their descendants were not known. For instance, ancestral lineages of the modern horse, rhinoceros, and the Biblical cony (*Hyrax*) can all be traced back through a succession of fossil forms to the Eocene period, fifty to sixty million years ago. At this period, these lineages have converged to such an extent that the forms representing them are much alike in size, shape, head form, and tooth structure. Furthermore, the different representatives of the same lineage which followed immediately after each other in time were usually so much alike that they could easily be visualized as having evolved through the accumulation of many relatively small genetic differences.

To be sure, many examples are known in which a new type of animal or plant appears suddenly and seems to be completely separate in respect to many large differences from any earlier fossil form. To explain these apparent saltations Simpson assumes that the fossil record contains many highly significant gaps. Furthermore, both his evidence and logical arguments suggest strongly that those conditions which would be most likely to bring about the origin of a new major adaptive complex and hence a new higher category would also be most likely to produce gaps in the fossil record. Organisms which exist as large populations in stable environments have the greatest chance of being preserved as fossils, but are the least likely to give rise to new adaptive types. New departures in evolution are most likely to occur when a system of relatively small populations, partly isolated from each other, is evolving in a rapidly changing environment. This combination of conditions is perhaps more unfavorable than any other for preserving such forms as fossils.

If, as Simpson believes, apparent saltations are produced by a combination of rapid evolution plus unfavorable conditions for fossilization, then those groups with the poorest fossil record should have the largest number of apparent saltations, and the improvement of our knowledge of the fossil record should progressively fill in the gaps. Recent progress in fossil discovery has shown this to be true in a striking fashion. In particular, the fossil history of man, which a generation ago had to be interpreted on the basis of fragments which could almost have been counted on the fingers of one's hands, now is illustrated by a variety of prehuman types, many of which are represented by a considerable number of individual fossils. As Le Gros Clark has emphasized, these new finds have definitely filled in some of the gaps. They have made it highly probable that the fossil primates which are waiting to be unearthed will eventually give us a continuous sequence extending from the ape- or monkey-like common ancestor which existed thirty or forty million years ago up to modern man.

SOME THOUGHTS ON AN
EVOLUTIONARY PHILOSOPHY

This discussion will close with some thoughts on how our present knowledge of evolution could affect our philosophy of life. The point of view adopted here is entirely personal, and I make no apologies for it. The facts upon which it is based are derived from a variety of sources, and most of the ideas have already been expressed by a number of other writers.

When we apply the concepts of evolution to our own past, we quickly realize that man is the product of two different kinds of evolution. Our bodies have evolved in the same way as those of other mammals, particularly primates. As mentioned above, the fossil record of man's ancestors is gradually being laid bare. We now can reconstruct with some assurance the way in which our ancestors first started to walk erect, to use tools and fire, and to hunt game in groups or primitive societies. We are sure that the size of the human brain increased gradually, as did also man's ability to make better tools. If, therefore, we consider only our bodies, we must conclude that we are no more than large apes that walk erect and have unusually large brains.

But our present way of life does not depend only upon our bodies and our brain power. Our minds and our social organization contribute far more to human nature than our bodies. Furthermore, our minds and social behavior, although based upon the foundation of our biological, genetic heredity, must nevertheless be reconstructed in each generation by learning. From our parents, our teachers, and from the leaders of our society we acquire a vast store of cultural heredity, which has been built up slowly and carefully by the thousands of generations of men who have preceded us. It is upon this heritage that our present way of life depends. When men first began to make tools, wear clothes, build shelters, and talk to each other, they set in motion a new kind of evolution, which we call socio-cultural evolution. Although built upon the foundations of organic evolution, socio-cultural evolution follows new directions and is governed by new principles. The familiar biological processes of mutation and genetic recombination are replaced by invention, learning, and cultural spread, or diffusion. Selection exists in socio-cultural evolution, but it makes progress through differential survival of customs and inventions rather than of men. It is thus radically different from the natural selection which guides organic evolution.

Finally, cultural evolution produces its effects in an entirely new way. Through organic evolution, organisms became modified to suit their environment; socio-cultural evolution enables man to modify the environment to suit his own needs. Animals became adapted to cold climates by developing fur; man, by building furnaces or by borrowing fur from animals. Birds became able to fly by growing wings and profoundly modifying their bodies; we fly infinitely higher and faster by elaborately designed machines, which even transport a bit of low-level, warm, temperate climate many miles above the earth.

Most important, organic evolution is opportunistic in direction. It is governed by the chance combination of environmental factors and the types of organisms which happen to exist at any one time. Socio-cultural evolution, on the other hand, is determined at least in part by man's own foresight and his ability to conceive of a better way of life for himself and his descendants.

We cannot overemphasize the fact that socio-cultural evolution is totally new in quality and has made man qualitatively different from all animals. This is true in spite of the fact that its beginning depended largely upon quantitative increases in brain power, and that in particular mental characteristics, like the ability to learn, memorize, and communicate with each other, we differ only in degree from the more intelligent kinds of apes. One of the most important facts about all of evolution is that from time to time new qualities emerge through more complex organization of simpler substances and systems. On the chemical level, we see this in many compounds which have properties very different from the chemical elements and simpler compounds of which they are built. The properties of salt and the elasticity of rubber are examples. Life itself differs from non-living matter only in having a special type of very complex organization. Since the dominant theme of cultural evolution has also been increasing complexity of organization, one need not be surprised that it has generated entirely new qualities. Our minds, our foresight, and our social structure, although they are the products of evolution, are nevertheless completely real and new. They set us apart from animals just as truly as if they had been specially created.

Another important fact about socio-cultural evolution is that it progressed for a very long time through traditions and learning which were passed down to each successive generation by word of mouth, without benefit of writing. Men have been able to speak to each other for at least five hundred thousand years; they have had brains as highly developed as ours for at least seventy-five thousand years; they have had such spiritual beliefs as that in an afterlife for at least fifty thousand years, as witnessed by ancient graves which include implements for use in the world to come. But writing as a means of perpetuating tradition is barely six thousand years old. Now everything we know about modern peoples who are not, or were not, able to write leads us to believe that among them reason dominates only the immediate events of their lives.

Their social structure and their plans for the future are bound up in their emotions and are passed on from generation to generation by spoken rules, stories, chants, poems, and incantations, surrounded with the symbols of religious worship. We do not know how religion began, but we can be sure that it has guided man's evolution for at least a hundred thousand years. Before the advent of writing, the stability of society depended upon the ability of children to learn from their elders the spoken word, and this was developed largely through the force which the symbols of religion gave to certain essential moral precepts. The ability to receive these words and to accept these precepts must, therefore, have had as high a selective value in primitive society as any other characteristic. Spiritual qualities must have been essential to the earliest rational men. Consequently, we must think of man as basically spiritual, regardless of whether we believe that religion was given to him by a supernatural supreme being, or whether, as I believe, we consider that it evolved through the socio-cultural process. The ability of men to put their ideas into writing, thus rendering them much more precise and constant, has enabled us to substitute rational thinking for many of the superstitions of the older religions, and we have not reached the end of this process. Nevertheless, the ties which bind us to our traditional heritage, which enable us to work together, and which stimulate our dreams for the future are still made up largely of emotional and spiritual attachments, and the experience of those nations which have attempted to sever them and substitute purportedly rationalistic philosophies like Marxism have emphasized sharply for us the dangers of such a course.

Hence to the questions, "Why am I here?" and "What is the meaning of life?" I give these answers: Whatever mind or spirit that I possess, as well as the comforts of the civilization in which I live, has been given to me by the work, care, and ideals of my own parents and teachers, their parents and teachers, and so on back through the ages. I owe to them an immense debt, which I can repay only through following their examples, and, like them, learning how to work with my fellow men and to develop ideals and dreams which I can pass on to future generations. And because I believe that human progress has been shaped in the past not by the unalterable will of an inscrutable supreme being, but by the hopes, ideals, and working together of men and women like ourselves, I can hope that whatever I do that is of worth will make the world better for future generations than it would have been if I had not made the effort. This is the greatest satisfaction for which I can hope in either the present life or any conceivable future existence.

4

DARWIN'S MISSING EVIDENCE

H. B. D. Kettlewell

In Darwin's time, certain species of moths were light in color. Today in many areas these same species are largely dark. If Darwin had noticed the color change occurring, he would have observed evolution in action. In the following article, H. B. D. Kettlewell describes experiments that demonstrate how the genetic variability stored in the gene pool of a population of moths enabled the population to survive successive environmental changes.

Charles Darwin's *Origin of Species* . . . was the fruit of 26 years of laborious accumulation of facts from nature. Others before Darwin had believed in evolution, but he alone produced a cataclysm of data in support of it. Yet there were two fundamental gaps in his chain of evidence. First, Darwin had no knowledge of the mechanism of heredity. Second, he had no visible example of evolution at work in nature.

It is a curious fact that both of these gaps could have been filled during Darwin's lifetime. Although Gregor Mendel's laws of inheritance were not discovered by the community of biologists until 1900, they had first been published in 1866. And before Darwin died in 1882, the most striking evolutionary change ever witnessed by man was taking place around him in his own country.

The change was simply this. Less than a century ago moths of certain species were characterized by their light coloration, which matched such backgrounds as light tree trunks and lichen-covered rocks, on which the moths passed the daylight hours sitting motionless. Today in many areas the same species are predominantly dark! We now call this reversal "industrial melanism."

It happens that Darwin's lifetime coincided with the first great man-made change of environment on earth. Ever since the Industrial Revolution commenced in the latter half of the 18th century, large areas of the earth's surface have been contaminated by an insidious and largely unrecognized fallout of smoke particles. In and around industrial areas the fallout is measured in tons per square mile per month; in places like Sheffield in England it may reach 50 tons or more. It is only recently that we have begun to realize how widely the lighter smoke particles are dispersed, and to what extent they affect the flora and fauna of the countryside.

In the case of the flora the smoke particles not only pollute foliage but also kill vegetative lichens on the trunks and boughs of trees. Rain washes the pollutants down the boughs and trunks until they are bare and black. In heavily polluted districts rocks and the very ground itself are darkened.

Now in England there are some 760 species of larger moths. Of these more than 70 have exchanged their light color and pattern for dark or even all-black coloration. Similar changes have occurred in the moths of industrial areas of other countries: France, Germany, Poland, Czechoslovakia, Canada and the U. S. So far, however, such changes have not been observed anywhere in the tropics. It is important to note here that industrial melanism has occurred only among those moths that fly at night and spend the day resting against a background such as a tree trunk.

These, then, are the facts. A profound change of color has occurred among hundreds of species of moths in industrial areas in different parts of the world. How has the change come about? What underlying laws of nature have produced it? Has it any connection with one of the normal mechanisms by which one species evolves into another?

In 1926 the British biologist Heslop Harrison reported that the industrial melanism of moths was caused by a special substance which he alleged was present in polluted air. He called this substance a "melanogen," and suggested that it was manganous sulfate or lead nitrate. Harrison claimed that when he fed foliage impregnated with these salts to the larvae of certain species of light-colored moths, a proportion of their offspring were black. He also stated that this "induced melanism" was inherited according to the laws of Mendel.

Darwin, always searching for missing evidence, might well have accepted Harrison's Lamarckian interpretation, but in 1926 biologists were skeptical. Although the rate of mutation of a hereditary characteristic can be increased in the laboratory by many methods, Harrison's figures inferred a mutation rate of 8 per cent. One of the most frequent mutations in nature is that which causes the disease hemophilia in man; its rate is in the region of .0005 per cent, that is, the mutation occurs about once in 50,000 births. It is, in fact, unlikely that an increased mutation rate has played any part in industrial melanism.

At the University of Oxford during the past seven years we have been attempting to analyze the phenomenon of industrial melanism. We have used many different approaches. We are in the process of making a survey of the present frequency of light and dark forms of each species of moth in Britain that exhibits industrial melanism. We are critically examining each of the two forms to see if between them there are any differences in behavior. We have fed large numbers of larvae of both forms on foliage impregnated with substances in polluted air. We have observed under various conditions the mating preferences and relative mortality of the two forms. Finally we have accumulated much information about the melanism of moths in parts of the world that are far removed from industrial centers, and we have sought to link industrial melanism with the melanics of the past.

Our main guinea pig, both in the field and in the laboratory, has been the peppered moth *Biston betularia* and its melanic form *carbonaria*. This species occurs throughout Europe, and is probably identical with the North American *Amphidasis cognataria*. It has a one-year life cycle; the moth appears from May to August. The moth flies at night and passes the day resting on the trunks or on the underside of the boughs of rough-barked deciduous trees such as the oak. Its larvae feed on the foliage of such trees from June to late October; its pupae pass the winter in the soil.

The dark form of the peppered moth was first recorded in 1848 at Manchester in England. Both the light and dark forms appear in . . . [Figures 4–1 and 4–2]. The background of each photograph is noteworthy. In . . . [Figure 4–2] the background is a lichen-encrusted oak trunk of the sort that today is found only in unpolluted rural districts. Against this background the light form is almost invisible and the dark form is conspicuous. In . . . [Figure 4–1] the background is a bare and blackened oak trunk in the heavily polluted area of Birmingham. Here it is the dark form which is almost invisible, and the light form which is conspicuous. Of 621 wild moths caught in these Birmingham woods in 1953, 90 per cent were the dark form and only 10 per cent the light. Today this same ratio applies in nearly all British industrial areas and far outside them.

We decided to test the rate of survival of the two forms in the contrasting types of woodland. We did this by releasing known numbers of moths of both forms. Each moth was marked on its underside with a spot of quick-drying cellulose paint; a different color was used for each day. Thus when we subsequently trapped large numbers of moths we could identify those we had released and established the length of time they had been exposed to predators in nature.

In an unpolluted forest we released 984 moths: 488 dark and 496 light. We recaptured 34 dark and 62 light, indicating that in these woods the light form had a clear advantage over the dark. We then repeated the experiment in the polluted Birmingham woods, releasing 630 moths: 493 dark and 137 light. The result of the first experiment was completely reversed; we recaptured proportionately twice as many of the dark form as of the light.

For the first time, moreover, we had witnessed birds in the act of taking moths from the trunks. Although Britain has more ornithologists and bird watchers than any other country, there had been absolutely no record of birds actually capturing resting moths. Indeed, many ornithologists doubted that this happened on any large scale.

The reason for the oversight soon became obvious. The bird usually seizes the insect and carries it away so rapidly that the observer sees nothing unless he is keeping a constant watch on the insect. This is just what we were doing in the course of some of our experiments. When I first published our findings, the editor of a certain journal was sufficiently rash as to question whether birds took resting moths at all. There was only one thing to do, and in 1955 Niko Tinbergen of the University of Oxford filmed a repeat of my experiments. The film not only shows that birds capture and eat resting moths, but also that they do so selectively.

These experiments lead to the following conclusions. First, when the environment of a moth such as *Biston betularia* changes so that the moth cannot hide by day, the moth is ruthlessly eliminated by predators unless it mutates to a form that is better suited to its new environment. Second, we now have visible proof that, once a mutation has occurred, natural selection alone can be responsible for its rapid spread. Third, the very fact that one form of moth has replaced another in a comparatively short span of years indicates that this evolutionary mechanism is remarkably flexible.

. . . [A study of the present status of the peppered moth that included more than 20,000 observations by 170 voluntary observers living in various parts of Britain makes the following points.] First, there is a strong correlation between industrial centers and a high percentage of the dark form of the moth. Second, populations consisting entirely of the light form are found today only in western England and northern Scotland. Third, though the counties of eastern England are far removed from industrial centers, a surprisingly high percentage of the dark form is found in them. This, in my opinion, is due to the long-standing fallout

FIGURE 4–1—Dark and light forms of the peppered moth were photographed on the trunk of an oak blackened by the polluted air of the English industrial city of Birmingham. The light form (*Biston betularia*) is clearly visible; the dark form (*carbonaria*) is well camouflaged. (Courtesy of Dr. H. B. D. Kettlewell, Genetics Laboratory, Department of Zoology, Oxford, England.)

FIGURE 4–2—The same two forms of the peppered moth were photographed against the lichen-encrusted trunk of an oak in an unpolluted area. Here it is the dark form which may be clearly seen. The light form, almost invisible, is just below and to the right of the dark form. (Courtesy of Dr. H. B. D. Kettlewell, Genetics Laboratory, Department of Zoology, Oxford, England.)

of smoke particles carried from central England by the prevailing south-westerly winds.

Now in order for the dark form of a moth to spread, a mutation from the light form must first occur. It appears that the frequency with which this happens—that is, the mutation rate—varies according to the species. The rate at which the light form of the peppered moth mutates to the dark form seems to be fairly high; the rate at which the mutation occurs in other species may be very low. For example, the light form of the moth *Procus literosa* disappeared from the Sheffield area many years ago, but it has now reappeared in its dark form. It would seem that a belated mutation has permitted the species to regain lost territory. Another significant example is provided by the moth *Tethea ocularis*. Prior to 1947 the dark form of this species was unknown in England. In that year, however, many specimens of the dark form were for the first time collected in various parts of Britain; in some districts today the dark form now comprises more than 50 per cent of the species. There is little doubt that this melanic arrived in Britain not by mutation but by migration. It had been known for a considerable time in the industrial areas of northern Europe, where presumably the original mutation occurred.

The mutation that is responsible for industrial melanism in moths is in the majority of cases controlled by a single gene. A moth, like any other organism that reproduces sexually, has two genes for each of its hereditary characteristics: one gene from each parent. The mutant gene of a melanic moth is inherited as a Mendelian dominant; that is, the effect of the mutant gene is expressed and the effect of the other gene in the pair is not. Thus a moth that inherits the mutant gene from only one of its parents is melanic.

The mutant gene, however, does more than simply control the coloration of the moth. The same gene (or others closely linked with it in the hereditary material) also gives rise to physiological and even behavioral traits. For example, it appears that in some species of moths the caterpillars of the dark form are hardier than the caterpillars of the light form. Genetic differences are also reflected in mating preference. On cold nights more males of the light form of the peppered moth appear to be attracted to light females than to dark. On warm nights, on the other hand, significantly more light males are attracted to dark females.

There is evidence that, in a population of peppered moths that inhabits an industrial area, caterpillars of the light form attain full growth earlier than caterpillars of the dark form. This may be due to the fact that the precipitation of pollutants on leaves greatly increases late in the autumn. Caterpillars of the dark form may be hardier in the presence of such pollution than caterpillars of the light form. In that case natural selection would favor light-form caterpillars which mature early over light-form caterpillars which mature late. For the hardier caterpillars of the dark form, on the other hand, the advantages of later feeding and longer larval life might outweigh the disadvantages of feeding on increasingly polluted leaves. Then natural selection would favor those caterpillars which mature late.

Another difference between the behavior of *B. betularia* and that of its dark form *carbonaria* is suggested by our experiments on the question of whether each form can choose the "correct" background on which to rest during the day. We offered light and dark backgrounds of equal area to moths of both forms, and discovered that a significantly large proportion of each form rested on the correct background. Before these results can be accepted as proven, the experiments must be repeated on a larger scale. If they are proven, the behavior of both forms could be explained by the single mechanism of "contrast appreciation." This mechanism assumes that one segment of the eye of a moth senses the color of the background and that another segment senses the moth's own color; thus the two colors could be compared. Presumably if they were the same, the moth would remain on its background; but if they were different, "contrast conflict" would result and the moth would move off again. That moths tend to be restless when the colors conflict is certainly borne out by recent field observations.

It is evident, then, that industrial melanism is much more than a simple change from light to dark. Such a change must profoundly upset the balance of hereditary traits in a species, and the species must be a long time in restoring that balance. Taking into account all the favorable and unfavorable factors at work in this process, let us examine the spread of a mutation similar to the dark form of the peppered moth. . . .

According to the mutation rate and the size of the population, the new mutation may not appear in a population for a period varying from one to 50 years. . . . Let us now assume the following: that the original successful mutation took place in 1900, that subsequent new mutations failed to survive, that the total local population was one million, and that the mutant had a 30-per-cent advantage over the light form. (By a 30-per-cent advantage for the dark form we mean that, if in one generation there were 100 light moths and 100 dark, in the next generation there would be 85 light moths and 115 dark.)

On the basis of these assumptions there would be one melanic moth in 1,000 only in 1929. Not until 1938 would there be one in 100. Once the melanics attain this level, their rate of increase greatly accelerates.

In the period between 1900 and 1938 natural selection is complicated by other forces. Though the color of the dark form gives it an advantage over the light, the new trait is introduced into a system of other traits balanced for the light form; thus the dark form is at first at a considerable physiological disadvantage. In fact, when moths of the dark form were crossed with moths of the light form 50 years ago, the resulting broods were significantly deficient in the dark form. When the same cross is made today, the broods contain more of the dark form than one would expect. The system of hereditary traits has become adjusted to the new trait.

There is evidence that other changes take place during the period [between 1900 and 1938]. Specimens of the peppered moth from old collections indicate that the earliest melanics were not so dark as the modern dark form: they retained some of the white spots of the light form. Today a large proportion of the moths around a city such as Manchester are jet black. Evidently when the early melanics inherited one gene for melanism, the gene was not entirely dominant with respect to the gene for light coloration. As the gene complex adjusted to the mutation, however, the new gene became almost entirely dominant.

When the dark form comprises about 10 per cent of the population, it may jump to 90 per cent in as little as 15 or 20 years. . . . Thereafter the proportion of the dark form increases at a greatly reduced rate.

Eventually one of two things must happen: either the light form will slowly be eliminated altogether, or a balance will be struck so that the light form continues to appear as a small but definite proportion of the population. This is due to the fact that the moths which inherit one gene for dark coloration and one for light (heterozygotes) have an advantage over the moths which inherit two genes for dark coloration (homozygotes). And when two heterozygotes mate, a quarter of their offspring will have two genes for light coloration, i.e., they will be light. Only after a very long period of time, therefore, could the light forms (and with them the gene for light coloration) be entirely eliminated. This period of removal . . . might be more than 1,000 years. Indications so far suggest, however, that complete removal is unlikely, and that a balance of the two forms would probably occur. In this balance the light form would represent about 5 per cent of the population.

The mechanisms I have described are without doubt the explanation of industrial melanism: normal mutation followed by natural selection resulting in an insect of different color, physiology and behavior. Industrial melanism involves no new laws of nature; it is governed by the same mechanisms which have brought about the evolution of new species in the past.

There remains, however, one major unsolved problem. Why is it that, in almost all industrial melanics, the gene for melanism is dominant? Many geneticists would agree that dominance is achieved by natural selection, that it is somehow related to a successful mutation in the distant past. With these thoughts in mind I recently turned my attention away from industrial centers and collected moths in one of the few remaining pieces of ancient Caledonian pine forest in Britain: the Black Wood of Rannoch. Located in central Scotland far from industrial centers, the Black Wood is probably very similar to the forests that covered Britain some 4,000 years ago. The huge pines of this forest are only partly covered with lichens. Here I found no fewer than seven species of moths with melanic forms.

I decided to concentrate on the species *Cleora repandata,* the dark form of which is similar to the dark form of the same species that has swept through central England. This dark form, like the industrial melanics, is inherited as a Mendelian dominant. Of just under 500 specimens of *C. repandata* observed, 10 per cent were dark.

C. repandata spends the day on pine trunks, where the light form is almost invisible. The dark form is somewhat more easily seen. By noting at dawn the spot where an insect had come to rest, and then revisiting the tree later in the day, we were able to show that on some days more than 50 per cent of the insects had moved. Subsequently we found that because of disturbances such as ants or hot sunshine they had had to fly to another tree trunk, usually about 50 yards away. I saw large numbers of these moths on the wing, and three other observers and I agreed that the dark form was practically invisible at a distance of more than 20 yards, and that the light form could be followed with ease at a distance of up to 100 yards. In fact, we saw birds catch three moths of the light form in flight. It is my belief that when it is on the wing in these woods the dark form has an advantage over the light, and that when it is at rest the reverse is true.

This may be one of many ways in which melanism was useful in the past. It may also explain the balance between the light and dark forms of *Cleora repandata* in the Black Wood of Rannoch. In this case a melanic may have been preserved for one evolutionary reason but then have spread widely for another.

The melanism of moths occurs in many parts of the world that are not industrialized, and in environments that are quite different. It is found in the mountain rain forest of New Zealand's South Island, which is wet and dark. It has been observed in arctic and subarctic regions where in summer moths must fly in daylight. It is known in very high mountains, where dark coloration may permit the absorption of heat and make possible increased activity. In each case recurrent mutation has provided the source of the change, and natural selection, as postulated by Darwin, has decided its destiny.

Melanism is not a recent phenomenon but a very old one. It enables us to appreciate the vast reserves of genetic variability which are contained within each species, and which can be summoned when the occasion arises. Had Darwin observed industrial melanism he would have seen evolution occurring not in thousands of years but in thousands of days—well within his lifetime. He would have witnessed the consummation and confirmation of his life's work.

SELECTED READINGS

Barnett, S. A., ed., 1959, *A Century of Darwinism*. Cambridge, Mass.: Harvard University Press.

Boyd, W., 1953, "The Contribution of Genetics to Anthropology," *Anthropology Today: An Encyclopedic Inventory*, A. C. Kroeber, ed. Chicago: University of Chicago Press.

———, 1963, "Four Achievements of the Genetical Method in Anthropology," *American Anthropologist*, 65:243–252.

Clark, W. E. Le Gros, 1959, "The Crucial Evidence for Human Evolution," *American Scientist*, 47:299–313.

Dobzhansky, Th., 1962, *Mankind Evolving; the Evolution of the Human Species*. New Haven, Conn.: Yale University Press.

Dunn, L. C., 1959, *Heredity and Evolution in Human Populations*. Cambridge, Mass.: Harvard University Press.

Mayr, Ernst, 1963, *Animal Species and Evolution*. Cambridge, Mass.: Belknap Press of Harvard University Press.

Merrell, D. J., 1962, *Evolution and Genetics; the Modern Theory of Evolution*. New York: Holt, Rinehart and Winston, Inc.

Moody, Paul A., 1962, *Introduction to Evolution*, 2d ed. New York: Harper & Row.

Neel, J. V., 1958, "The Study of Natural Selection in Primitive and Civilized Human Populations," *Human Biology*, 30:43–72.

———, and W. J. Schull, 1954, *Human Heredity*. Chicago: University of Chicago Press.

Rensch, B., 1960, *Evolution above the Species Level*. New York: Columbia University Press.

Sheppard, P. M., 1959, "Blood Groups and Natural Selection," *British Medical Bulletin*, 15:134–139.

Simpson, G. G., 1966, "The Biological Nature of Man," *Science*, 152:472–478.

————, 1960, "The World into Which Darwin Led Us," *Science,* 131: 966–974.

Smith, J. M., 1958, *The Theory of Evolution.* Baltimore, Md.: Penguin.

Tax, Sol, ed., 1960, *Evolution after Darwin; the University of Chicago Centennial,* Vol. I. *The Evolution of Life. Its Origin, History and Future.* Vol. II. *The Evolution of Man, Mind, Culture, and Society.* Chicago: University of Chicago Press.

PART THREE

THE DYNAMICS
OF HOMINID
EVOLUTION

If we are ever to understand how human beings evolved from nonhumans, if we are ever to grasp the significance of human body form and changes in structure as evidenced by the hominid record, we must study human evolution in a larger context than simply the close examination and comparison of fossils. The realization that human evolution is in large part the evolution of man's capacity for culture now influences most research in physical anthropology. It is to the larger comprehension of human evolution that the modern generation of paleoanthropologists are addressing themselves. Results of the reconstruction of the history of plant life and animal life in areas inhabited by human populations have gone into the synthesis, as have studies of the relation between anatomical structure and behavior as well as the study of the evolutionary processes themselves. Precise determination of dating, by careful stratigraphic and chemical analysis, has also helped to wring every last bit of data from the fossil record.

In the articles that follow, some of the major problems of hominid evolution are discussed. Washburn and Lancaster examine the characteristics of hunting as a way of life, and assess their significance for human biological and social evolution. Garn attempts to see the similarities among the successive fossil groups as an antidote to the traditional emphasis on the differences.

The articles have been selected not only to offer a balanced view of the present disagreements among anthropologists about hominid evolution but also to provide a picture of the area of consensus particularly with regard to the major importance of culture in the evolution of man. Even when anthropologists are talking about teeth and molar-cusp structure, they are well aware that the evolution of the capacity for culture is the real topic of their conversation.

5

THE EVOLUTION OF HUNTING[1]

S. L. Washburn and C. S. Lancaster

The fossil record of human evolution indicates that the Hominidae separated from the other hominoid lines 15 to 20 million years ago, and that by 2 to 3 million years ago, adaptations for bipedalism, tool-use, and cultural modes of behavior were already firmly established. The 2-million-year span of the Pleistocene epoch was marked by further transformations in human genotypes that were to equip populations of bipedal, tool-making, and symbol-using humans to make a unique niche for themselves among the earth's living creatures. What were these prehistoric human beings really like? How did they live? What goals for living did their societies develop? What did they think about? What did they believe in? What were they afraid of? Such questions are not beyond all conjecture; they are not even beyond the scope of investigation. In Part Three, an article by Geertz and one by Prost and Milner will discuss the ways that different lines of evidence may converge in reconstructing the life of early man.

An illustration of how such reconstruction may be effected is provided in the following selection. Starting with the fact that man has lived as a hunter for almost his entire history, the authors explore the implications of the hunting way of life. They utilize data from the fossil record, ecology, primate studies, and ethnography of contemporary hunting cultures to present a picture of early human populations living as hunters.

("The Evolution of Hunting" appears with alterations in the symposium *Man the Hunter*, edited by Irven DeVore and Richard Lee. By permission of the authors and the editors.)

[1] This paper was presented as part of a program on primate behavior supported by the United States Public Health Service (Grant No. 8623) and aided by a Research Professorship in the Miller Institute for Basic Research in Science at the University of California at Berkeley. The authors wish to thank Dr. Phyllis C. Jay for her helpful criticism and suggestions.

S. L. Washburn is Professor of Anthropology at the University of California, Berkeley. C. S. Lancaster is also at the University of California, engaged in research in the evolution of behavior.

. . . Human hunting is made possible by tools, but it is far more than a technique, or even a variety of techniques. It is a way of life, and the success of the hunting adaptation (in its total social, technical, and psychological dimensions) has dominated the course of human evolution for hundreds of thousands of years. In a very real sense our intellect, interests, emotions, and basic social life are evolutionary products of the success of the hunting adaptation. When anthropologists speak of the unity of mankind, they are stating that the selection pressures of the hunting and gathering way of life were so similar and the result so successful that populations of *Homo sapiens* are still fundamentally the same everywhere. In this essay we are concerned with the general characteristics of man that we believe can be attributed to the hunting way of life.

Perhaps the importance of the hunting way of life in producing man is best shown by the length of time hunting has dominated human history. The genus *Homo*[2] has been existent for some 600,000 years, but agriculture has been important only during the last few thousand years. Even 6000 years ago large parts of the world's population were nonagricultural, and the entire evolution of earliest *Homo erectus* into existing races took place during the period in which man was a hunter. The common factors that dominated human evolution and produced *Homo sapiens* were preagricultural. Agricultural ways of life have dominated less than 1 percent of human history, and there is no evidence of major biological changes during that period of time. The kinds of minor biological changes that occurred and which are used to characterize some modern races are not common to *Homo sapiens*. The origin of all common characteristics must be sought in preagricultural times. Probably all experts would agree that hunting was a part of the social adaptation of populations of the genus *Homo*, and many would regard *Australopithecus*[3] as an earlier hominid who was already a hunter, although possibly much less efficient than the later forms. If this is true and if the Pleistocene period had a duration of 3 million years, then pre-*Homo erectus* human tool-using and hunting lasted for at least four times as long as the duration of the genus *Homo*. No matter how the earlier times may ultimately be

[2] The term *Homo* includes Java, Peking, Maur, and later forms.

[3] This term is used to include both the small *A. africanus* and *A. robustus* large forms. Simpson (1966) briefly and clearly discusses the taxonomy of these forms and of the fragments called *Homo habilis*.

interpreted, the observation of more hunting among apes than was previously suspected and increasing evidence of hunting by *Australopithecus* strengthens the position that less than 1 percent of human history has been dominated by agriculture. It is for this reason that the consideration of hunting is so important for the understanding of human evolution.

When hunting and the way of life of successive populations of the genus *Homo* are considered, it is important to remember that there must have been both technical and biological progress during this vast period of time. Although the locomotor system appears to have changed very little in the last 500,000 years, the brain did increase in size, and the form of the face evolved. But for present purposes it is particularly necessary to direct attention to the cultural changes that occurred in the last ten or fifteen thousand years before agriculture. There is no convenient term for this period of time, traditionally spoken of as the end of the Upper Paleolithic and the Mesolithic, but Binford has rightly emphasized its importance.

During most of human history water must have been a major physical and psychological barrier and the inability to cope with water is shown in the archeological record by the absence of remains of fish, shellfish, or any object that would have required either going deeply into water or the use of boats. There is no evidence that the resources of river and sea were utilized until this late preagricultural period, and since the consumption of shellfish in particular leaves huge middens, the negative evidence is impressive. It is likely that the basic problem in utilization of resources from sea or river was that man cannot swim naturally and to do so must learn a difficult skill. The normal quadrupedal running motions of monkeys serve to keep them afloat and moving quite rapidly. A macaque, for example, does not have to learn any new motor habit in order to swim. But the locomotor patterns of gibbons and apes will not keep them above the water surface, and even a narrow, shallow stream is a barrier for the gorilla. For early man, water was a barrier and a danger, not a resource.

In addition to the conquest of water, there seems to have been great technical progress in the late preagricultural period. Besides a wide variety of stone tools of earlier kinds, the archeological record shows bows and arrows, grinding stones, boats, house of more advanced types and even villages, sledges drawn by animals and used for transport, and the domestic dog. These facts have two special kinds of significance . . . First, the technology of *all* the living hunters belongs at the earliest to this late Mesolithic era, and many have elements borrowed from agricultural and metal-using peoples. Second, the occasional high densities of hunters mentioned as problems and exceptions . . . are based on a very late and modified extension of the hunting and gathering way of life. For example, the way of life of the tribes of the Northwest Coast, with polished stone axes for woodworking, boats, and extensive reliance on products of river and sea, should be seen as a very late adaptation.

The presence of the dog is a good index of the late preagricultural period, and domestic dogs were used by hunters in Africa, Australia, and the Americas. Among the Eskimos, dogs were used in hunting, for transportation, as food in time of famine, and as watchdogs. With dogs, sleds, boats, metal, and complex technology, Eskimos may be better examples of the extremes to which human adaptation can go than examples of primitive hunting ways. . . . Dogs were of great importance in hunting for locating, tracking, bringing to bay, and even killing. Lee mentions that one Bushman with dogs brought in much more game than the other hunters. Dogs may be important in hunting even very large animals; in the Amboseli Game Reserve in Kenya one of the present authors saw two small dogs bring a rhinoceros to bay and dodge repeated charges.

With the acquisition of dogs, bows, and boats, it is certain that hunting became much more complex in the last few thousand years before agriculture. The antiquity of traps, snares, and poisons is unknown, but it appears that until a few thousand years ago man was able to kill large game close in with spear or axe. As Brues has shown, this kind of hunting limits the size of the hunters, and there are no very large or very small fossil men. Pygmoid hunters of large game are probably possible only if hunting is with bows, traps, and poison. It is remarkable that nearly all the estimated statures of fossil men fall between 5 feet 2 inches and 5 feet 10 inches. This suggests that strong selection pressures kept human stature within narrow limits for hundreds of thousands of years and that these pressures relaxed a few thousand years ago, allowing the evolution of a much wider range of statures.

Gathering and the preparation of food also seem to have become more complex during the last few thousand years before agriculture. Obviously gathering by nonhuman primates is limited to things that can be eaten immediately. In contrast, man gathers a wide range of items that he cannot digest without soaking, boiling, grinding, or other special preparation. Seeds may have been a particularly important addition to the human diet because they were abundant and could be stored easily. Since grinding stones appeared before agriculture, grinding and boiling may have been the necessary preconditions to the discovery of agriculture. One can easily imagine that people who were grinding seeds would see repeated examples of seeds sprouting or being planted by accident. Grinding and boiling were certainly known to the preagricultural peoples, and this knowledge could have spread along an arctic route, setting the stage for a nearly simultaneous discovery of agriculture in both the New and Old Worlds. It was not necessary for agriculture itself to have spread through the arctic but only the seed-using technology, which could have then led to the discovery of seed planting. If this analysis is at all correct, then the hunting-gathering adaptation of the Indians of California, for example, should be seen as representing the possibilities of this late preagricultural gathering, making possible much higher population densities than would have been the case in a pre-grinding and preboiling economy.

Whatever the fate of these speculations, we think that the main conclusion, based on the archeological record, ecological considerations, and the ethnology of the surviving hunter-gatherers, will be sustained. In the last few thousand years before agriculture, both hunting and gathering became much more complex. The final adaptation, including the use of products of river and sea and the grinding and cooking of otherwise inedible seeds and nuts, was worldwide, laid the basis for the discovery of agriculture, and was much more effective and diversified than the previous hunting and gathering adaptations.

Hunting by members of the genus *Homo* throughout the 600,000 years that the genus has persisted has included the killing of large numbers of big animals. This implies the efficient use of tools, as Birdsell has stressed. . . . The adaptive value of hunting large animals has been shown by Bourlière, who has demonstrated that 75 percent of the meat available to human hunters in the eastern Congo was elephant, buffalo, and hippopotamus. It is some measure of the success of human hunting that when these large species are protected in game reserves (as in the Murchison Falls or Queen Elizabeth Parks in Uganda) they multiply rapidly and destroy the vegetation. As evidenced in the Masai Amboseli Reserve in Kenya, elephants alone can destroy trees more rapidly than can be replaced naturally. Since the predators are also protected in reserves, it appears that human hunters have been killing enough large game to maintain the balance of nature for many thousands of years. It is tempting to think that man replaced the saber-toothed cat as the major predator of large game, both controlling the numbers of the game and causing the extinction of Old World saber-tooths. We think that hunting and butchering large animals put a maximum premium on cooperation among males, a behavior that is at an absolute minimum among the nonhuman primates. It is difficult to imagine the killing of creatures such as cave bears, mastodons, mammoths—or dinotherium at a much earlier time—without highly coordinated, cooperative action among males. It may be that the origin of male-male associates lies in the necessity of cooperation in hunting, butchering, and war. Certainly butchering sites, such as those described by Clark Howell in Spain, imply that the organization of the community for hunting large animals goes back for many, many thousands of years. From the biological point of view, the development of such organizations would have been paralleled by selection for an ability to plan and cooperate (or reduction of rage). Because females and juveniles may be involved in hunting small creatures, the social organization of big-game hunting would also lead to an intensification of a sexual division of labor.

As noted before, it is important to stress that human hunting is a set of ways of life. It involves division of labor between male and female, cooperation among males, planning, knowledge of many species and large areas, and technical skill. Recently, the old idea has been revived that the way of life of our ancestors was similar to that of wolves, rather than that of apes or monkeys. But this completely misses the special nature of the human adaptation. Human females do not go out and hunt and then regurgitate to their young when they return. Human young do not stay in dens but are carried by mothers. Male wolves do not kill with tools, butcher, and share with females who have been gathering. In an evolutionary sense the whole human pattern is new, and it is the success of a particularly human way that dominated human evolution and determined the relation of biology and culture for thousands of years. Judging from the archeological record, it is probable that the major features of this human way, possibly even including the beginnings of language, had evolved by the time of *Homo erectus*.[4]

---

[4] In speculations of this kind, it is well to keep in mind the purpose of the speculation and the limitation of the evidence. Our aim is to understand human evolution. What shaped the course of human evolution was a succession of successful adaptations, both biological and cultural. These may be inferred in part from the direct evidence of the archeological record. But the record is very incomplete. For example, Lee has described how large game may be butchered where it falls and only meat brought back to camp. This kind of behavior means that analysis of bones around living sites is likely to underestimate both the amount and variety of game killed. If there is any evidence that large animals were killed, it is probable that far more were killed than the record shows. Just as the number of human bones gives no indication of the number of human beings, the number of animal bones, although providing clues to the existence of hunting, gives no direct evidence of how many animals were killed. The Pleistocene way of life can only be known by inference and speculation. Obviously, speculations are based on much surer ground when the last few thousand years are under consideration. Ethnographic information is then directly relevant and the culture bearers are of our own species. As we go farther back in time, there is less evidence and the biological and cultural differences become progressively greater. Yet it was in a remote time that the human way took shape, and it is only through speculation that we may gain some insights into what the life of our ancestors may have been.

THE WORLD VIEW OF THE HUNTER

Lévi-Strauss has urged that we study the world view of hunters, and, perhaps surprisingly, some of the major aspects of this world view can be traced from the archeological record. We have already mentioned that boats and the entire complex of fishing, hunting sea mammals, and using shellfish developed late. With this new orientation, wide rivers and seas changed from barriers to pathways and sources of food, and the human attitude toward water must have changed completely. But many hundreds of thousands of years earlier, perhaps with *Australopithecus,* the relation of the hunters to the land must also have changed from an earlier relationship that may be inferred from studies of contemporary monkeys and apes. Social groups of nonhuman primates occupy exceedingly small areas, and the vast majority of animals probably spend their entire lives within less than four or five square miles. Even though they have excellent vision and can see for many miles, especially from the tops of trees, they make no effort to explore more than a tiny fraction of the area they see. Even for gorillas the range is only about fifteen square miles, and it is of the same order of magnitude for savanna baboons; they refuse to be driven beyond the end of their range and double back. The known area is a psychological reality, clear in the minds of the animals. Only a small part of even this limited range is used, and exploration is confined to the canopy, lower branches, and bushes, or ground, depending on the biology of the particular species. Napier has discussed this highly differential use of a single area by several species. In marked contrast, human hunters are familiar with very large areas. In the area studied by Lee eleven waterholes and several hundred square miles supported a smaller number of Bushmen than the number of baboons supported by a single waterhole and a few square miles in the Amboseli Reserve in Kenya. The most minor hunting expedition covers an area larger than most nonhuman primates would cover in a lifetime. Interest in a large area is human. The small ranges of monkeys and apes restrict the opportunities for gathering, hunting, and meeting conspecies, and limit the kind of predation and the number of diseases. In the wide area, hunters and gatherers can take advantage of seasonal foods, and only man among the primates can migrate long distances seasonally. In the small area, the population must be supported throughout the year on local resources, and natural selection has been for biology and behavior that efficiently utilize these limited opportunities. But in the wide area selection is for the knowledge that enables the group to utilize seasonal and occasional food sources. Gathering over a wide and diversified area implies a greater knowledge of flora and fauna, knowledge of the annual cycle, and a different attitude toward group movements. Clearly one of the great advantages of slow maturation is that learning covers a series of years, and the meaning of events in these years become a part of the individual's knowledge. With rapid maturation and no language the chances that any member of the group will know the appropriate behavior for rare events is greatly reduced.

Moving over long distances creates problems of carrying food and water. Lee has called to our attention that the sharing of food even in one locality implies that food is carried, and there is no use in gathering quantities of fruit or nuts unless they can be moved. If women are to gather while men hunt, the results of the labors of both sexes must be carried back to some agreed-upon location. Meat can be carried easily, but the development of some sort of receptacle for carrying vegetable products may have been one of the most fundamental advances in human evolution. Without a way of carrying, the advantages of a large area are greatly reduced. However that may be, the whole human pattern of gathering and hunting to share is unique to man. In its small range a monkey gathers only what it itself needs to eat at the moment; the whole complex of economic reciprocity that dominates so much of human life is unique to man. Wherever archeological evidence can suggest the beginnings of movement over large ranges, cooperation, and sharing, it is dating the origin of some of the most fundamental aspects of human behavior, of the human world view. We believe that hunting large animals may demand all these aspects of human behavior that separate man so sharply from the other primates. If this is so, then the human way appears to be as old as *Homo erectus*.

The price that man pays for his high mobility is well illustrated by the problems of living in the African savanna. Man is not adapted to this environment in the same sense that baboons or vervet monkeys are. Man needs much more water, and without preparation and cooking he can only eat a limited number of the foods on which the local primates thrive. Unless there have been major physiological changes, the diet of our ancestors must have been far more like that of chimpanzees than like that of a savanna-adapted species. Further, man cannot survive the diseases of the African savanna without lying down and being cared for. Even when sick, the locally adapted animals are usually able to keep moving with their troop; and the importance to their survival of a home base has been stressed elsewhere [see the article by DeVore and Washburn in this volume]. Also, man becomes liable to new diseases and parasites by eating meat, and it is of interest that the products of the sea, which we believe were the last class of foods added to the human diet, are widely regarded as indigestible and carry diseases to which man is particularly susceptible. Although many humans die of disease and injury, those who do not, almost without exception, owe their lives to others who cared for them when they were unable to hunt or gather, and this uniquely human caring is one of the patterns that builds social bonds in the group and permits the species to occupy almost every environment in the world.

A large territory not only provides a much wider range of possible foods but also a greater variety of potentially useful materials. With tool use this variety takes on meaning, and even the earliest pebble tools show selection in size, form, and material. When wood ceases to be just something to climb on, hardness, texture, and form become important. Availability of materials is critical to the tool-user, and the interest of early men in their environment must have been very different from that of monkeys or apes. Thus, the presence of tools in the archeological record is not only an indication of technical progress but also an index of interest in inanimate objects and in a much larger part of the environment than is the case with nonhuman primates.

The tools of the hunters include the earliest beautiful man-made objects, the symmetrical bifaces, especially those of the Acheulian tradition. Just how they were used is still a matter of debate, but, as contemporary attempts to copy them show, their manufacture is technically difficult, taking much time and practice and a high degree of skill. The symmetry of these tools may indicate that they were swung with great speed and force, presumably attached to some sort of handle. A tool that is moved slowly does not have to be symmetrical, but balance becomes important when an object is swung rapidly or thrown with speed. Irregularities will lead to deviations in the course of the blow or the trajectory of flight. An axe or spear to be used with speed and power is subject to very different technical limitations from those of scrapers or digging sticks, and it may well be that it was the attempt to produce efficient high-speed weapons that first produced beautiful, symmetrical objects.

When the selective advantage of a finely worked point over an irregular one is considered, it must be remembered that a small difference might give a very large advantage. A population in which hunters hit the game 5 percent more frequently, more accurately, or at greater distance would bring back much more meat. There must have been strong selection for greater skill in manufacture and use, and it is no accident that the bones of small-brained men (*Australopithecus*) are never found with beautiful, symmetrical tools. If the brains of contemporary apes and men are compared, the areas (both in cerebellum and cortex) associated with hand skills are at least three times as large in man. Clearly, the success of tools has exerted a great influence on the evolution of the brain and has created the skills that make art possible. The evolution of the capacity to appreciate the product must evolve along with the skills of manufacture and use, and the biological capacities that the individual inherits must be developed in play and practiced in games. In this way the beautiful, symmetrical tool becomes a symbol of a level of human intellectual achievement, representing far more than just the tool itself.

In a small group the necessity of practice in developing skills to a very high level restricts the number of useful arts. Where there is little division of labor, all men must learn to use the weapons of the hunt and of war. In sports we take it for granted that one person will not achieve a very high level of performance in more than a limited set of skills. This limitation is in part biological, but it is important socially as well because great proficiency in a skill necessitates practice. In warfare a wide variety of weapons is useful only if there are enough men so that there can be division of labor and different groups can practice different skills. Handedness, a feature that separates man from ape, is a part of this biology of skill. To be ambidextrous might seem ideal, but in fact the highest level of skill is attained by concentrating both biological ability and practice primarily on one hand.

Hunting changed man's relationship to other animals and his view of what is natural. The human notion that it is normal for animals to flee and the whole concept of animals being wild, is the result of man's habit of hunting. In game reserves many different kinds of animals soon learn not to fear man, and they no longer flee. Woodburn took a Hadza into the Nairobi Park, and the Hadza was amazed and excited, because although he had hunted all his life, he had never seen such a quantity and variety of animals close at hand. His whole previous view of animals was the result of his having been their enemy, and they had reacted to him as the most destructive carnivore. In the park, the Hadza hunter saw for the first time the peace of the herbivorous world. Prior to hunting, the relationship of our ancestors to other animals must have been very much like that of the other noncarnivores. They could have moved close among the other species, fed beside them, and shared the same waterholes. But with the origin of human hunting the peaceful relationship was destroyed, and for at least half a million years man has been the enemy of even the largest mammals. In this way the whole human view of what is normal and natural in the relation of man to animals is a product of hunting, and the world of flight and fear is the result of the efficiency of the hunters.

Behind this human view that the flight of animals from man is natural lie some aspects of human psychology. Men enjoy hunting and killing, and these activities are continued as sports even when they are no longer economically necessary. If a behavior is important to the survival of a species (as hunting was for man throughout most of human history), then it must be both easily learned and pleasurable [See the article by Hamburg in this volume]. Part of the motivation for hunting is the immediate pleasure it gives the hunter, and the human killer can no more afford to be sorry for the game than a cat can be for its intended victim. Evolution builds a relation between biology, psychology, and behavior, and, therefore, the evolutionary success of hunting exerted a profound effect on human psychology. Perhaps this is most easily shown by the extent of the efforts devoted to maintain killing as a sport. In former times royalty and nobility maintained parks where they could enjoy the sport of killing, and today the United States government spends many millions of dollars to supply game for hunters. Many people dislike the notion that man is naturally aggressive, that he naturally enjoys the destruction of other creatures. We all know people who, for example, although denying human aggressive tendencies, use the lightest fishing tackle to prolong the fish's futile struggle, to maximize the personal sense of mastery and skill. And until recently war was viewed in much the same way as hunting. Other human beings were simply the most dangerous game, and war has been far too important in human history for it to be other than pleasurable for the males involved. It is only recently, with the entire change in the nature and conditions of war, that this institution has been challenged and the wisdom of war as a normal part of national policy or as an approved road to personal social glory has been questioned.

Human killing differs from killing by carnivorous mammals in that the victims are frequently of the same species as the killer. In carnivores there are submission gestures or sounds that normally stop a fatal attack, but in man there are no effective submission gestures. It was the Roman emperor who might raise his thumb; the victim could make no sound or gesture that might restrain the victor or move the crowd to pity. The lack of biological controls over killing conspecies is a character of human killing that separates this behavior sharply from that of other carnivorous mammals. This difference may be interpreted in a variety of ways. From an evolutionary point of view, it may be that human hunting is so recent that there has not been enough time for controls to evolve. Or it may be that killing other humans was a part of the adaptation from the beginning, and the sharp separation of war and hunting is due to the recent development of these institutions. Or it may be simply that in most human behavior stimulus and response are not tightly bound. Whatever the origin of this behavior it has had profound effects on human evolution, and almost every human society has regarded killing members of certain other human societies as desirable.

Certainly this has been a major factor in man's view of the world, and every folklore contains the tales of the cultural heroes whose fame is based on the human enemies they destroyed.

The extent to which the biological bases for killing have been incorporated into human psychology may be measured by the ease with which boys can be interested in hunting, fishing, fighting, and games of war. It is not that these behaviors are inevitable, but that they are easily learned, satisfying, and have been socially rewarded in most cultures. The skills for killing and the pleasures of killing are normally developed in play, and the patterns of play prepare the children for their adult roles. . . . Woodburn's excellent motion pictures show Hadza boys killing small mammals, and Laughlin describes how Aleuts train boys from early childhood so that they will be able to throw harpoons with accuracy and power while seated in kayaks. The whole youth of the hunter is dominated by practice and appreciation of the skills of the adult males, and the pleasure of the game motivates the practice that is necessary to develop the skills of weaponry. Even in monkeys rougher play and play fighting are largely the activities of the males, and the young females explore less and show a greater interest in infants at an early age. These basic biological differences are reinforced in man by the division of labor that makes adult sex roles differ far more in humans than they do in nonhuman primates. Again, hunting must be seen as a whole pattern of activities, a wide variety of ways of life, the psychobiological roots of which are reinforced by play and by a clear identification with adult roles. Hunting is more than a part of the economic system, and the animal bones in Choukoutien are evidence of the patterns of play and pleasures of our ancestors.

THE SOCIAL ORGANIZATION
OF HUMAN HUNTING

The success of the human hunting and gathering way of life lay in its adaptability. It permitted a single species to occupy most of the earth without biological adaptation to local conditions. The occupation of Australia and the New World probably occurred entirely after the end-Paleolithic-Mesolithic development discussed earlier, but even so there is no evidence that any other primate species occupied more than a fraction of the area of *Homo erectus*. Obviously this adaptability makes any detailed reconstruction impossible, and we are not looking for stages in the traditional evolutionary sense. However, using both knowledge of the contemporary primates and the archeological record, certain important general conditions of our evolution may be reconstructed. For example, the extent of the distribution of the species noted above is remarkable and gives the strongest sort of indirect evidence for the adaptability of the way of life, even half a million years ago. Likewise all evidence suggests that the local group was small—twenty-five to fifty individuals has been suggested as the average size. Such a group size is common in nonhuman primates and so we can say with some assurance that it did not increase until after agriculture. This means that the number of adult males who might cooperate in hunting or war was very limited, and this restricted the kinds of social organizations that were possible. Probably one of the great adaptive advantages of language was that it permitted the planning of cooperation between local groups, temporary division of groups, and the transmission of information over a much wider area than that occupied by any one group.

Within the group of the nonhuman primates the mother and her young may form a subgroup that continues even after the young are fully grown. This grouping affects dominance and grooming and resting patterns, and, along with dominance, is one of the factors giving order to the social relations in the group. The group is not a horde in the traditional sense, but it is ordered by positive affectionate habits and by strength, that is, dominance. Both these principles continued into human society, and dominance based on personal achievement must have been particularly powerful in small groups living dangerous physical lives. The mother-young group certainly continued and the bonds must have been intensified by the prolongation of infancy. In human society economic reciprocity was added, and this created a wholly new set of interpersonal bonds.

When males hunt and females gather, the results are shared and given to the young, and the habitual sharing among a male, a female, and their offspring is the human family. According to this view the human family is the result of the reciprocity of hunting—the addition of a male to the mother-plus-young social group of the monkeys and apes.

This view of the family offers a reason for incest tabus. According to Sade, young sexually mature males do not mate with their mothers. How long this avoidance continues is not known at the present time, but at least some elements of the mother-son incest tabu are present among the nonhuman primates. This emphasizes the point mentioned above that the primate social group is not a horde, but is an orderly organization with principles that are seen to be both more lasting and more complex as the data become richer. If the function of the addition of a male to the group is economic, then the male who is added must be able to fulfill the role of a socially responsible provider. In the case of the hunter this necessitates a degree of skill in hunting and a social maturity that is attained some years after puberty. The necessary delay in the assumption of the role of provider for female and young can be achieved only by an incest tabu because brother-sister mating would result in an infant while the brother was still years away from effective social maturity. Father-daughter incest would produce a baby without adding a male; this is quite different from taking a second wife, which, if permitted, is allowed only for those males who have shown they are able to provide for more than one female.

To see how radically hunting changed the economic situation, it is necessary to remember that in the case of monkeys and apes an individual simply eats what it needs. After an infant is weaned, it is economically on its own and is not dependent on adults. This means that adult males never have economic responsibility for any other animal, and adult females have it only when they are nursing. In such a system there is no economic gain in delaying any kind of social relationship. But when hunting makes females and young dependent on the success of male skills, there is a great gain in not allowing the male to take the role of provider until he has proved his full effectiveness. These considerations in no way alter the importance of the incest tabu as a deterrent to role conflict in the family and as the necessary precondition to all other rules of exogamy. The more functions a set of behaviors fulfills the more likely such behaviors are to be widespread, and the rule of parsimony is completely wrong when applied to the explanation of social situations. However, these considerations do alter the emphasis and the conditions of the discussion of incest. First, the existence of mother-son incest in monkeys requires a different explanation from that for brother-sister or father-daughter incest. Incest is not a single problem, nor is the tabu to be accounted for in any one way. Second, the central consideration is that incest produces pregnancies, and the most fundamental adaptive value of the tabu is the provision of situations in which infants are more likely to survive. . . .

That family organization may be attributed to the hunting way of life is supported by ethnography. Since the same economic and social problems under hunting continued under agriculture, the institution continued. The data on the behavior of contemporary monkeys and apes also show why this institution was not necessary in a society in which each individual gets its own food.[5] Obviously the origin of the custom

[5] The advantage of considering both the social group and the facilitating biology is shown by considering the ''family'' of the gibbon. The social group consists of an adult male, an adult female, and their young. But this group is maintained by extreme territorial behavior in which no adult male tolerates another, by aggressive females with large canine teeth, and by very low sex drive in the males. The male-female group is the whole society. The gibbon group is based on a different biology

cannot be dated in the sense that we can prove *Homo erectus* had a family organized in the human way. But it can be shown that the conditions making the family adaptive existed at the time of *Homo erectus*. The evidence of hunting is clear from the archeological record. A further suggestion that the human family is old comes from physiology: the loss of estrus is essential to the human family organization. It is unlikely that this physiology, which is universal in contemporary mankind, evolved recently.

If the local group is looked upon as a source of male-female pairs (an experienced hunter-provider and a female who gathers and who cares for the young), then it is apparent that a small group cannot produce pairs regularly, since chance determines whether a particular child is a male or female. If the number maturing in a given year or two is small, then there may be too many males or females (either males with no mates or females with no providers). (The problem of excess females may not seem serious in our society or in agricultural societies, but among hunters it was recognized and was regarded as so severe that female infanticide was often practiced.) How grave the problem of imbalance can become is shown by the following hypothetical example: In a society of approximately forty individuals there might be nine couples. With infants born at the rate of about one in three years, this would give three infants per year, but only approximately one of these three would survive to become fully adult. The net production in the example would be one child per year. Because the sex of the child is randomly determined, all children might be male for a three-year period once every eight years, and similarly all might be female once every eight years. Smaller departures from a fifty-fifty sex ratio would be very common.

In monkeys, because the economic unit is the individual, not a pair, a surplus of females causes no problem. Surplus males may increase fighting in the group, or males may migrate to other groups.

For humans, the problem of imbalance in sex ratios may be met by exogamy, which permits mates to be obtained from another group. The orderly pairing of hunter males with females requires a much larger group than can be supported locally by hunting and gathering, and this problem is solved by reciprocal relations between several local groups. It takes something on the order of 100 pairs to produce enough children so that the sex ratio is near enough to fifty-fifty for society to function smoothly, and this requires a population of approximately 500 people.

from that of the human family and has none of its reciprocal economic functions. Although the kind of social life seen in chimpanzees lacks a family organization, to change it into that of man would require far less evolution than would be necessary in the case of the gibbon.

With smaller numbers there will be constant random fluctuations in the sex ratio significant enough to cause social problems. This argument shows the importance of a sizable linguistic community, one large enough to cover an area in which people may find mates. It does not mean that either the large community or exogamy does not have many other functions, as outlined by Mair. As indicated earlier, the more factors that favor a custom, the more likely it is to be geographically widespread and long lasting. What the argument does stress is that the finding of mates and the production of babies under the particular conditions of human hunting and gathering favor both incest tabus and exogamy for basic demographic reasons.

Assumptions behind the argument are that social customs are adaptive, and that nothing is more crucial for evolutionary success than the orderly production of the number of infants that can be supported. This argument also presumes that, at least under extreme conditions, these reasons are obvious to the people involved, as infanticide attests. Or, as Whiting has mentioned . . . when a boy could find no suitable mate locally, his mother might well have suggested he try her brother's group.

If customs are adaptive and if humans are necessarily opportunistic, it might be expected that social rules would be labile under the conditions of small hunting and gathering societies. . . . Murdock has pointed out the high frequency of bilateral kinship systems among hunters, and experts on Australia all seem to believe that the Australian systems have been described in much too static terms. Under hunting conditions, systems that allow for exceptions and local adaptation make sense, and surely political dominance and status must have been largely achieved.

CONCLUSION

While stressing the success of the hunting and gathering way of life with its great diversity of local forms and while emphasizing the way it influenced human evolution, we must also take into account its limitations. There is no indication that this way of life could support large communities or more than a few million people in the whole world. To call the hunters "affluent," as Sahlins has, is to give a very special definition to the word. During much of the year many monkeys can obtain enough food in only three or four hours of gathering each day, and under normal conditions baboons have plenty of time to build the Taj Mahal. The restriction on population, however, is the lean season or the atypical year, and, as Sahlins recognized, building by the hunters was limited by motivation and technical knowledge, not by time. Where monkeys are fed, population rises, and Koford estimates the rate of increase on an island at 15 percent per year.

After agriculture human populations increased dramatically in spite of disease, war, and slowly changing customs. Even with fully human (*Homo sapiens*) biology, language, technical sophistication, cooperation, art, the support of kinship, the control of custom and political power, and the solace of religion—in spite of this whole web of culture and biology—the local group in the Mesolithic was no larger than that of baboons. Regardless of statements . . . on the ease with which hunters obtain food, it is still true that food was the primary factor in limiting early human populations, as is shown by the events subsequent to agriculture.

The agricultural revolution, continuing into the industrial and scientific revolutions, is now freeing man from the conditions and restraints of 99 percent of his history, but the biology of our species was created in the long gathering and hunting period. To assert the biological unity of mankind is to affirm the importance of the hunting way of life. It is to claim that, however much conditions and customs may have varied locally, the main selection pressures that forged the species were the same. The biology, psychology, and customs that separate us from the apes—all these we owe to the hunters of time past. Although the record is incomplete and speculation looms larger than fact, for those who would understand the origin and nature of human behavior, there is no choice but to try to understand man the hunter.

6

THE HOMINIZATION PROCESS

F. Clark Howell

In this article, F. Clark Howell discusses the evolutionary transformation of infrahominid populations into full hominid status in the early stages of human evolution. He draws on recently accumulated evidence from the fossil record and the archeological record, as well as data about ancient Pleistocene animal and plant populations and climatic fluctuations. Howell has made important contributions to our understanding of the status of the "Neanderthal" fossils and the emergence of modern man. He is presently at the University of Chicago.

Modern paleoanthropological studies seek to understand, in both biological and cultural perspective, those factors which effected the evolution of man. The biologically oriented anthropologist is especially concerned with the nature and adaptive significance of major anatomical and physiological transformations in the evolution of the body from an apelike higher primate to the single variable species, *Homo sapiens*. He must equally concern himself with the origin and evolution of distinctively human patterns of behavior, especially capabilities for culture and the manifestations of such capacities, and not only with their biological bases.

The fossil record of man and his higher primate relatives is still far from adequate. However, in the last several decades significant discoveries have been made which considerably expand our knowledge of ancient human and near-human populations. There is not now a single major range of Pleistocene time from which some one or more parts of the world has not at last yielded some hominid skeletal remains. Hence, there is now some pertinent evidence to suggest the general sequence and relative order of those bodily transformations during this process of hominization. In this process major changes were effected at quite unequal rates, in: the locomotor skeleton, the teeth and their supporting facial structures, the size and proportions of the brain, and the enveloping skull bones. And there were equally significant and accompanying changes in behavior. In the course of the last decade the earlier phases of this process have received considerable investigation. Some significant aspects of that work are to be considered here.

Man is a primate and within the order Primates is most closely related to the living African anthropoid apes. How immediate the relationship, or to put it another way, how far removed in time the point of common ancestry prior to divergence, is still unsettled. Except under special circumstances skeletal remains are not readily preserved in the acid soils of forested habitats; hence fossil remains of anthropoid apes from the requisite late Tertiary time range, some twenty to a few million years ago, are uncommon, and when found are often very inadequately preserved. Nevertheless, apelike higher primates are known to have had a widespread Eurasiatic distribution (up until five to ten million years ago, by which time such creatures had disappeared from increasingly temperate Europe); they were presumably also common in parts of Africa, although there, fossiliferous beds of that age are singularly rare. Fragmentary jaws and teeth of such creatures indicate their higher primate—indeed, specifically ape—affinities. They also suggest substantial diversity in anatomical structure as well as in over-all size. The rare and fortunate occurrence of other skeletal parts (such as limb bones) indicate that some distinguishing characteristics of modern apes were later evolutionary "specializations" rather than the "primitive" ancestral condition. Several specimens of jaws and teeth, from regions as widely separate as northern India and eastern Africa, and some ten to fourteen million years in age, show some hominid resemblances.[1] Until more adequately preserved skeletal remains are recovered, these few provocative fragments will remain enigmatic. The antecedents of the hominids, the so-called proto-hominids, are still really unknown, and one can only speculate about the very early formative phases in the process of hominid emergence.

The anatomical-physiological basis of the radiation of the hominids is generally acknowledged to have been a major transformation in structure and function of the locomotor system. The lower limb skeleton and associated musculature were modified under selection pressures eventually

---

[1] See E. L. Simons, "The Early Relatives of Man," in this volume, pages 213-230 for a discussion of some of these fossils, notably *Kenyapithecus* and *Ramapithecus*.

to permit a fully erect posture and efficient, habitual bipedal gait. The changes effected in the lower limb were extensive and revolutionary. The characteristic curvature of the loins, the short, broad and backwardly shifted hip bones and their displaced and strengthened articulation with the sacrum, their sinuous distortion to form a basin-like structure about the lower abdomen, as well as the shortened ischial region, were all part of a complex of largely interrelated modifications adaptive for terrestrial bipedalism. There were related changes in the musculature of the hip and thigh, in relative proportions and in structure and function of specific muscle groups, all to afford power to run and to step off in walking, to maintain the equilibrium of the upright trunk during the stride, and to extend fully and to stabilize the elongated lower limb at hip and knee— an impossible stance for any ape. And the foot was fully inverted, with the lateral toes shortened and the hallux enlarged and immobilized, the rigidity of the tarsus enhanced through the angularity of joints and strengthened ligaments, with the development of prominent longitudinal and transverse arches, and the heel broadened to become fully weight-bearing.

The singularity of the erect posture was long ago recognized from comparative anatomical studies of man and the nonhuman primates. Its priority in the hominization process has been fully confirmed by the discovery in Africa of the still earliest known hominids, the australopithecines (genus *Australopithecus*), creatures with small brains, but with lower limbs adapted to the erect posture and bipedal gait, or at least for upright running. Some evidence suggests that the full-fledged adaptation to bipedalism, that which permitted leisurely and prolonged walking, was not yet wholly perfected. The hominid type of dental structure, with small incisor teeth, reduced and spatulate-shaped canines, and noninterlocking canines and anterior premolar teeth all set in a parabolic-shaped dental arch, was also fully differentiated. Brain size, as estimated from skull capacities, was only about a third to two-fifths that of the size range of anatomically modern man. There are several distinct forms of the genus *Australopithecus,* surely distinct species (and probably valid subgenera), with consistent differences in skeletal anatomy as well as in body size. One larger form attained a body weight of some one hundred twenty to one hundred fifty pounds, whereas another was much smaller with a body weight of only some sixty to seventy-five pounds.

Although thus far restricted to Africa, these earliest known hominids were nonetheless fairly widely distributed over substantial portions of that continent. Their ecological adjustments are now known in some measure and can even be paralleled among certain present-day African environments within the same regions. One small South African species is recorded under rainfall conditions some 50 per cent less than that of the present-day (now twenty-eight to thirty inches) in the same region—a rolling, high veld country of low relief and little surface water. Other occurrences testify to more favorable climatic and environmental situations. Generally speaking, the environments were relatively open savanna. In southern Africa remains of these creatures, along with other animals, occur in caves in a limestone plateau landscape where caverns, fissures, and sink holes probably afforded fairly permanent sources of water which was otherwise scarce. But there, and also in eastern Africa, sites were in proximity to more wooded habitats fringing shallow water courses, or mantling the slopes of adjacent volcanic highlands. It is just such transitional zones, the "ecotones" of the ecologist, which afford the greatest abundance and diversity of animal and plant life.

The absolute age of some of these creatures can now be ascertained as a consequence of refinements in the measurement of radioactivity (potassium/argon or K/A) in some constituent minerals of volcanic rocks. Their temporal range extends back nearly two million years with some representatives apparently having persisted until less than a million years ago. Their discovery has therefore tripled the time range previously known for the evolution of the hominids.

Culturally patterned behavior appears concurrently with these creatures. In several instances there is direct association with some of their skeletal remains. The field investigation of undisturbed occupation places, maximizing the possibility for the recovery of evidence in archeological context, has culminated in these significant discoveries. Traditional prehistoric archeological studies, on the other hand, were largely preoccupied with the sequential relationships of relics of past human endeavors, often in secondary contexts. The careful exposure of undisturbed occupation places has permitted wholly new inferences into the nature of past hominid adaptations and patterns of behavior. This work has broader implications for it forces complete rejection of the traditional viewpoint of some anthropologists which envisioned the sudden appearance of human behavior and culture at a "critical point" in man's phylogeny. . . .

This most primitive cultural behavior is manifest in several ways. There was a limited capability to fashion simple tools and weapons from stone (and presumably in other media, although perishable materials are not preserved). These objects, the raw material of which was not infrequently brought from sources some distance away, include deliberately collected, sometimes fractured or battered, natural stones or more substantially modified core (nodular) and flake pieces fashioned to produce chopping, cutting, or piercing edges. Several undisturbed occupation places with associated animal bones attest also to the acquisition of a meat-eating diet. It was limited, however, to the exploitation of only a narrow range of the broad spectrum of a rich savanna and woodland fauna. It comprised predominantly various freshwater fish, numerous sorts of small amphibians, reptiles (mostly tortoises and lizards), and birds, many small mammals (rodents and insectivores), and some infants (or the very young) of a few moderate-sized herbivorous ungulates. Vegetal products doubtlessly constituted a very substantial part of the diet of these predaceous-foragers, but the conditions of preservation prohibit other than inferences as to what these may have been. At any rate carnivorous behavior of these earliest hominids contrasts markedly with the essentially vegetarian proclivities of recent apes (and monkeys).

Such food remains and associated stone artifacts are concentrated over occupation surfaces of restricted extent—in part at least seasonally exposed mud flats around ephemeral lakes adjacent to periodically active volcanoes. These occupational concentrations have a nonuniform distribution over the occupation surfaces; there are dense central clusters of tools and much broken-up and crushed bones (presumably to extract the marrow), and peripherally more sparse occurrences of natural or only battered stones and different, largely unbroken skeletal parts of their prey. In one case a large ovoid-shaped pattern of concentrated and heaped-up stony rubble, with adjacent irregular piles of stone, suggests a structural feature on the occupation surface. These uniquely preserved sites in eastern Africa, sealed in quickly by primary falls of volcanic ash, afford some tantalizing glimpses into the activities of these primitive creatures. Such occupation places may well represent an ancient manifestation of the adjustment to a "home base" within the range, a unique development within the hominid adaptation.

We can now delineate some of the basic features of the early radiation of the hominids to include: (1) differentiation and reduction of the anterior dentition; (2) skeletal and muscular modifications to permit postural uprightness and erect cursorial bipedalism; (3) effective adjustment to, and exploitation of, a terrestrial habitat; (4) probably a relatively expanded brain; (5) extensive manipulation of natural objects and development of motor habits to facilitate toolmaking; and (6) carnivorous predation adding meat protein to a largely vegetal diet.

The adaptation was essentially that of erectly bipedal higher primates adjusting to a predaceous-foraging existence. These adaptations permitted or perhaps were conditioned by the dispersal into a terrestrial environment and the exploitation of grassland or parkland habitats. The African apes (and also the Asiatic gibbon), especially the juvenile individuals, show occasional though unsustained efforts at bipedalism; it is highly probable that this preadaptive tendency, which developed as a consequence of the overhand arboreal climbing adaptation of semierect apes, was pronounced in the still unknown proto-hominids of the Pliocene. Wild chimpanzees are now recognized sometimes to eat meat from kills they have made, and also to manipulate inanimate objects, and even to use and occasionally to shape them for aid in the food quest. This would surely suggest that such tendencies were at least equally well developed among the closely related proto-hominids.

Terrestrial environments were, of course, successfully colonized long previously by other primates. These are certain cercopithecoid monkeys, the secondarily ground-dwelling quadrupedal patas monkeys and baboons of Africa and the macaques of Asia (and formerly Europe). Hence their adaptations, social behavior, and troop organization provide a useful analogy for inferences into the radiation of the proto-hominids. Comparative investigations of the nonhuman primates, including the increasingly numerous and thorough behavioral and ecological studies of monkeys and apes in natural habitats, . . . have substantially broadened our understanding of the primate background to human evolution. These studies serve to emphasize those particular uniquenesses of the human adaptation.

A half million or probably nearly a million years ago, hominids were in the process of dispersal outside the primary ecological zone exploited by the australopithecines. In part, this dispersal can be understood only in respect to the opportunities for faunal exchange between the African and Eurasiatic continents, and the prevailing paleogeographic and paleoecological conditions of the earlier Pleistocene. The diverse Saharan zone failed to constitute a barrier to this dispersal, or to that of Pliocene and early Pleistocene mammal faunas for that matter. Moreover the extensive seas of the Pliocene and earliest Pleistocene were sufficiently lowered, either due to continental uplift, or, less likely, as a consequence of the incorporation of oceanic waters in extensive arctic-subarctic ice caps, so as to afford substantial intercontinental connections.

Probably within a hundred thousand years, or less, representatives of the genus *Homo* were dispersed throughout most of the Eurasian subtropics and had even penetrated northward well into temperate latitudes in both Europe and eastern Asia. This dispersal involved adjustment to a diverse new variety of habitats. Cultural and perhaps physiological adaptations permitted, for the first time, man's existence outside the tropics under new and rigorous climatic conditions, characterized by long and inclement winters. It was unquestionably facilitated by anatomical-physiological modifications to produce the genus *Homo* including prolongation of growth and delayed maturation, and behavioral changes favoring educability, communication, and over-all capabilities for culture.

The fully human pattern of locomotion was probably perfected by this time. These final transformations in the hip, thigh, and foot permitted a fully relaxed standing posture, with the body at rest, as well as sustained walking over long distances. The skeletal evidence is unfortunately still incomplete, but some four to six hundred thousand years ago the lower limb skeleton appears not to have differed in any important respect from that of anatomically modern man. Brain size, and especially the relative proportions of the temporal-parietal and frontal association areas, were notably increased to some one-half to two-thirds that of *Homo sapiens* (and to well within that range which permits normal behavior in the latter species). And some further reduction and simplification also occurred in the molar (and premolar) teeth and the supporting bony structures of the face and lower jaw.

Hunting was important as a basis for subsistence. Meat-eating doubtless formed a much increased and stable portion of the normal diet. Much of the mammalian faunal spectrum was exploited, and the prey included some or all of the largest of herbivorous species, including gregarious "herd" forms as well as more solitary species, and a variety of small mammals. Several occupation places of these early and primitive hunters, some of which are quite undisturbed, are preserved and have been excavated in eastern Africa and now also in Europe. These localities preserve prodigious quantities of skeletal remains of slaughtered and butchered mammals. The famous and enormous cave locality (Locality I) of Choukoutien (near Peking) in eastern Asia is a unique occurrence of occupation of a site of this type at such an early time. At Choukoutien, although other ungulate and carnivorous mammals are also present, about 70 per cent of the animal remains are represented by only two species of deer. In Africa the impressive quarry included a number of gigantic herbivorous species, as well as other extinct forms. In two such occupation sites in eastern Africa, over five hundred thousand years old, the very abundant fauna included species of three simians, two carnivores, two rhinos, eight pigs, two to three elephants, sheep and buffalo, two hippos, three giraffids, a chalicothere, six horses, as well as numerous antelopes and gazelles, and other remains of small mammals (rodents), birds, and some reptiles (tortoises). Preferential hunting of certain herd species is recognized at several somewhat younger occupation sites in Europe. At one of two sites in central Spain recently worked by the writer only five large mammalian species are represented, and of these a woodland elephant and wild horse are most numerous, with infrequent wild oxen (aurochs) and stag (red deer), and very rare rhinoceros. The remains of some thirty individual elephants, many of which were immature, are represented in an area of approximately *three hundred* square meters! At another such open-air site, on the edge of the Tyrrhenian Sea north of Rome, remains of horse predominated over all other species. Some indication of the level of cultural capability and adaptation, as well as requisite plasticity for local ecological adjustment is afforded by the diversity of game species which were exploited and the corresponding distinctions in occurrence, habitat preference, size of aggregation, and their species-specific patterns of behavior.

Toolmaking capabilities are notably improved along with the establishment of persistent habits of manufacture. These reflect, in part at least, more dexterous and effective control of manual skills. Corresponding evolutionary changes in the structure and function of the hand, especially development of the fully and powerfully opposable thumb, with expansion and complication of the corresponding sector of the cerebral motor cortex and interrelated association areas, were all effected under the action of natural selection.

Not only was the over-all quantity and quality of the stone tools increased. New techniques were developed for the initial preparation as well as for the subsequent fashioning of diverse and selected sorts of stone into tools (and weapons). New types of stone tools make their appearance, including in particular sharply pointed and cutting-edged tools of several sorts, seemingly most appropriate for butchery of tough-skinned game. Certain stones already of favorable form were deliberately trimmed into a spheroidal shape, it is thought, as offensive missiles. These and other forms of tools subsequently become remarkably standardized. This fact, and the very broad pattern of geographic distribution throughout Africa, southern and western Europe, and through western into southern Asia and the Indian subcontinent, suggest also a sophisticated level of communication and conceivably even the capability of symbolization.

More perishable stuffs, such as wood and fiber, are unfortunately very rarely preserved. However, several such early sites in Europe attest the utilization and working of wood, fashioned into elongate, pointed, and spatulate shapes. The discovery had doubtless been made of the thrusting spear, a major offensive weapon in the pursuit of large, thick-skinned mammals. Again, although traces of the utilization of fire are nearly equally as rarely preserved, there is incontrovertible evidence of its discovery and utilization (whether for heat or cookery is uncertain), both in Europe and in eastern Asia.

The development of a hunting way of life, even at a very unsophisticated level of adaptation, it has been argued, set very different requirements on early human populations. It led to markedly altered selection pressures and was, in fact, responsible for profound changes in human biology and culture. Many workers regard this adaptation as a critical factor in the emergence of fundamentally human institutions. Some of those changes which represent the human (*Homo*) way of life would include: (1) greatly increased size of the home range with defense of territorial boundaries to prevent infringement upon the food sources; (2) band organization of interdependent and affiliated human groups of variable but relatively small size; (3) (extended) family groupings with prolonged male-female relationships, incest prohibition, rules of exogamy for mates, and subgroups based on kinship; (4) sexual division of labor; (5) altruistic behavior with food-sharing, mutual aid, and cooperation; and (6) linguistic communities based on speech.

It may appear impossible ever to obtain direct evidence of this sort from the fossil and archeological record. Yet an approach which combines the field and laboratory study of the behavior of living nonhuman primates with analysis of basic patterns of adaptation and behavior of human hunter-gatherer populations can enhance enormously the sorts of inferences usually drawn from the imperfect evidence of paleoanthropological investigations. The favorable consequences of active cooperation between students concerned with the origin and evolution of human behavior, however diverse in background and orientation, is already evident and has considerably advanced understanding of the process of hominization. In the coming years it may be comparable with those advances in paleoanthropological studies effected through the fullest cooperation with colleagues in the natural sciences.

7

THE SCARS
OF HUMAN EVOLUTION

Wilton M. Krogman

Although man stands on two legs, his skeleton was originally designed for four. The result is some ingenious adaptations, not all of them successful. Wilton M. Krogman is Chairman of the Department of Physical Anthropology at the Graduate School of Medicine, University of Pennsylvania.

It has been said that man is "fearfully and wonderfully made." I am inclined to agree with that statement—especially the "fearfully" part of it. As a piece of machinery we humans are such a hodgepodge and makeshift that the real wonder resides in the fact that we get along as well as we do. Part for part our bodies, particularly our skeletons, show many scars of Nature's operations as she tried to perfect us.

I am not referring to our so-called vestiges—those tag-ends of structures which once were functional, such as the remnant of a tail at the base of the spine, the appendix, the pineal or "third" eye, the misplaced heart openings of "blue babies," or the like. Nor do I mean the freak variations that crop up in individuals. I am discussing the imperfect adaptations the human race has made in getting up from all fours.

We have inherited our "basic patents," as W. K. Gregory of the American Museum of Natural History calls them, from a long line of vertebrate (backboned) ancestors; from fish to amphibian to reptile to mammal and finally from monkey to ape to anthropoid to *Homo sapiens*. In all this evolution the most profound skeletal changes occurred when we went from a four-legged to a two-legged mode of locomotion.

Gregory has very aptly called a four-legged animal "the bridge that walks." Its skeleton is built like a cantilever bridge: the backbone is the arched cantilever; the vertebrae of the forward part of the backbone are slanted backward and those of the rear forward, so that the "thrust" is all to the apex of the arch; the four limbs are the piers or supports; the trunk and abdomen are the load suspended from the weight-balanced arch; in front the main bridge has a draw-bridge or jointed crane (the neck) and with it a grappling device (the jaws). [See Figure 7–1.]

When all this was up-ended on the hind limbs in man, the result was a terrific mechanical imbalance. Most of the advantages of the cantilever system were lost, and the backbone had to accommodate itself somehow to the new vertical weight-bearing stresses. It did so by breaking up the single-curved arch into an S-curve. We are born, interestingly enough, with a backbone in the form of a simple ancestral arch, but during infancy it bends into the human shape. When we begin to hold our head erect, at about the age of four months, we get a forward curve in the backbone's neck region; when we stand up, at about a year, we get a forward curve in the lower trunk; in the upper trunk and pelvic regions the backbone keeps its old backward curve.

But we achieve this at a price. To permit all this twisting and bending, Nature changed the shape of the vertebrae to that of a wedge, with the thicker edge in front and the thinner in back. This allows the vertebrae to pivot on their front ends as on hinges, like the segments of a toy snake. On the other hand, it also weakens the backbone, particularly in the lower back region, where the wedge shape is most pronounced. Heavy lifting or any other sudden stress may cause the lowermost lumbar vertebra to slip

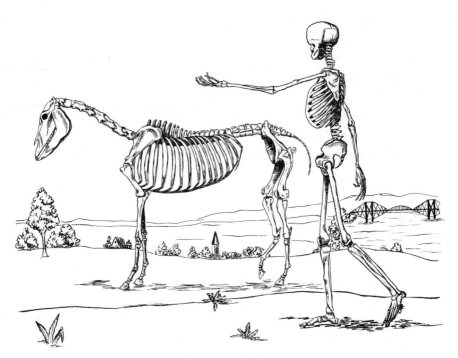

FIGURE 7–1—Backbones of the horse and man illustrate the principal problem of adapting the quadruped skeleton to biped purposes. The horizontal backbone of the horse is gently arched between two supports, rather like the cantilever bridge in the right background. The vertical backbone of man, in contrast, is curved like an S. (Adapted by Margaret Kowalczyk.)

backward along the slope of the next vertebra. The phrase ''Oh my aching back'' has an evolutionary significance!

There are other ways in which the backbone may literally let us down. The human backbone usually has 32 to 34 vertebrae, each separated from its neighbor by a disk of cartilage which acts as a cushion. Of these vertebrae 7 are cervical (in the neck), 12 thoracic (upper trunk), 5 lumbar (lower trunk), 5 sacral (at the pelvis), and 3 to 5 caudal (the tail). Every once in a while the seventh cervical vertebra may have an unusually long lateral process; if long enough, this protruding piece of bone may so interfere with the big nerves going down to the arm that it has to be sawed off by a surgeon. Most people have 12 pairs of ribs, borne by the 12 thoracic vertebrae, but occasionally the transverse processes of the next lower segment, the first lumbar vertebra, are so exaggerated that they form a 13th pair of ribs. In some people the lowest (fifth) lumbar vertebra is fused with the sacral vertebrae. The latter are usually united into one bone, called the sacrum, but sometimes the first sacral vertebra fails to join with its mates. All these idiosyncrasies can cause trouble.

The "Achilles' heel" of our backbone is the unstable lower end of the vertebral column. This is where we reap most of the evil consequences of standing up on our hind legs. It is a crucial zone of the body—the pathway for reproduction and the junction point where the backbone, the hind end of the trunk and the legs come together. The skeletal Grand Central Station where all this happens is a rather complicated structure consisting of the sacrum and the pelvis. The pelvis is not only a part of the general skeletal framework of the body but also a channel for the digestive and urogenital systems and the coupling to which the muscles of the hind legs are attached. When we stood up on our hind legs, we burdened the pelvis with still another function, namely, bearing the weight of the upper part of the body. How have we changed our pelvis to adapt it to its new position and burdens?

The pelvic structure is made up of three sets of paired bones, the ilium, the ischium, and the pubis. The three bones meet at each side in the hip socket, where the head of the thighbone articulates. In standing erect man tilted the whole structure upward, so that the pelvis is at an angle to the backbone instead of parallel to it. The relative position of the three pelvic bones changed, with the pubis now in front instead of below. The bones also were altered in shape. The iliac bones, formerly elongate and blade-like (in the anthropoids), are now shortened and broadened. They form the crests of our hips, and they help support the sagging viscera, especially the large intestine. The pubic bones help to form the subpubic arch—that "arch of triumph" beneath which we must all emerge to life and to the world. The ischial bones retreat to the rear; they are the bones that bear the brunt of sitting through a double feature or before a television screen. [See Figure 7–2.]

The greatest change is in the zone of contact between the iliac bones and the wedgelike sacrum—the so-called sacroiliac articulation. Here are focused the weight-bearing stresses set up by the erect posture. Two things have happened to adapt the pelvic structure for "thrusting" the weight of the trunk to the legs. The area of contact between the sacrum and the iliac bones has increased, strengthening the articulation. In the process the sacrum has been pushed down, so that its lower end is now well below the hip socket and also below the upper level of the pubic articulation. This has brought trouble, for the sacrum now encroaches upon the pelvic cavity and narrows the birth canal that must pass the fetus along to life. Furthermore, the changes have created an area of instability which far too often results in obscure "low back pain" and in "slipped sacroiliacs."

The shortening of the iliac bones has increased the distance between the

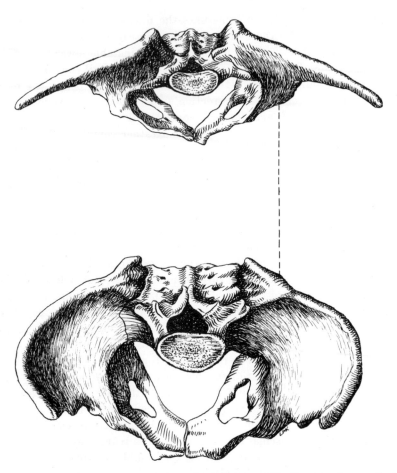

FIGURE 7–2—Top view of the pelvis of the gorilla (top) and man (bottom) shows how the latter has developed to support the weight of the abdominal organs. The dotted line indicates the width of the sacrum in man. (Adapted by Margaret Kowalczyk.)

12th (lowest) rib and the top or crest of the ilium. This has given us our waist, but it has also materially weakened the abdominal wall, which now, for about a palm's breadth, has only muscle to support it. The greatest weakness of the upright posture is the lower abdominal wall. In four-legged animals, the gut is suspended by a broad ligament from the mechanically efficient convex vertebral arch. The burden of carrying the weight of the viscera is distributed evenly along the backbone. Up-end all this and what happens? First of all, the gut no longer hangs straight down from the backbone but sags parallel to it. Secondly, the supporting ligament has a smaller and less secure hold on the backbone. One result of the shift in weight-bearing thrust of the abdominal viscera is that we are prone to hernia.

Nature has made a valiant effort to protect our lower belly wall. She invented the first "plywood," and made it of muscle. Three sheets of muscle make up the wall, and their fibers criss-cross at right and oblique angles. This is all right as far as it goes, but it has not gone far enough: there is a triangular area in the wall which was left virtually without muscular support—a major scar of our imperfect evolution.

The upright posture required a major shift in the body's center of gravity, but here Nature seems to have done a pretty good job. The hip sockets have turned to face slightly forward instead of straight to the sides; the sockets and the heads of the thighbones have increased in size, and the neck of the thighbone is angled a bit upward. As a result of this complex of adjustments the bodily center of gravity is just about on a level with a transverse line through the niddly of the hip sockets, and the weight of the trunk upon the pelvis is efficiently distributed on the two legs. [See Figure 7–3.]

Though it does not directly involve the skeleton, I might mention here

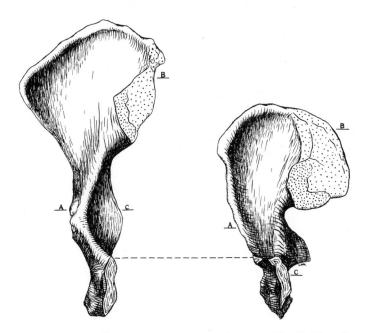

FIGURE 7–3—Inside view of the hipbone of the gorilla (left) and man (right) shows how the latter has become shorter. The dotted line and the letters A, B, and C indicate similar anatomical features in both structures. (Adapted by Margaret Kowalczyk.)

that the blood circulation is another factor that is not helped by our upright position. Since the heart is now about four feet above the ground, the blood returned to the heart from the veins of the legs must overcome about four feet of gravitational pull. Often our pumping system and veins find the job too much, and the result is varicose veins. The lower end of the large intestine also is affected, for its veins, when up-ended in a vertical position, become congested more easily, so we get hemorrhoids.

Even more serious is the danger to the circulation along the vertebral column. Two great vessels, an artery and a vein, run down this column. At the level where these vessels divide into two branches, one for each leg, the right-sided artery crosses over the left-sided vein. In a quadruped this presents no problems, but in the erect position the two vessels must cross a sharp promontory of bone at the junction of two vertebrae, and the viscera piled up in the pelvis press down on them. During pregnancy the pressure may increase so much that the vein is nearly pressed shut, making for very poor venous drainage of the left leg. This is the so-called "milk leg" of pregnancy.

Going back to the skeleton, it is clear that the two-legged posture places a much bigger burden on our feet. They have adapted themselves to this by becoming less of a grasping tool (as in the monkeys) and more of a load-distributing mechanism. We have lost the opposability of the big toe, shortened the other toes, and increased the length of the rest of the foot. The main tarsal bones, which form the heel, ankle joint, and most of the instep, now account for half the total length of the foot, instead of only a fifth as in the chimpanzee. We have also achieved a more solid footing by developing two crosswise axes, one through the tarsals and the other through the main bones of the toes. The little-toe side of our foot is relatively neglected—the toe is little because it is not so useful. Our fallen-arch troubles, our bunions, our calluses, and our foot miseries generally hark back to the fact that our feet are not yet healed by adaptation and evolutionary selection into really efficient units.

Now let us go to the other extreme—to the head. A lot has gone on there, too. We have expanded our brain case tremendously, and there can be no doubt that many of the obstetrical problems of Mrs. H. Sapiens are due to the combination of a narrower pelvis and a bigger head in the species. How long it will take to balance that ratio we have no idea. It seems reasonable to assume that the human head will not materially shrink in size, so the adjustment will have to be in the pelvis; i.e., evolution should favor women with a broad, roomy pelvis.

If the head has increased in size, the reverse is true of the facial skeleton. Bone for bone the face has decreased in size as we proceed from anthropoid to man. To put it succinctly, we have a face instead of a snout.

What about the teeth, in that face of ours? All mammals have four kinds of teeth: incisors in front, canines at the corner, premolars and molars along the sides. With but few exceptions the mammals have both a milk set and a permanent set of teeth. About 100 million years ago, or maybe a bit more, the first mammals had 66 permanent teeth, of which 44 were molars or premolars. Most mammals today have 44 teeth, including 28 molars and premolars. But man, and the anthropoid, has only 32 teeth —8 incisors (upper and lower), 4 canines, 8 premolars, and 12 molars. The loss has been greatest in molars, next in incisors, then in premolars, with the canine a veritable Rock Of Gibraltar.

While the face bones have decreased in size, our teeth have remained relatively large. Many orthodontists believe that this uneven evolutionary development may be partly responsible for the malocclusion of teeth in children. Certain it is that some human teeth are apparently on the way out: the third molars ("wisdom teeth") are likely to be impacted or come in at a bad angle, and many people never have them at all. Perhaps in another million years or so we shall be reduced to no more than 20 teeth.

It is mayhap a form of human conceit—the egotism born of a highly evolved brain—to worry about our bodily imperfections or inadequacies. As the philosopher said:

> The world is old and thou art young;
>   The world is large and thou art small;
> Cease, atom of a moment's span
>   To hold thyself an All-in-All.

8

CULTURE
AND THE DIRECTION
OF HUMAN EVOLUTION

Stanley M. Garn

*In the minute analysis of the fossil fragments that comprise
the record of hominid evolution, it is understandable that stress
has been laid on the ways in which fossil hominid populations
seem to have differed from one another. In this article,
Stanley M. Garn approaches the fossil record from another
direction, seeing the differences as less important than the similarities and reminding us of the immensely significant role that
the capacity for culture has played in the transformation of
fossil man from clever ape to wise man.*

In the last million years, our own genus *Homo* has made considerable
and apparently rapid evolutionary progress. From a rather small ground-
scampering animal, man has emerged as a distance runner, attaining an
adult fat-free weight of over 55 kilograms. Starting with a small brain
of no more than pongid proportions, there has been a threefold increase
in human brain-volume. And, from a molar row not far from 60 mm in
length, there has been a full 50% linear reduction. Truly, evolution has
reshaped us at both ends of the vertebral column, increasing our capacities to plan and to pursue, but decreasing our capacities to masticate.

Now it is tempting to speculate about the various directions that human
evolution has taken, and to fit our trends into the broader picture of

(Reprinted from ''Culture and the Direction of Human Evolution,'' *Human
Biology*, Vol. 35, No. 3, September 1963, pages 221–235, by Stanley M.
Garn. By permission of the Wayne State University Press and the author.
Copyright 1963 Wayne State University Press, Detroit 2, Michigan. This
article also appeared in *Culture and the Direction of Human Evolution;
A Symposium Arranged and Edited by Stanley M. Garn*, Wayne State Uni-
versity Press, Detroit 1964.)

animal evolution. The human size increase during the Pleistocene may well be viewed as an example of Predator's Progress. The larger brain may represent organizational success on the part of smarter and less tolerant hominids. The smaller teeth we now possess may be due to relaxation of selection pressure following the development of food technology. But when we come to super-theories of human evolution, attempts to explain diverse trends in terms of a single set of adaptations, the probability of intellectual success becomes small. The literature now constitutes a graveyard of explanations for human evolution, explanations that no longer hold promise for explaining the multiple directions of evolutionary change. To quote Darwin on this matter, "Any fool can speculate." And sheer speculation we must conscientiously avoid.

And I think that it is important that many of the older speculations about the causes of evolutionary change in man were based upon the assumption of maximum differences between the fossils and us. Textbooks still emphasize these differences, and college students parse them at the tone of a Pavlovian bell. But, like the reports of Mark Twain's death, the morphological gap between Pleistocene man and contemporary man has been exaggerated and inflated. It is now necessary to adjust our thinking to the evidence that the major, postcranial reshaping of man was largely complete with *Homo erectus*, that despite changes in the way of life since the fossils from Java and China, man has remained very much the same below the cranial base.

But to speak of higher things, when we turn to the size of the brain there is no doubt of an increase from the African and Asiatic megadonts through the Javanese and Chinese fossils and on through to the forms we accept as cospecific with us today. Some of this increase in brain size is necessarily allometric, the simple growth-associated relationship between bigger frames and bigger brains. Some of this brain increase, perhaps the largest portion, is a true increase in the volume of the brain; and here we must rack our brains to explain our brains. It is no longer enough to attribute even the first increase of hominid brain size to the mere rudiments of technology, and certainly not the second increase that followed Pithecanthropus. Surely man did not double and nearly redouble his cerebral volume merely to pick up sticks.

When we look upon the social adaptations man has made, adaptations to the improbable rules of his own making, when we observe (in even simplest societies) the highly complicated game of human relations, we wonder about the alterations in brain structure and brain physiology necessary to make such behaviors possible. The ability to adjust to complex relationships with an ever-changing set of age-specific rules, the needs for imagining, worrying, dreaming, and even speculating seem more closely related to our direction of brain evolution than simply using tools.

And now, in studies of ongoing human evolution, we have succeeded in climbing out of the bones and into the laboratory-based area of biochemical evolution. The clear fact is that man continually changes in response to new directions of selection. Over the last few thousand years, the rate of biochemical change in some populations has certainly been rapid, a rate attributable to intensive disease-selection. And, we now can demonstrate that the directions of disease-selection are due to changes in the way of life. Thus, the role of culture in directing the course of human evolution has first become clear for serological factors, for the hemoglobins, and for various enzymatic polymorphisms, rather than for the classical parameters of skulls and bones and teeth.

CULTURE AND THE PROBLEM OF FOSSIL DIFFERENCES

In describing the Pithecanthropus-Sinanthropus fossils from Java and China and the various "Neanderthals," much is commonly made of differences between them and us. According to textbook descriptions (usually copied from previous textbook descriptions), these old-world fossils were unique in various ways. "Fossils" are supposedly characterized by unusually thick skulls, exceptionally large teeth, extra-massive mandibular symphyses, and patterns of tooth size and of tooth eruption not found in living man. Such characterizations heighten student acceptance of the notion that a taxonomic "chasm" separates the classical old-world fossils from contemporary man. And they suggest that selection pressure had to go far to convert palaeanthropic hominids into us.

But the fossils that achieve textbook immortality (like those that have gained newspaper notoriety) are a picked-over lot, remembered primarily because they were (or were once said to be) most unusual. Less extreme fossils have drifted into monographic obscurity and in some cases have not even been described at all. Fossil collections reviewed at a later date frequently reveal a cache of neglected breccia-mates, whose existence becomes known too late to change the taxonomic position now ascribed to the type specimen.

And fossil describers have rarely enjoyed the large comparative collection we have in our great museums today. Far too often, the past standard of comparison has been the dissecting-room pauper (plus an occasional "Hindoo" or "Kaffir" for skeletal variety). With inadequate facilities to compare the fossils, and inadequate bases to judge fossil variability against that of living hominids, it is not surprising that characterizations made fifty, thirty, and in some cases only ten years ago tend to exaggerate the picture of fossil uniqueness.

Now many of the fossils selected for description *were* thick-skulled, if published measurements can be trusted. But they were not so unique in skull thickness as we were wont to believe. And it is not necessary to search museums for isolated cranial extremes simply to demonstrate this important point, nor is it necessary to center upon thick-vaulted Florida and California coastal Indians. A contemporary series of living Americans extends well into the fossil range of skull thickness. With due precautions to exclude possible cases of Paget's disease, it is quite possible to show that contemporary Americans and palaeanthropic fossils do not form separate distributions: the fossils are quite overlapped by living men and women.

Many fossils have been described as big-toothed, and surely the megadonts of Asia and Africa were as big-toothed as their name properly suggests. But from Pithecanthropus on, the exceptional nature of fossil tooth size (at least for the premolars and molars) is again open to question. With perhaps one classical exception (Pithecanthropus 4) modern and fossil tooth sizes quite overlap. The Neanderthals, as variously described, fit comfortably within contemporary ranges, and this observation is remarkably true for the Lower-Cave teeth from Choukoutien. The metrical position of these fossil teeth can best be portrayed and appreciated by a new comparison with living Americans who are by no means huge in tooth size (Figure 8–1). It is clear that the distribution of tooth sizes in contemporary American whites encompasses the "fossil" range to the extent that, as with skull thickness, there is no suggestion of a true taxonomic chasm.

Certain fossil teeth have been described as "taurodont" with pulp cavities huge by contemporary adult standards. Taurodont teeth are indeed remarkable, with enlarged pulp cavities extending deep into the root area. But the many allegedly "taurodont" fossil teeth are those of children, and it is with respect to children that comparisons should properly be made. Early in tooth formation, shortly after the bifurcate roots of the molars begin to calcify, enlarged pulp cavities may still be seen in occasional modern American boys and girls. With 45 degree oblique views of developing dentitions, it should be possible to make a careful comparison of pulp-cavity growth in fossil children and contemporary Americans. Meanwhile, the term "taurodontism" should be restricted to those situations where pulp cavity enlargement extends well into the root area, after apical union is complete.

For some years, too, the notion has been current that fossil man and modern man were differentiated by the order of tooth eruption. Franz Weidenreich championed such a belief, arguing a real taxonomic "chasm"

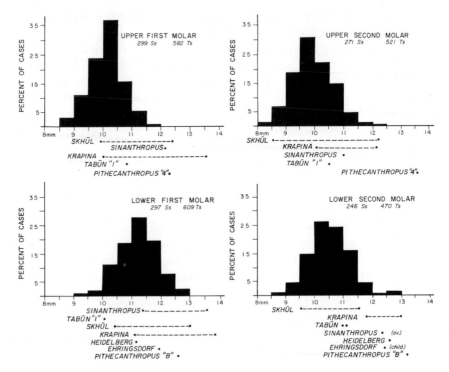

FIGURE 8–1—Tooth-size and tooth-size range of major fossils plotted against the combined-sex frequency distributions for contemporary American whites. While these fossils do tend to be large-toothed by our standards, it is clear that the majority of them fall within the contemporary range. (Adapted by Jacquelyn Hetrick.)

in this respect. Broom and Robinson, and Dart, in turn, have gone further by suggesting different sequences of tooth eruption for individual Australopithecines, sequences which they claim to be "unknown in modern man." But the idea of one tooth-eruption sequence for fossils and another for modern man falls when subjected to careful review. It is a mistake to compare the order of eruption of the teeth through the *jaws* (that is, alveolar eruption) with the order of eruption of the teeth through the *gums* (*i.e.*, gingival eruption). The two orders are not the same. Actually, and as we have shown, the M_2P_2 or "fossil" order is the usual order of alveolar eruption in modern children (Figure 8–2). And in ascertaining these facts we have further shown that the alleged uniqueness of fossil eruption-sequences is merely a lack of knowledge of the normal progress of the developing human dentition. Once again, and in a respect previously held to have great taxonomic importance, the fossils prove to be quantitatively not different from us.

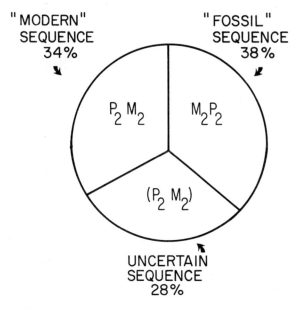

"MODERN" SEQUENCE 34%

"FOSSIL" SEQUENCE 38%

P_2M_2

M_2P_2

(P_2M_2)

UNCERTAIN SEQUENCE 28%

FIGURE 8–2—Frequency of the P_2M_2 (P_2M_2) and M_2P_2 sequences of alveolar eruption in contemporary children. Although the M_2P_2 has been claimed to be characteristic of fossil man, this order of eruption *through the bones* is actually the most common sequence in contemporary whites. Paradoxically, the M_2P_2 order is not diagnostic of the very fossils for which it was claimed. (Adapted by Jacquelyn Hetrick.)

Now this particular example, wherein an information gap simulates a basic biological difference, can easily be duplicated in yet another area of presumed taxonomic significance. Paleoanthropic fossils, according to the textbooks, are said to have massive mandibular symphyses, and high mandibular symphyses as well, as befits forms with supposedly massive dentition. Yet, by comparison to a rather small series of contemporary American adults (N–258) it would seem that *we* hold equal claim to the extremes of symphyseal size and massivity (Figure 8–3). All except one or two fossil specimens fall within the contemporary combined-sex bivariate distribution. All other euhominids, *erectus* or *sapiens* (taken from the listing of Weidenreich), fall well into the contemporary American white distribution. Many of the fossils (we might add) fall into the area that we now consider to be female by analysis of discriminant functions. Once again it would appear that the fossils are not qualitatively different from us.

Now I am not interested in displacing our ossified ancestors from their hard-won phylogenetic position. Nor am I interested in deflating their devoted describers, who worked without the manifold investigative ad-

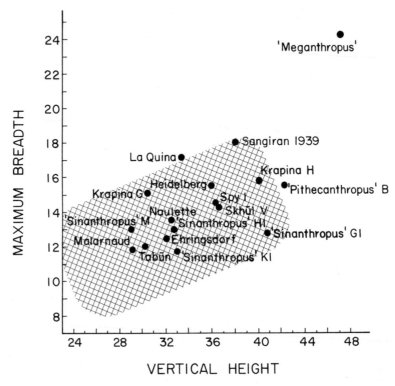

FIGURE 8–3—Bivariate distribution of symphyseal sizes showing major fossils plotted against combined-sex data for 258 Fels adults. While it is true that these fossils tend to cluster above the combined-sex contemporary means, it is also true that most fall below the discriminant line for American females. Note that Sinanthropus specimens G, H, K, and M have narrow symphyseal widths compared to modern Americans, even though the techniques of measurement used for the fossils tends to maximize this mandibular dimension. Shaded area denotes contemporary adult data. (Adapted by Jacquelyn Hetrick.)

vantages we enjoy today. Rather, it is my purpose to show particular respects in which the differences between the fossils and us are less than onetime claimed.

And if these famous fossils were not so uniquely thick of skull, so large of tooth, so massive of mandibular symphysis, or so different in the order of tooth eruption, how hard did culture have to work to convert them into us? I think that we all now realize that the *postcranial* skeleton of Pithecanthropus was contemporary in every respect. We no longer utter *caveats* about the limb bone of Sinanthropus, nor do we now picture Neanderthals as slouching, bent-knee half-men. And now, it would appear appropriate to observe that the facial skeletons of fossil and modern man are by no means so greatly different. Has culture modified man so very much below the cranial base?

The proposition is open that changes in the way of life have been concerned much more with modifying the brain of man than his jaws or teeth, at least since *Homo erectus*. And even here we must reconsider the evidence that still assigns the Java-China fossils to a separate species from us. Just as the provisional genus *Pithecanthropus* was ultimately reassigned to *Homo,* one may question the extent of differentiation between *H. erectus* and the successional species *H. sapiens.*

CULTURE AND THE DIRECTION OF BRAIN EVOLUTION

After reviewing tooth-size, symphysis-size, skull-thickness and tooth-eruption data on the Sinanthropus-Pithecanthropus fossils from Java and China, and on various "Neanderthals" and Neanderthal-like fossils, it is difficult to remain convinced of a major taxonomic gap between them and us. Depending upon the modern population selected for comparison, and exigencies of sampling within that population, it is easy to surpass individual fossils with individual Americans or whole groups of Australians. I am inclined to agree with Weidenreich, therefore, that *all* the hominids now known belong morphologically to a single species, or successional species at most, and to suggest that below the braincase macro-evolution in the genus *Homo* came to an early end.

But the cranial contents provide a qualitatively different picture. The Javanese fossils within or slightly beyond the American range in tooth size had vastly smaller cranial capacities. The Lower-Cave finds from Choukoutien had smaller brains too. Now it is possible that some part of the smallness was allometric in nature, the natural consequence of small body size. Unfortunately, good stature estimates do not exist for the "Sinanthropus" fossils, the oft-quoted estimate of 165 cm being based on but one bone. The estimate of 175-178 cm for Pithecanthropus is again a very limited estimate. Still, it would appear that no great correction need be made for body size in these fossils, and that subsequent human evolution raised cranial volume from below 1000 cc to perhaps 1400 cc, or roughly by one-half.

It does not seem sufficient to explain this cerebral increase by a simple improvement in manipulative skills. There is no reason to believe that the Java-China fossils were less handy with their hands than we. It is impossible to gauge linguistic skills by gazing at the backside of a mandible, so I will make no effort to introduce language. And, since neither Sinanthropus B-I nor the Ehringsdorf child was buried with a grave marker giving the true age at death, there is no confirmation for the belief that brain evolution has been paralleled by an increase in the period of juvenile dependency.

What, we may ask, is the adaptive advantage of more brains? Here we are truly stumped for a testable hypothesis. Do more brains make a better hunter? Does a more capacious skull make a more provident food gatherer? Do the personal qualities associated with more brains give greater access to females, and therefore more living children? What is the value of a 500 cc increase in brain volume, having 800 cc of brains to begin with? Does brain size have taxonomic meaning within the Pithecanthropus-sapiens range?

It may well be that early hominids with more brains were so intolerant of those with less as to eliminate them in wars of intellectual superiority, as Mayr has suggested. This presupposes an early origin of the battle between eggheads and pinheads, for which we have but one bit of evidence—the incidence of abrupt death and subsequent dismemberment in so many fossil remains. We should have to grant the larger-brained hominids the advantages of deviousness, cunning and guile—preaching peace while practicing war. This is no flattering portrait of our forebears, arguing that they were no better then than we are now.

But these Pleistocene ancestors of ours were moving into an era of complex societies, an era in which equally complex rules were increasingly the way of life. As we know now, life in a horde is hemmed about by rules no less complicated than life in Outer Suburbia. Exactly how much brains does it take to learn that one's father's sister's daughter (if of appropriate totem) is fair sexual game, but one's mother's brother's daughter, not?

There is a need, even in the least complex cultures, to accept age-grading, otherwise the Leopard Society (or the accrediting board) will make short work of the upstart. There is a need to accept property rights, to observe tabus, and to cut the lawn at least once a week. There is a need for the young to recognize kinfolk (and therefore potential supporters), especially kinfolk with political power. But how much brains does political consciousness need?

There is a positive value in worry, if we mean by worry the vicarious living-through of potential events. There is a value in enjoying purely social and non-utilitarian games that mark one as a good guy (one might say a potential Dean). But does the game of power politics require more than 1000 cc of brains; and if it does, do the advantages accrue early enough to guarantee differential survivorship? Given the early average age at death in man till quite recently, plus the retention of fertility through the fifties at least, it is possible that in fossil years such intellectual abilities *did* convey an appreciable adaptive advantage.

When we view the increase in human-brain size from 900 cc to 1400 cc, it is natural for us to equate the additional volume with increased intelligence; but increased intelligence for what? Is intelligence as we customarily measure it by the Binet or Wechsler scales inherently adaptive? Or is intelligence, the function that we now test for, a chance by-product of brain changes that were truly adaptive during the middle Pleistocene?

Technically and technologically it is by no means certain that the hominids of Java and China (the small-brained men) were so far behind the larger-brained hominids that we all accept as co-specific with us. But social and even intercultural relations did increase, if we can judge from sites like the Shanidar Cave, bringing with them heightened interpersonal relations, with exponentially increasing possibilities for interpersonal conflict. With increasing chances for conflict, there obviously arose rules for minimizing conflict and hence the need for a personality structure that could withstand both conflict and rules.

It is no secret that we are today surrounded by an extraordinary amount of informational noise, thousands of bits of information that are effectively irrelevant to survival or even to personal competence. But the signal-to-noise ratio is low, thus requiring (by analogy with vacuum-tube systems) rather complex circuitry to operate at a low signal-to-noise (S/N) ratio. Moreover, in a system where "information" is buried, there is need for a further type of circuitry, one that scans incoming signals for *pattern*. In the chaos of exhortations to buy this, do that, or vote for somebody, there are some few bits that are important (like the date for filing income tax), and some patterns that must be recognized (such as repeated failures to get grants). Circuits that discriminate at a low S/N ratio and circuits that are pattern-reading as well tend to be bulky. Is this the meaning of our 50% larger brain, as cyberneticists have been wont to suggest?

With increasing social (as against technological) complexity, it was inevitable that information input increased, and with it that kind of information that is effectively noise. The noisiness, we may presume, put a premium on the ability to discriminate between signal and noise. As total input increased, with larger groups and with more social complexities, the ability to discern pattern became of further use. Is this the key to human brain changes, *i.e.*, finer tuning, noise limiters, cathode followers and the like, all of them requiring more complicated and hence more bulky cerebral circuitry, neural component size being fixed?

The fact is that human-brain size did increase, either because brainier individuals were at an adaptive advantage, or because *groups* with larger brains survived and groups with smaller brains did not. It gratifies our ego to believe that selection favored intelligence, that our own ancestral lines came to genetic fulfillment because they were so very smart. But it may be that our vaunted intelligence is merely an indirect product of the kind of brain that càn discern meaningful signals in a complex social context generating a heavy static of informational or, rather, misinformational noise.

CULTURE AND BIOCHEMICAL EVOLUTION IN RECENT MAN

In contrast to older and more familiar concerns with the skulls, teeth and jaws of fossil hominids, the newer interest in biochemical evolution may seem far removed. Substantively, the amino acids, hemoglobins and tissue enzymes represent an invisible world to paleontologists accustomed to osseous ontogeny. Methodologically, chromatography and electrophoresis are procedures a planet apart from skeletal comparisons and odontometrics. Even the time depth considered, thousands of years, at best, is minuscule to specialists who have pictured man over his million-year existence. But the biochemical and immunochemical evidence returns us to the initial quest for source and direction in human evolution. For the biochemical evidence clearly points to culture (*i.e.*, the way of life) as the directing force in recent evolutionary change.

The abnormal hemoglobin S in Africa, the abnormal hemoglobin responsible for thalassemia in Europe and the Middle East, and red-cell phosphate dehydrogenase deficiency are all examples of adaptive polymorphisms. Elevated gene frequencies for hemoglobins S and e and G6P deficiency similarly owe their existence to the fact that the heterozygotes are relatively protected against malaria. But, while malaria is the immediate agent of natural selection (with respect to these particular polymorphisms), it is man and his way of life that made malaria an important disease.

Malaria, and therefore hemoglobin S in Africa, may be traced to slash-and-burn agriculture which opened the forest floor to the stagnant pools in which the larvae of *A. gambias* breed. Elsewhere man made malaria important by developing agricultural techniques that supported large human populations in potentially malarial areas. Such technological advances brought man to the insects and vice versa and they built populations of sufficient size to maintain a reservoir of infection. It is not the scattered nomadic tribesmen in Saudi Arabia who are the sicklers, but rather the inhabitants of settled oasis villages who have traded mosquito-free poverty for an enriched if more malarial existence.

Population size is crucial in disease selection. Small, isolated or nomadic human populations are effectively isolated both from each other and from infectious diseases as well. And hunting-and-gathering populations, limited by the amount of game a man can kill and carry, or the roots and fruits a woman can gather and pack, are likely to remain both small and isolated. But with the advent of agriculture, especially cereal-crop agriculture, larger populations eventuate and such larger populations constitute a disease reservoir. Permanent populations, moreover, attract traders who dispense both trinkets and microorganisms along their yearly trading rounds.

The impact of cultural level on disease and disease-selection is perhaps best shown for the African Bushmen. Continually on the move and few in numbers the South African Bushmen do not overtax the ability of dung-burying beetles to do an adequate sewage-disposal job. But in contrast to the Bushmen, stable agricultural populations in Africa have a permanent sanitary problem to the point where intestinal parasites (coupled with protein malnutrition) become an important cause of death. Nomadic and peregrinating peoples outwalk and outrun both parasites and vermin, twin hazards of permanent civilization. Villages set in forest clearings, mud houses, and granaries all attract mice, rats, cockroaches and other domesticable insect vectors of disease. So it is that the great technological advances that made civilization possible brought with them diseases in turn, some carried by man, some by flies and mosquitoes, some by rodents and some by snails. Each of these communicable diseases, malaria, typhus, typhoid, paratyphoid and many others became actual or potential directors of human evolution.

Now the shift from hunting and gathering to genuine food producing has had a profound directional impact on human evolution. The populations that acquired animal husbandry first, or those who learned to till the ground first, expanded first and thus achieved genetic predominance over the others. In history, as we know it, gene flow has generally been outward from the food producers. And more effective techniques of food producing brought new directions of selection in the form of disease, and (perhaps) a relaxation of certain other previously important directions of natural selection in man.

But agriculture, especially cereal and root agriculture, carries with it a potential danger, the ubiquitous danger of exclusive reliance upon a single crop. With the surrounding game exhausted, and with an increasing population to support, there is a too-common tendency to rely almost exclusively on the one crop that produces the greatest caloric yield. This tendency toward crop exclusiveness we see in the rice areas of Asia and corn areas of the Americas, particularly in the *Altaplana*. One-crop dependence carries disadvantages for each cereal has its own limiting amino acids. Moreover, the one crop of major importance tends to be deified, exalted out of all reasonable proportion, and ultimately viewed as an all-purpose food good for man, beast and in particular, child. And so in many parts of the world one-crop agriculture has resulted in protein-deficiency anemia, kwashiorkor, in part stemming out of the low-protein content of a particular grain or root, and in part stemming out of the culturally induced belief in this grain as the perfect food for the weaning and post-weaning period.

I need merely point out here the interaction between protein-deficiency disease, infection and the dysenteries. The evidence is now considerable that infection is more morbidogenic in areas of protein deficiency and that protein deficiency, in turn, constitutes a greater health hazard in areas where dysentery is common. Thus the very cultural advances that have resulted in large populations supported on a single climatologically adapted, highly productive crop constitute a directing force affecting both the tempo and the mode of recent human evolution.

We may view much of recent human evolution as a series of local adaptations (primarily in food-producing peoples) to disease situations arising out of food producing. In some cases man has made room for his diseases simply by favoring the insect or rodent vectors of the disease. In other cases man has moved to potential disease areas in actual pursuit of some particular food-producing economy. In general he has favored disease by increasing his numbers and by increasing the number of contacts with other populations. And he has favored disease-selection by developing dietaries that are themselves growth-limiting, and inimical to the maintenance of an optimum immunochemical (defense) system.

With respect to the cultural direction of hominid evolution in the early Pleistocene, we have at best speculations and conjectures. For the later Pleistocene we may postulate certain directions of cultural selection favoring increased brain size and (by relaxation of selection pressure) allowing reduction of tooth size. But all in all, and recognizing the extent to which the fossils are not as different from us as we once thought, the evidence for cultural direction of paleoanthropic evolution is far from good today. Yet, by the very same standards, it is apparent that the recent evolution of man has been profoundly influenced by a succession of psychological and cultural events. The very advances that made large populations possible brought about intensified disease-selection and rapid genetic change, as is now being demonstrated by students of geographical medicine today.

9

THE TRANSITION
TO HUMANITY

Clifford Geertz

It is tempting to glorify man and his uniqueness among animals, stressing his behavioral flexibility, the variety of his life styles, and the potentialities that are encompassed in his capacity for symbolic transaction, tool-making, and learning. Certainly, although perhaps without meaning to, cultural anthropologists have provided abundant evidence to lead us to consider the uniqueness of man. Yet this has had one unfortunate result for anthropology as a field, namely, to split off the study of human evolution from the main body of anthropology. Core anthropology has been cultural anthropology, and it has required the tortuous manipulations of anthropologists and observers of anthropology as a unified discipline to relate the activities of the investigators of human evolution to that of the investigators of human culture.

One of the encouraging results of the recent re-examination of human evolution and its relation to culture has been the realization that all anthropologists really are talking about the same animal—an animal that evolved the capacity for culture-building. In the following article, Clifford Geertz, a cultural anthropologist, describes the split and the ways in which cultural anthropology has been constructing a unified view of man, the cultural animal.

The question of the relationship of man to the other animals has been a persisting one in the human sciences. Since Darwin, it has hardly

(From *Horizons of Anthropology*, Sol Tax, editor, pages 37–48. Copyright © 1964 by Aldine Publishing Company. All rights reserved. First published 1964 by Aldine Publishing Company, 64 East Van Buren Street, Chicago 5, Illinois. By permission of the author and the publisher.)

been doubted that there is such a relationship. But concerning its nature, and particularly its closeness, there has been very much more debate, not all of it enlightening. Some students, especially those in the biological sciences—zoology, palaeontology, anatomy and physiology—have tended to stress the kinship between man and what we are pleased to call the lower animals. They see evolution as a relatively unbroken flow of biological process, and they tend to view man as but one of the more interesting forms life has taken, along with dinosaurs, white mice and dolphins. What strikes them is continuity, the pervasive unity of the organic world, the unconditioned generality of the principles in terms of which it is formed. However, students in the social sciences—psychologists, sociologists, political scientists—while not denying man's animal nature have tended to view him as unique, as being different, as they often put it, not just in "degree" but in "kind." Man is the toolmaking, the talking, the symbolizing animal. Only he laughs; only he knows that we will die; only he disdains to mate with his mother and sister; only he contrives those visions of other worlds to live in which Santayana called religions, or bakes those mudpies of the mind which Cyril Connolly called art. He has, the argument continues, not just mentality but consciousness, not just needs but values, not just fears but conscience, not just a past but a history. Only he, it concludes in grand summation, has culture.

The reconciliation of these two points of view has not been easy, particularly in a field such as anthropology, which, in the United States at least, has always had a foot in both camps. On the one hand, anthropologists have been the main students of human physical evolution, tracing the stages by which modern man emerged out of a general primate background. On the other, they have been the students par excellence of culture, even when they were not entirely certain what they meant by that term. Unlike some biological scientists, they could not ignore man's cultural life as belonging "over on the Arts side," beyond the confines of Science althogether. Unlike some social scientists, they could not dismiss his physical history as irrelevant to an understanding of his present condition. As a result, the problem of the origin of culture, no matter how often ignored as unimportant or derided as insoluble, has continually come pressing back to the center of our attention as, piece by piece, the story of the physical evolution of *Homo sapiens* has been put together. It is the peculiar genius of such an eclectic discipline as American anthropology that the triumphs of one branch of it expose the failures of the others; and in such a way the science is built.

For the past half century or so, the reigning solution of the origin-of-culture problem has been what might be called the "critical point" theory. This term, which I take from the recently deceased dean of American anthropology, Alfred Kroeber, postulates that the development of the capacity for acquiring culture was a sudden, all-or-none, quantum-leap type of occurrence in the phylogeny of the primates. At some specific moment in the history of hominidization—i.e., the "humanization" of one branch of the primate line—a portentous, but in genetic or anatomical terms probably quite minor, organic alteration took place. This change, presumably in cortical structure, enabled an animal whose parents had not been competent, in Kroeber's words, "to communicate, to learn and to teach, to generalize from the endless chain of discrete feelings and attitudes" to become competent. With him culture began and, once begun, set upon its own course so as to grow wholly independently of the further organic evolution of man. The whole process of the creation of modern man's capacity for producing and using culture was conceptualized as one of a marginal quantitative change giving rise to a radical qualitative difference. Kroeber used the simile of the freezing of water, which can be reduced degree by degree without any loss in fluidity until suddenly it solidifies at $0°C$. Another anthropologist compared the process to that of a taxiing plane as it accelerates along the ground toward that tremulous instant when it is launched into flight. A physical anthropologist, critical of the notion, referred to it drily as the appointment to rank view of the appearance of man, "as if he had suddenly been promoted from colonel to brigadier general." Man's humanity, like the flare of a struck match, leaped into existence.

There were three major considerations which led to and supported this general view. First, there was the tremendous apparent gap between the mental abilities of man and his closest living relatives, the great apes. Man can talk, can symbolize, can fabricate tools, etc.; no other contemporary animal can even approximate such accomplishments. One primatologist couple even undertook the heroic experiment of raising a chimpanzee in their household as though it were an adopted sibling to their natural daughter, giving it, in a rough sort of way, the same care and education given to the human child. But though the chimp learned a good many rather unusual things for a chimp to learn—how to operate a spray gun, how to pry the lids off of tin cans with a screwdriver, and, at one glorious point, how to pull an imaginary toy around by an imaginary string—it never even began to learn to talk. And, unable to talk, it was soon left far behind by its less agile but more loquacious human sister who proceeded onward, one presumes, to spin complicated theories about the uniqueness of the human condition.

Second, language, symbolization, abstraction, etc., seemed, on purely logical grounds, to be all-or-none, yes-or-no matters. One either spoke or did not; made tools or did not; imagined demons or did not. Half-religions, half-arts, half-languages did not seem even conceivable, for the essential process which lay behind them—i.e., the imposition of an arbitrary framework of symbolic meaning upon reality—was not the sort of activity of which there were partial versions. The progress from simple reflex activity, through conditioned responses and complex sign behavior, to symbolic thought was seen as a series of jumps, not an ascending continuum. Between the perception of the natural relationship of dark clouds to rain and the establishment of the arbitrary relationship of dark clouds to hopelessness there were, so it was thought, no intermediate stages.

And, third, there was the more delicate problem of what is usually called "the psychic unity of mankind." This has reference to the proposition—today not seriously questioned by any reputable anthropologist—which asserts that there are no important differences in the nature of the thought process among the various living races of mankind. If one assumes that culture appeared full-blown at some instant of time at a period before racial differentiation began, then this proposition becomes true virtually by deduction. To raise the question as to whether there might be historical differences in the ability to acquire culture among different species of hominids—i.e., among the various sorts of "men," living and extinct—seemed to raise it with respect to different races of modern men. And as the empirical evidence against such differences among the various groups of *Homo sapiens* was, and is, overwhelming, the hypothesis seemed disproved on the face of it. Thus comparative psychology, semantics, and ethnology converged to support the critical point theory of the origin of culture.

One branch of anthropology, however, did not so converge—human paleontology, i.e., the study of human evolution by means of the discovery and analysis of fossil remains. Ever since that strange Dutch physician, Eugene DuBois, found the skull cap of *Pithecanthropus erectus,* the "erect ape-man," in a Javanese river bed in 1891, historical physical anthropology has been steadily piling up evidence that makes the drawing of a sharp line between man and non-man on an anatomical basis increasingly difficult. Despite some halfhearted attempts to establish a "cerebral Rubicon"—a critical brain size at which the ability to behave in a properly human manner springs full-grown into existence like Athena from the brow of Zeus—the findings of human paleontologists have, bit by fossil bit, smoothed the curve of the descent of man to the point where flat assertions about what is human and what is not human have come to have a painfully arbitrary air about them. Whether or not human minds or souls come in degrees, human bodies most assuredly do.

The most disturbing fossil finds in this connection have been the various sorts of australopithecine "man-apes" which have been coming out of southern and eastern Africa since Raymond Dart dug the first one up out of the Transvaal in 1924. Certainly the most momentous discoveries in the history of human paleontology, these fossils, which date anywhere from three-quarters of a million to a million and three-quarters years ago, show a striking mosaic of primitive and advanced morphological characteristics, in which the most outstanding features are a pelvis and leg formation strikingly similar to that of modern man and a cranial capacity hardly larger than that of living apes. The initial tendency was to regard this puzzling conjunction in one animal of a "manlike" bipedal locomotive system and an "apelike" brain as indicating that the australopithecines represented an aberrant and ill-fated line of development separate from both the human and the great ape lines—better to be a thoroughgoing ape than half a man, as Ernest Hooton once put it. But the present consensus is that they represent the oldest known forms in the evolutionary process which eventually produced modern man out of some generally simian stock. In these bizarre half-men our own full humanity is rooted.

. . . My interest in . . . [the australopithecines] here is in their implications for the critical point theory of the origin of culture. These more or less erect, small-brained proto-men, their hands freed from locomotion, manufactured tools and probably hunted small animals—or at least some of them did so. But that they could have had a developed culture comparable to that of, say, the Australian aborigine or possessed language in the modern sense of the term with a brain about a third the size of our own seems wholly unlikely. In the australopithecine we seem to have, therefore, a kind of "man" who evidently was capable of acquiring some elements of culture—simple toolmaking, sporadic hunting, and perhaps some system of communication more advanced than that of contemporary apes and less advanced than that of true speech—but not others, a state of affairs which casts something of a shadow on the critical point theory. What seemed presumptively unlikely, or even logically impossible, turns out to have been empirically true—like man himself, the capacity for culture emerged gradually, continuously, step by step, over a quite extended period of time.

But the situation is even more desperate. Because if the australopithecines had an elementary form of culture (what one anthropologist has called "proto-culture") with a brain one-third the size of that of modern man, then it follows that the greater part of human cortical expansion has followed, *not* preceded, the "beginning" of culture. In the critical point [of] view man was considered more or less complete, neurologically at least, before the growth of culture commenced, because the biological capacity for culture was an all-or-none thing. Once achieved it was achieved entirely; all else was a mere adding on of new customs and developing of older ones. Organic evolution proceeded up to a certain point and then, the cerebral Rubicon crossed, cultural evolution took over, a process in itself autonomous and not dependent upon or productive of further nervous system alterations. The fact that this is apparently not the case, that cultural development was underway well before organic development ceased, is of fundamental significance for our view of the nature of man. He becomes, now, not just the producer of culture but, in a specifically biological sense, its product.

This is true because the pattern-of-selection pressures during the terminal phases of the evolution of the human animal were partly determined by the initial phases of human cultural development, not simply by natural environmental factors alone. A reliance upon tool manufacture, for example, puts a premium on both manual dexterity and on foresight. Within a population of australopithecines an individual somewhat better endowed with these characteristics would have had a selective advantage over an individual somewhat less well endowed. Hunting small animals with primitive weapons involves, among other things, great patience and persistence. The individual with more of these sober virtues would have an advantage over a flightier individual with less of them. All these various abilities, skills, dispositions, or whatever, are, of course, dependent in turn upon nervous system development. And so the introduction of tool manufacture and hunting must have acted to shift selection pressures so as to favor the rapid growth of the forebrain, as, in all likelihood, did the advances in social organization, communication, and moral regulation which, there is reason to believe, also occurred during this period of overlap between cultural and biological change.

Much of the work in this area is, of course, still speculative, and we are just beginning to ask the questions rather than to answer them. The systematic study of primate behavior under natural conditions which DeVore described, and which is having such an impact on our interpretations of the social life of early man, is, save for a few isolated exceptions, scarcely a decade old, for example. The fossil record itself is now expanding at such a fantastic rate and dating procedures are becoming so rapidly refined that only the foolhardy would attempt to set out definitive opinions on particular matters. But, details, evidence, and specific hypotheses aside, the essential point is that the innate, generic constitution of modern man (what, in a simpler day, used to be called "human nature") now appears to be both a cultural and a biological product. "It is probably more correct," the physical anthropologist Sherwood Washburn has written, "to think of much of our [physical] structure as a result of culture rather than to think of men anatomically like ourselves slowly discovering culture." The slogan "man makes himself" now comes to have a more literal meaning than originally supposed.

The ice age, with its rapid and radical variations in climate, land formations, and vegetation, has long been recognized to be a period in which conditions were ideal for the speedy and efficient evolutionary development of man. Now it seems also to have been a period in which a cultural environment increasingly supplemented the natural environment in the selection process so as to further accelerate the rate of human evolution to an unprecedented speed. It appears not to have been merely a time of receding brow ridges and shrinking jaws, but a time in which were forged nearly all those characteristics of man's existence which are most graphically human: his thoroughly encephalated nervous system, his incest-taboo-based social structure, and his capacity to create and use symbols. The fact that these distinctive features of humanity emerged together in complex interaction with one another rather than serially, as for so long supposed, is a fact of exceptional importance in the interpretation of human mentality, because it suggests that man's nervous system does not merely enable him to acquire culture, it positively demands that he do so if it is going to function at all. Rather than culture acting only to supplement, develop, and extend organically based capacities genetically prior to it, it would seem to be ingredient to those capacities themselves. A cultureless human being would probably turn out to be not an intrinsically talented though unfulfilled ape, but a wholly mindless and consequently unworkable monstrosity. Like the cabbage it so much resembles, the *Homo sapiens* brain, having arisen within the framework of human culture, would not be viable outside of it.

The general implications of this revised view of the transition to humanity are many, only a few of which can be touched upon here. On the one hand, it has forced a reinvestigation and reformulation of the theoretical considerations which supported the critical point theory in the first place. The argument from comparative primate psychology, for example, it is now apparent, established not the uniqueness of modern man, but rather the distinctiveness of the whole five- to twenty-five-million year hominid line of which he is but the culminating and, it so happens, the only living representative, but which includes a large number of different kinds of extinct animals, all of them much "closer" to man than is any living ape. The fact that chimpanzees do not talk is both interesting and important, but to draw from that fact the conclusion that speech is an all-or-nothing phenomenon is rather like assuming that, since the giraffe is the only living quadruped with such a long neck, he must have achieved it by a sort of quantum stretch. The great apes may be man's closest living relatives, but "close" is, to commit a pun, a relative term. Given a realistic time scale they are not actually so close at all, the last common ancestor being at the very least fifty thousand centuries back in what geologists call the Pliocene, and perhaps even further back than that.

As for the logical argument, that too has come to be questioned. The rapidly increasing interest in communication as a general process which has marked disciplines from engineering to ethology in the last decade or two has, on the one hand, reduced speech to but one—admittedly highly flexible and efficient—mechanism for the transmission of meanings among many, and, on the other hand, provided a theoretical framework in terms of which series of graded steps leading up to true speech can be conceived. This work cannot be reviewed here, but as an example one linguist has compared eight different systems of communication ranging from bee dancing, fish courtship and bird singing through gibbon calls, instrumental music and human language. Rather than pivoting his entire analysis around the simple, and by now somewhat overburdened, sign-*vs.*-symbol distinction, he distinguishes thirteen design features of language and attempts in terms of them to analyze the difference between human and subhuman communication more precisely and to construct a possible course from the gradual development of true speech out of proto-speech during the ice age. This kind of work, too, is only in its infancy. But the day seems to be coming to an end when the only thing that could usefully be said about the origins of language was that all humans equally possess it and all non-humans equally do not.

Finally, the established fact that there are no significant differences in innate mental capacity among the living races of man is not contradicted, but if anything supported and deepened by the postulation of differences in the capacity to acquire culture among different forms of presapiens men. The physical divergence of the human races is, of course, a very recent matter, beginning perhaps only fifty thousand years or so ago, or, by the most conservative estimates, less than one hundredth of the length of the whole hominid, i.e., man-forming, line. Thus mankind has not only spent the overwhelming proportion of its history in an altogether common evolutionary process, but this period now seems to have been precisely the one during which the fundamental features of its humanity were forged. Modern races are just that: modern. They represent very late, and very secondary, adaptation in skin color, facial structure, etc.— probably mainly to climatic differences—as *Homo sapiens* dispersed throughout the world toward the close of the glacial period. These adaptations are thus entirely subsequent to the basic formative processes of neural and anatomical development which occurred between the founding of the hominid line and the emergence, fifty to one hundred fifty millennia ago, of *Homo sapiens*. Mentally, man was made in the ice age, and the really decisive shaping force in producing his uniqueness—the interaction of the initial phases of cultural development and the culminating ones of biological transformation—is part of the common background of all modern races. Thus, the view that the capacity for carrying culture, rather than bursting into full flower at a single point, was hammered out in old stone age toolshops over an extended period of time, far from undermining the doctrine of psychic unity explains and specifies it. It gives it a realistic historical grounding it previously rather lacked.

But even more important than the revision or reinterpretation of older theories which the synchronous, rather than the sequential, view of the relationship between the evolution of human anatomy and the birth of human culture necessitates, are its implications for a novel way of thinking about culture itself. If man grew up, so to speak, within the context of a developing cultural environment, then that environment must needs be viewed not as a mere extrasomatic extension, a sort of artificial amplification, of already given innate capacities, but as ingredient to the existence of those capacities themselves. The apparent fact that the final stages of the biological evolution of man occurred after the initial stages of the growth of culture implies, as I have already noted, that "basic," "pure," or "unconditioned" human nature, in the sense of the innate constitution of man, is so functionally incomplete as to be unworkable. Tools, hunting, family organization, and later, art, religion, and a primitive form of "science," molded man somatically, and they are therefore necessary not merely to his survival but to his existential realization. It is true that without men there would be no cultural forms. But it is also true that without cultural forms there would be no men.

The symbolic network of belief, expression, and value within which we live provides for us the mechanisms for ordered behavior which in lower animals are genetically built in to their bodies but which in ourselves are not. The uniqueness of man has often been expressed in terms of how much and how many different things he is capable of learning. And, although chimpanzees who learn to play with imaginary toys may give us some pause, this is true enough. But what is of perhaps even more fundamental theoretical importance is how much there is for man to learn. Without the guiding patterns of human culture, man's intellectual life would be but the buzzing, booming confusion that William James called it; cognition in man depends upon the existence of objective, external symbolic models of reality in a way no ape's does. Emotionally, the case is the same. Without the guidance of the public images of sentiment found in ritual, myth, and art we would, quite literally, not know how to feel. Like the expanded forebrain itself, ideas and emotions are cultural artifacts in man.

What this heralds, I think, is a fundamental revision in the theory of culture itself. We are going, in the next few decades, to look at culture patterns less and less in terms of the way in which they constrain human nature, and more and more in the way in which, for better or for worse, they actualize it; less and less as an accumulation of ingenious devices to extend preexisting innate capacities, and more and more as part and parcel of those capacities themselves; less and less as a superorganic cake of custom, and more and more as, in a vivid phrase of the late Clyde Kluckhohn's, designs for living. Man is the only living animal who needs such designs for he is the only living animal whose evolutionary history has been such that his physical being has been significantly shaped by their existence and is, therefore, irrevocably predicated upon them. As the full import of this fact becomes recognized, the tension between the view of man as but a talented animal and the view of him as an unaccountably unique one should evaporate, along with the theoretical misconceptions which gave rise to it.

SELECTED READINGS

Baker, Paul T., and others, 1962, "Ecology and Anthropology: A Symposium," *American Anthropologist*, 64:15–59.

Buettner-Janusch, J., 1965, *The Origin of Man*. New York: Wiley.

Campbell, Bernard G., 1966, *Human Evolution; An Introduction to Man's Adaptations*. Chicago: Aldine Publishing Company.

Garn, Stanley, ed., 1963, "Culture and the Direction of Human Evolution, Symposium," *Human Biology*, 35:3.

Hallowell, A. Irving, 1956, "The Structural and Functional Dimensions of a Human Culture," *Quarterly Review of Biology*, 31:88–101.

Howell, F. Clark, 1965, *Early Man*, from *Life Nature Library*, New York: Time Inc.

Howells, William W., ed., *Ideas on Human Evolution, Selected Essays, 1949–1961*. Cambridge, Mass.: Harvard University Press.

Koenigswald, G. H. R. von, 1962, *The Evolution of Man*. Ann Arbor, Mich.: University of Michigan Press.

La Barre, Weston, 1954, *The Human Animal*. Chicago: University of Chicago Press.

Montagu, M. F. Ashley, 1955, "Time, Morphology, and Neoteny in the Evolution of Man," *American Anthropologist*, 57:13–27.

Oakley, K. P., 1957, "Tools Maketh Man," *Antiquity*, 31:199–209.

Spuhler, J. N., 1959, "Somatic Paths to Culture," *Human Biology*, 31:1–13.

Washburn, S. L., 1959, "Speculation on the Interrelations of the History of Tools and Biological Evolution," *Human Biology*, 31:21–31.

———, 1960, "Tools and Human Evolution," *Scientific American*, 203:62–75.

———, ed., 1961, *Social Life of Early Man*. Chicago: Aldine Publishing Company.

PART FOUR

STUDIES
OF PRIMATES

A traditional interest of physical anthropologists has been the comparison and contrast of the different infrahuman primates (apes, monkeys, and others) with one another and with man himself. Since the time of Thomas Huxley, systematized descriptions and comparisons of the primates with man have figured prominently in the evidence supporting the theory that man shares a common ancestry with the apes and monkeys. Moreover, as fossil fragments of early forms of man were recovered, it became a convention to compare the skeletal anatomy of early man not only with that of modern man but also with that of the apes.

Today, contemporary anthropology is extending comparisons of man and infrahuman primates into other areas. The interest in the evolution of human behavior, or more specifically, the evolution of the biological capacity for human behavior, has made it necessary to know more about apes and monkeys than what can be learned by comparative anatomy and laboratory study of primates. Accordingly, in recent years there has been a sharp increase in the number of students who have conducted research on free-ranging troops of monkeys and apes in their natural haunts. Social behavior, the relation of such animals to their resources and physical characteristics of their habitats (ecology), and proto-cultural behavior are all extensively observed in studies of an increasing number of different species.

The articles that comprise this section will convey some impression of the questions that anthropologists have to answer through the study of infrahuman primates. Prost and Milner provide a description—part biological and part functional—of the relation of primate studies to the central problems of evolution and human culture. DeVore and Washburn's discussion of primate ecology and Goodall's description of free-ranging chimpanzees demonstrate the procedures and results of such field studies as well as their implications for an understanding of human behavior from the anthropological point of view. Hall reviews the evidence for tool-using behavior in animals other than man, putting the human capacity for tool-making and tool-using in a context of ethological studies.

The following articles will not only form a bridge from the considerations of ongoing human evolution and evolutionary theory presented in previous sections of this volume, but they will also prepare us for seeing the emergence of man in its unique aspects as the evolution of man's biological capacity for culture.

10

THE SIGNIFICANCE
OF PRIMATE BEHAVIOR
FOR ANTHROPOLOGY

Richard B. Milner and Jack H. Prost

*Why are anthropologists—purportedly students of "man"—
interested in free-ranging monkeys and apes? What can be
learned about human evolution by studying the living nonhuman
primates? In reconstructing human origins, early anthropologists
attempted to use descriptions of primitive people and the behavior of children as well as observations of the insane. They
reasoned that commonalities in the behavior of these groups would
represent "throwbacks" to the primitive condition of mankind.
A great deal of information about human behavior was gained
by these studies, but this very information led to the demise of
"throwback" theories. It was discovered that various tribal peoples of the world were no more "primitive" than civilized men.
All living groups of men are recognized today as members of the
single species* Homo sapiens, *possessing equivalent biological potentialities.*

*Children and the mentally-ill, whose behaviors were thought
to be atavistic, are now recognized as exhibiting immature and
pathological forms of uniquely human behavior, forms that have
little in common with the competent nonsapient adults who were
our ancestors.*

*Today anthropologists approach the question of "origins" by
seeking the commonalities pervading the behavior of man's nonhuman relatives. If these contemporary nonhuman primates share
certain behavioral traits, reasonable inferences may be made that
man's nonhuman ancestors did also.*

In the following article, Richard B. Milner and Jack H. Prost

(This article was prepared for inclusion in *Human Evolution,* 1967. By
permission of the authors. All rights reserved.)

provide some of the background we need in order to place primate studies in an anthropological perspective.

Richard B. Milner is now at the University of California, Berkeley. Jack H. Prost is Associate Professor of Anthropology at Duke University. Despite the 2500 miles that separate them, they have collaborated to prepare the article especially for this volume.

The cardinal principle of modern evolutionary theory is that adaptive changes occur, through time, in the existing gene pools of populations. Changes are slow and cumulative, altering the basic gene pool a little at a time. Therefore, evolution does not produce radically new things but modifies the old. If we apply this principle to the origin of human anatomy and behavior, we conclude that those traits that we call "human" are accretions to an already elaborate primate inheritance. In science the question of "origins" generally means an attempt to reconstruct an actual developmental history. Attempts to uncover the origins of man must therefore be attempts to reconstruct the history of the biological and behavioral complexes that are coded in the human gene pool, and that are based upon the gene pools of our primate ancestors.

Social and cultural anthropologists compare social systems and cultures of widely scattered peoples in order to understand the range of man's ways and to extract underlying regularities in behavior. Since all living groups of men are of one species, however, such comparisons tell us little of the prehuman situation. Yet it is true that peoples who still live as hunters and gatherers share important ecological characteristics with our ancestors and can provide important information for understanding early man. Linguists reconstruct "extinct" languages, such as Indo-European, by seeking commonalities and differences in related languages that are spoken today. In an analogous manner, physical anthropologists use the comparative method to reconstruct the antecedents of man by comparing *Homo sapiens* with the various living primates to which he is related by common ancestry in the remote past.

As the comparative behavior of many kinds of primates is collected, the peculiarities of each species are separated from the broader common picture of the primate way of life. These commonalities are the base for the evolution of the Hominoidea, including man. When viewed against this total primate pattern, man's way of life appears less unique than was once believed. At the same time, the distinctive features of human behavior are thrown into bold relief.

But direct comparisons between man and the living primates are difficult to make. Each primate now alive on the earth has a history at least as old as man's, and most of them have histories that are much older. Each has diverged to some extent from our common ancestors, some more and some less. All have evolved distinctive modes of behavior appropriate to the various ecologic niches that they occupy. Without some basic evolutionary and ecological understanding, one can easily draw false inferences from these comparisons.

This article will discuss the ways in which primate behavior studies can contribute to the question of human origins and man's "place in nature." We have already seen that the focus of these studies is that of the comparative method. However, as we have just indicated, the judicious use of this method requires some understanding of the ways in which structure, behavior, environment, and evolutionary change are related. A major purpose of this article will be to sketch an introductory picture of those relationships. In addition, we will discuss the nature of behavior, the ways behavior is studied, and how the behavior of living primates can illuminate the evolution of human behavior.

WHAT IS BEHAVIOR?

The difference between a dead animal and a live one is behavior. Dead animals do not behave. However, it is no simple matter to define precisely what constitutes the behavior of a living animal. Everyone has observed the behavior of an angry dog. He stands stiffly with muscles tensed, ears flattened, tail down, and fur bristling. He bares his teeth in a snarl and emits a low growling sound. For some practical purposes, this would be sufficient description of his behavior. But if we examined him closely, we might also find that his eye muscles are contracted, producing pupil dilation, that his endocrine system was releasing adrenalin and other chemicals into his bloodstream, increasing his heart and respiration rates, and that his nerve processes were pulsating with coordinating and controlling messenger currents. If we could see into his brain, we might find other mechanisms of memory, aggression, fear, and attention at work. The whole biological mass of a living animal is involved in behavior, and it is constantly behaving.

It is therefore spurious to attempt to separate physiology, anatomy, and behavior. All are aspects of the same phenomenon, and there can be no clear distinction made among them. For certain purposes, however, by *behavior* we generally mean the gross observable actions of an animal as perceived by an unaided human observer. When the human observer increases his powers by means of microscopes or electrocardiographs we say that he is measuring *physiology*—the internal workings of an animal that are not directly observable. When the structures of an animal are observed, particularly in the dead, we call the study *anatomy*. But behavior, physiology, and anatomy are merely different facets of the same die. They are all descriptive aspects of that unity that is the living organism.

Observers of behavior record what animals do—when, where, and for how long. Field workers restrict their descriptions to behavior because it is difficult to take complex laboratory equipment into natural habitats and because they do not wish to disturb the behavior of the animals. Under natural conditions field workers can observe how animals react to changing environmental conditions, how animals interact with one another, and how animals get their food. If the animals are social by nature, as many primates are, they can attempt to describe the structure and workings of the animal society.

BEHAVIOR AND EVOLUTION

Before going on to discuss the role of behavior in evolution, it is necessary to define two crucial evolutionary concepts: *adaptation* and *ecological niche*. When these are understood, the implications of behavioral studies for understanding evolution will become much clearer.

What is adaptation? According to G. G. Simpson, "*an* adaptation is a characteristic of an organism advantageous to it or to the conspecific group in which it lives, while adaptation or the process of adaptation is the acquisition within a (genetic) population of such individual adaptation." Usually, we mean hereditary characteristics when speaking of adaptation, and always we view adaptation as a relationship between the organism and its environment. In a given environment, the better adapted animal will tend to leave more offspring, and thus the adaptation is perpetuated.

We can see striking evidence of adaptation in cases of convergent evolution, where unrelated animals which live in similar environments have developed similar adaptations. Thus, the mammalian porpoise and certain fish have come to resemble one another because of similar locomotor adaptations to aquatic life. Although the porpoise's limbs are constructed entirely differently from the fins of fishes, they have assumed the flipper form that is superficially similar to fin shapes. Indeed, the entire streamlined "torpedo" body of the porpoise resembles that of certain fish because of the efficiency of that shape for deep-sea swimming. In semi-aquatic birds, such as the puffin or penguin, we can see similar adaptations along the same general lines. These birds, like porpoises, rely on underwater speed and efficiency for capturing the aquatic organisms on which they feed. Note that in this example we have included both the structure (flipper shape, body form) and the behavior (swimming, underwater food-getting) as integral and inseparable aspects of the adaptation.

A second important concept for understanding behavior and evolution is that of the *ecological niche. Ecology* is the study of the interrelations between living things and their organic and inorganic environments. An ecologic community, such as a sawgrass-palm swamp, a sage prairie, or a pine-oak forest, supports characteristic life forms that participate in a complicated web of life activities. Within each ecologic community, each animal species characteristically occupies a specific and circumscribed place—its ecological niche. One does not find alligators perched in oak trees or beavers living in the desert.

This niche may involve living in a particular physical part of the community (for example, the treetop canopy), eating only certain foods found there (for example, certain insects and fruits of the canopy), and being well adapted for locomotion and food-getting in that particular niche. Gibbons, for example, have long arms, flexible shoulder joints, and hands that are well adapted for swinging through treetop branches and for hanging while feeding on the ends of branches. In any given community there may be thousands of niches (counting all the insects and other small organisms) so that different species may occupy their different niches and rarely come into conflict over food or territorial rights. Indeed, that is why such a diversity of animal forms is able to persist today. It is only when two species must compete for the same niche that the evolutionary struggle becomes intense, and the best adapted species will outcompete, (that is, leave more progeny than) its rivals.

To understand the reasons for evolutionary change is to reconstruct "how" and "why" one particular set of modifications became incorporated in the gene pools of evolving lineages. The "how" is explained by an understanding of the processes of mutation, selection, drift, and hybridization. The "why" is explained by an understanding of the processes of adaptation. The key to solving the "why" riddle is behavior, because an organism's behavior is its touchstone for survival and reproduction.

An animal behaves to exploit its environment, gaining its food for sustenance; it behaves to attract a mate, reproducing and perpetuating its species. It behaves to locomote itself efficiently from place to place. If its behavior is adaptive, its survival and reproduction are assured. If its behavior is maladaptive, the animal perishes, and the genetic modifications that it carries disappear from the gene pool. Adaptive behavior adjusts organisms to their environment and gives them the exploitative efficiency demanded for successful competition and survival. Were environments static, evolution would cease, but because the en-

vironments in which organisms live constantly change, so must the behaviors of organisms—and so must the gene pools that determine these
behaviors. Hence there is the unfolding of new life forms and new modes
of behavior.

We have said that evolutionary processes never produce radically
new things over short periods of time. But, because these processes
have cumulative effects, they can produce dramatically new forms over
long periods of time. By slow and gradual modification, amphibians
arose from fish, birds from reptiles, and humans from apes.

PRIMATES AND THEIR BEHAVIOR

The primates are the order of mammals in which man shares membership. It includes, besides man, the monkeys, apes, and prosimians.
The prosimians, such as tarsiers, lemurs, and pottos, are the descendants
of the earliest primates. Their ancestry goes back to Paleocene and
Eocene times. Man's closest relative are the Old World monkeys (which
include langurs, guenons, mangabeys, macaques, and baboons) and the
apes (of which there are four types: gibbon, orangutan, gorilla, and
chimpanzee). Both the Old World monkeys and apes have histories dating back to the Oligocene. The New World monkeys are far removed
from the line of human development, having undergone a separate
parallel evolution since the Eocene.

Despite their diversity, primates can be characterized by a basic locomotor adaptation—that of climbing by grasping. Most possess a well-developed prehensile hand that is equipped with flat nails rather than
claws. Unlike other climbing mammals (for example, cats) that dig their
claws into tree bark when they climb, the primates "hold on" by opposing their digits. Many are agile animals with highly developed motor
areas of the brain. They are rarely carnivorous but are usually either
omnivores or vegetarians. Vision is well developed; stereoscopic vision
is the rule, and many have color vision as well. Generally, the sense of
smell is poorly developed, since most primates rely largely on their
visual sense to guide them in their movements and to warn them of dangers. The arboreal world in which primates developed is a three-dimen-
sional lattice of branches where a misstep could mean death. It is therefore not surprising that many primates have stereoscopic vision and that
there is in most primates an unusually rich and complex nervous coordination between hand, eye, and brain.

Apes and monkeys live surprisingly well-ordered lives. They live
in organized social groups according to established statuses of age, sex,
and relative dominance. These statuses include sexually receptive fe-

males, females with young, infants, juveniles, and adult males of varying dominance rank. For each of these statuses, there is an appropriate
role for the actors to play and appropriate behaviors for others to exhibit when interacting with them. Among the males there are a very
few dominant individuals who are most active in defending the group
and in preventing fights between group members. The remaining adult
and subadult males carry lower ranks of dominance and have subordinate roles in group defense. Other individuals perform and elicit different types of behaviors, depending on their statuses. For example, access to food and sexual contacts is often regulated by the dominance
status of adult males; infants are entitled to special attention by group
members.

Although dominance relations are usually based on the ultimate threat
of physical force, there are few serious fights once hierarchies have been
established. Such activities as mutual grooming and play provide positive advantages to group integration. The united power of the group
is a deterrent to predation by carnivores. When danger threatens a
baboon troop, as when a leopard approaches, the dominant and sub-
dominant males rush to the fore, shielding the females and the juveniles
from attack.

Group patterns of flight, solidarity, or defense in the face of danger
relieve the individual of many potential hazards. Learning and communication make such group behavior possible. Primates learn from
imitating their mothers and other troop members, and by the time they
are adults they have learned to avoid certain foods, know local food
sources, recognize danger, and perform many other highly advantageous
learned behaviors. By means of complex systems of facial and vocal
expression, they are able to understand and communicate various states
of fear, interest, and excitement. Individual animals would quickly
perish without the support and protection provided by the group.

Many kinds of animals live in societies, but primate societies have
certain unique features. As DeVore has pointed out, they are permanent,
year-around organizations as opposed to the seasonal groupings of most
other social animals. In contrast to other mammalian groups wherein
the mother rears her young exclusively, the primate infant is raised
and socialized within the stable social group. Social behavior is the key
to understanding primate life.

The highly social nature of the primates makes it necessary to view
natural groups, as well as the individuals, as the adaptive units of the
species. Primate evolution (including our own) can only be understood
when we think of natural societies of animals adapting to their ecologic
environment. The gibbon, with his long arms, has anatomical equipment suitable for certain locomotor and feeding behaviors in the tree-

tops, while the baboon's limbs and hands have become highly efficient for quadrupedal walking on the ground. However, as Washburn and DeVore have shown, the baboon's crucial terrestrial adaptation is its social behavior. It is only by viewing the ecological context of social groups that we can understand the evolutionary adaptation of the total animal.

In effect, social life acts as a "buffer" between the individual animal and the hazards of its environment. The individual primate, therefore, is doubly adapted. He is adapted both to his ecological environment and to his socio-ecological environment. In other words, a macaque is not only equipped to walk on the ground; he is also equipped with the kind of brain and nervous system that is keyed to learning and functioning in macaque society. Similarly, man is adapted both to an ecological environment and to social living. His basin-shaped pelvis, elongated lower limbs and feet (with their double arches and well-developed heels) are specifically adapted to terrestrial walking and running. The human brain, with its capacities for symbolic learning, memory, and language, is man's supreme adaptation to a complex social environment.

Social life places learning at a premium. Many less intelligent animals, such as birds and fish, have social behaviors, but these are largely dependent on fixed and innate cues. For example, young herring gulls, without having been taught, will peck at the red spot on their mother's beak. Since the beaks hold food, the youngsters survive by responding to this cue. But the response is so fixed that young gulls will also peck at dabs of red paint. Primates, however, respond not only to fixed cues, but also to subtle variances. Since there is great variability among individuals and their behaviors, a monkey or ape must be more flexible and discriminating in his responses. In complex social life, animals must learn to adjust to one another. Primate society has not only the greatest differentiation among individuals but also the greatest differentiation of social roles in the animal world. Thus, the primate brain has evolved into a highly complex and efficient learning mechanism. Man, whose social life is by far the most complex of all primates, has developed the largest, most complex and efficient brain of all.

PRIMATE BEHAVIOR AND PALEOANTHROPOLOGY

When we turn to the question of man's origin, it is with the above facts and concepts about evolution and behavior. Those particular characteristics that we call human must have been accumulations and modifications incorporated into the evolving human lineage during man's prehuman history. The physical base upon which these changes occurred was that of man's prehuman genetic constitution. To understand the steps of human evolution is to separate those attributes that are modifications of this base from those that are unmodified retentions from this base, and those that are new and unique accumulations to this base. For some human attributes the question is: How did man evolve these unique characters? For others: How did man's prehuman primate inheritance become modified in this particular way? With some human attributes, a knowledge of the primates makes no explanation necessary, since they represent the inherited commonality that man received unmodified from his prehuman ancestors.

Much of the early thinking about the evolution of man's behavior came from nineteenth-century anatomists who worked on dead laboratory specimens. From these studies, they were able to properly assess man's close anatomical relation to the nonhuman primates. Where they erred was in their judgments about man's exclusive behavioral possessions. For example, these early anatomists, impressed with man's complexly constructed eyes, marveled at their existence and questioned the efficacy of natural processes purported to produce such structures. Today behaviorists see the primate eye, including the human eye, as a necessary and efficient sensory mechanism for arboreal behavior. Millions of years of arboreal living by the early Tertiary ancestors of monkeys, apes, and men were needed to accumulate the modifications that culminated in the optical apparatus used so profitably by man. But there is nothing unique about this apparatus; man shares it with his close relatives, the monkeys and apes.

Interpreting evolution means not only studying commonalities but also understanding the processes that shaped them. As S. L. Washburn has noted, physical anthropology is increasingly concerned "with process and with the mechanism of evolutionary change, whereas the older point of view was chiefly concerned with sorting the results of evolution." This concern with evolutionary dynamics has called for deeper and wider understanding of the nature and scope of primate behavior so that results can be applied to solving paleoanthropological problems. For example, recent work has made much use of the still limited behavioral data in the taxonomy of fossil man, which was traditionally a morphological province. It is obvious that if we were to encounter a new hominid on the street we would judge his humanity more by the way he acted than by the way he looked. We would want to know, for example, whether he had a true language or a primate communication system of sounds, postures, and facial expressions. Indeed, Washburn has also suggested that behavioral criteria should be used in fossil taxonomy. The recent practice in classifying the australopithecines is to collect the fossil data, then to reconstruct the living animal's behavior, and only then to attempt an evolutionary conclusion.

Paleontologists and comparative anatomists have developed the art of reconstructing the appearance of ancient animals from fossil remains. In many cases, familiarity with the muscles and soft parts of living animals enabled the paleontologists to visualize the missing soft parts of animals long extinct. Since the methods were derived from comparative anatomy, however, little could be said about the behavior of extinct animals. A knowledge of the anatomy of primate cadavers enables one to reconstruct the probable appearance of an ancient primate from its bones; but how can one reconstruct the way this ancient primate walked or moved without any clear idea of how living animals behave?

Today we are beginning to acquire the knowledge that will make such behavioral reconstructions possible. Careful analysis of positional behavior in primates is leading to an understanding of the ways in which animals utilize their bodies and limbs for running, walking, and climbing. Such studies may eventually provide clues to the nature of the shifts in locomotor behavior, including the emergence of bipedalism in hominids. In addition, naturalistic field studies have provided data on tool-using, communication, and social behavior that are helping to construct a well-rounded picture of the primate lifeway. These various kinds of behavioral studies are building a solid base for behavioral reconstructive extrapolation.

PRIMATE BEHAVIOR AND ANTHROPOLOGY

Part of the reason for studying evolution is to seek a definition of man and an understanding of his place in nature. This involves an analytical separation of those characteristics that are peculiar to man from those he shares with the other primates. Many attributes that were once thought to be unique to man are now seen as widespread primate phenomena. A popular definition used to be "man is the tool-using animal." Field studies of primate behavior have demonstrated, however, that man is not alone in making and using tools. Chimpanzees use tools to capture termites in their forest home by inserting prepared twigs into the termite mounds, as described by Goodall. In addition, they use bundles of dry leaves as sponges to gather otherwise inaccessible water during the dry season. Studies of primate behavior have also given new insights into the nature of man. For example, early social theorists postulated that man "in the state of nature" must have been a solitary creature who was always "at war with every other man." Primate studies show us that man could never have been a solitary animal, for his sociality is as much a part of his primate inheritance as are his hands.

It used to be supposed that man was unique in having learned and shared behavior. Primate studies have revealed, however, that monkeys and apes have social traditions. Baboons maintain fear reactions to dangerous situations that were experienced years ago by only a few individuals in the group. The very selective diet of gorilla groups and the chimpanzee tool-using mentioned above are other examples of adaptive behavior that are perpetuated through learning or social tradition. Japanese macaques have demonstrated that innovations made spontaneously by individual animals may be adopted and perpetuated by the entire group. In one case the monkeys adopted the custom of washing out sandy wheat in the sea without having been shown how to perform this action by human observers. Such recent observations have led many anthropologists to redefine the term "culture" as applied to humans, since it is clear that its familiar definition as "learned and shared behavior" is not an exclusive behavioral attribute of man.

Recent field studies of macaques may illuminate problems in the origin of human kinship systems that have long eluded anthropologists. It was discovered by Donald Sade and others that macaques born of the same mother groom each other much more frequently than they groom other animals in the troop. Sade also found other evidence for special social bonds between primate kin. For example, when a fight occurred among his free-living rhesus monkeys, the animals that came to an adult male's aid were identified as that animal's siblings and his old mother! It may well be that the primate pattern includes a much more complicated set of kinship relations that we can presently guess from observing animals whose genealogical relationships are unknown. In Sade's unusual study, the animals had all been marked and records kept on their genealogy for several generations. Similar studies of primate genealogies may some day help us to know whether or not there is a biological basis for the widespread taboos against incest in human groups.

Since anthropology deals with human behavior and with the evolution of man, it must also deal with the evolution of human behavior. Nonhuman primates possess social organization, cooperation, status differentials, a sense of territory, a communications system, and the rudiments of tool-using and social tradition. Against this background, it is plain that culture is a greatly elaborated expression of the primate way of life. Its distinctively human hallmark is language, which is uniquely peculiar to man. Unlike other primates, all normal humans are genetically capable of learning language, although the particular language a man learns is determined by the culture in which he is brought up. Although language makes possible complex cumulative cultural achievements, such as science and technology, it is not the only way in which humans communicate. We still supplement linguistic communication with facial expressions, gestures, and postures—the old primate communication system. Of course, even many of these are greatly modified in man by cultural traditions. A major task of anthropology is to account for the emergence of a human way of life from a prehuman, nonlinguistic one. As E. W. Count has stated, it is precisely this task that gives cultural, social, and physical anthropology "the junction for their integration." Primate behavioral studies now stand alongside ethnology, human ecology, and paleolithic archeology in helping anthropology achieve an integrated approach to the origin, development, and nature of man.

11

BABOON ECOLOGY
AND HUMAN EVOLUTION

Irven DeVore and Sherwood L. Washburn

In the following article, Irven DeVore and Sherwood L. Washburn relate social behavior, demographic data, and information about the geographic environment in presenting the ecology of baboons. They suggest the ways that terrestrial baboons may be adapted to the availability of food and geography. Since the baboons have followed an evolutionary course somewhat parallel to that of another land primate—man—in adapting to life on the ground, there are many implications for reconstructing prehominid evolution in a study of the baboons' adaptations to their ecological niche.

Sherwood L. Washburn, Professor of Anthropology at the University of California, Berkeley, has probably influenced the course of modern physical anthropology more than any other

(From *African Ecology and Human Evolution*, F. Clark Howell and Francois Bourliere, editors, pages 335–367. Copyright © 1963 by Wenner-Gren Foundation for Anthropological Research, Inc. First published 1963 by Aldine Publishing Company. By permission of the author and the publisher.)

single individual. His classic article, "The New Physical Anthropology," pointed out the direction in which anthropology was to go and heralded the beginning of many modern studies of evolution. This article was published in 1951 in Transactions of the New York Academy of Sciences.

Irven DeVore has spent many months on field trips for the purpose of observing free-ranging troops of baboons in east Africa. Primate ethnography is a relatively new field, and DeVore is one of its pioneers. Prior to his work with baboons, only a handful of researchers had studied primates in the wild, and most of our information about monkeys and apes was distorted on the basis of zoo studies of these animals.

The ecology of baboons is of particular interest to the student of human evolution. Aside from man, these monkeys are the most successful ground-living primates, and their way of life gives some insight into the problems which confronted early man. We have been concerned with an attempt to reconstruct the evolution of human behavior by comparing the social behavior and ecology of baboons with that of living hunter-gatherer groups, and applying these comparisons to the archaeological evidence. The following description of baboon behavior and ecology is based on field data collected during 200 hours of observation by Washburn in the game reserves of Southern Rhodesia in 1955, and on more than 1200 hours of observations by both of us in Kenya game reserves during 1959. The original study was financed by the Wenner-Gren Foundation for Anthropological Research, and the second trip was part of a study of the origin of human behavior supported by the Ford Foundation. Analysis of the field data is being completed under a National Science Foundation grant for the study of primate behavior. We wish to thank the foundations, and the numerous people who helped us in Africa —especially J. Desmond Clark, Stephen Ellis, L. S. B. Leakey, B. L. Mitchell, and B. Verdcourt.

CLASSIFICATION

This paper will primarily consider troop size, range, population density, and diet, but before discussing these topics we wish to give our views on the classification of these primates. Baboons are large, primarily ground-living monkeys of the family Cercopithecidae. As has been true of many of the primates, this group has been so divided that generic names have been applied to taxonomic groups which amount to no more than species. The most widely distributed baboon group occurs in the savanna and forest from the Tibesti Plateau in the north to Cape Town in the south, and across Central Africa from Dakar to the east coast. This group, the genus *Papio*, is usually divided into several species, including "chacma," "yellow," and "olive." There is no evidence that these forms are more than racially distinct, however, and "chacma" and "yellow" baboons occur in the same troops in the Rhodesias, although not in extreme form. It is not known whether the East and West African forms are distinct species, but it is likely that intermediate forms exist there, as they do between East and South Africa. When separated by long distances, individuals from these races appear to be quite distinct, as is the cases of the "chacma" from the Cape, the "yellow" in Nyasaland, or the highland and coastal races in Kenya. But if intermediate forms exist and reproductive isolation cannot be demonstrated, these varieties are best considered races.

In West Africa there are two species of short-tailed forest baboons, the drill and the mandrill. These forest types differ no more from the widely distributed form of savanna *Papio* than the pig-tailed macaque (*Macaca nemestrina*) differs from the crab-eating macaque (*M. irus*). In North Africa and Arabia the desert baboon, *Papio hamadryas,* lives in country which is too dry and open for the other species. In summary, the genus *Papio* is divided into a number of races, and into at least four species, including the savanna species with several races, two forest species, and a desert species.

The gelada baboon, *Theropithecus gelada,* is very distinct from *Papio.* Its facial skeleton is constructed differently; it jumps and uses its tail differently; and it should probably not be regarded as a baboon at all. Today *Theropithecus* is confined to the mountains of Ethiopia, in the same region in which hamadryas occupy the lowland desert and "olive" baboons the savanna between the two extremes. But *Simopithecus* is probably *Theropithecus,* indicating that the *Theropithecus* group formerly extended into East Africa. The practice of putting almost every fossil primate in a new genus nullifies the utility of the genus as a taxonomic concept. *Cercopithecoides,* for example, is a *Colobus* monkey. The increased understanding which the presence of such forms might contribute to the reconstruction of the ecology of Olduvai or Sterkfontein is lost by the multiplication of names which separate the fossils from similar living forms.

The African baboons are very similar to the Asiatic ground monkeys, the macaques. Both groups have forty-two chromosomes, and their distribution does not overlap. The newborn are usually black, changing to brown. Skulls, teeth, and general physical structures are much the same. In social life and basic habits the two groups are very similar. In contrast to all other monkeys (both New and Old World), the macaques and baboons do most of their feeding on the ground. They can cross rivers and may live in dry areas, moving far from trees. Compared to other monkeys they are more aggressive and dominance-oriented, and their average troop size is considerably larger than any other species yet studied. These characteristics have enabled the baboon-macaques to occupy a much larger area than that of any other group of monkeys. It is an area very comparable to that utilized by *Homo* before the time of the last glaciation. Ground living, ability to cross water, an eclectic, varied diet, the protective troop, and aggressive males permitted the baboon-macaques to occupy this vast area with a minimum of speciation. The contrast in the number of species between ground-living and tree-living monkeys emphasizes this point. There are more species in the genus *Cercopithecus* in the African forests than among all the baboon-macaques from Cape Town to Gibraltar to Japan. There are more species of langurs in Southeast Asia alone than species of *Cercopithecus*. Further, the most ground-living of the langurs (*Presbytis entellus*) has the widest distribution, and the same is true for the most ground-living vervet (*C. aethiops*). The taxonomic contrast between tree and ground monkeys is clearly seen in Ceylon where the island is occupied by one macaque, one dry country langur, and four forest forms. Apparently in Ceylon the rivers have been a major factor in isolating the langurs, but they do not form barriers for the macaques. The general relation between ecology and taxonomy in the monkeys appears clear; the more ground-living, the less speciation. There are many more adaptive niches in the forests than in the drier regions.

The men of the Middle Pleistocene, genus *Homo,* occupied the same range as the baboon-macaques but without speciation. Their way of life (based on tools, intelligence, walking, and hunting) was sufficiently more adaptable and effective so that a single species could occupy an area which ground monkeys could occupy only by evolving into at least a dozen species. This comparison gives some measure of the effectiveness of the human way of life, even at the level of Pekin and Ternifine man. Obviously, there is nothing to be gained by being dogmatic about the number of species of Middle Pleistocene men. Perhaps when many more specimens have been found it will be convenient to recognize two or three species, but the general form of this argument will still hold. There is no suggestion that any of the known fossil men (genus *Homo*) differ in size or form as much as a chacma baboon and a drill, or a crab-eating macaque and a pig-tail macaque. Even in its most primitive form the human way of life radically alters the relation of the organisms to the environment. As early as Middle Pleistocene times man could migrate over three continents without major morphological adaptation.

Australopithecus may have occupied an adaptive position midway in effectiveness between the ground monkeys and early *Homo.* Small-brained, bipedal tool-makers probably occupied larger areas than baboons, and without speciation. It is most unlikely that the East African and South African forms of *Australopithecus* are more than racially distinct. Robinson's suggestion that the jaws from Java called "Meganthropus" are closely allied to the Australopithecoid from Swartkrans supports the notion that *Australopithecus* was already able to disperse widely with minimum biological change. The presence of small and large Australopithecoids in South Africa at the same time suggests that their adaptation was much less effective than that of *Homo*. It may be possible to reconstruct more of this stage in human evolution with a more thorough study of the ecology of baboons, and by contrasting their mode of adaptation to that of man. With this hope in mind we will now consider the ecology of baboons in East Africa.

THE TROOP

TROOP SIZE

Careful counts of more than 2,000 baboons showed a range in troop size from 9 to 185. Estimates by the Tanganyika Game Department, for troops in the Wankie Game Reserve (Southern Rhodesia), and carefully repeated counts in the Royal Nairobi National Park all give an average troop size of 36–42. The *largest* troop in Nairobi Park numbered 87. In the Amboseli Reserve, the *average* troop size was 80 and the largest troops numbered 171 and 185. The fact that troops are twice as large at Amboseli indicates the need to study several localities before generalizing. Table 1 summarizes the size of troops in the Nairobi Park and in the Amboseli Reserve.

The smallest troops we observed numbered only 9 (Tsavo Reserve), 11, 12 (Wankie Reserve), 12 (Nairobi Park), and 13 (Amboseli Reserve). Three of these troops contained two adult males, and one only a single adult male; our data do not show the number of adult males in the fifth troop. These small troops are independent, functioning societies and not temporarily detached parts of larger troops. Baboon troops are closed social systems with a high degree of inbreeding. Often, adjacent troops can be distinguished from each other by the characteristic color patterns, length of hair, and form of face or tail. During both field trips, in over 1400 hours of observation, we saw only two individuals change from one troop to another. In these very small troops, inbreeding may be very important, and a whole generation may be the offspring of a single male.

The largest troops (103, 171, 185) were seen only at Amboseli, but for our study we selected open areas where the baboons would be visible as

TABLE 1

Troop Size

NAIROBI PARK	AMBOSELI RESERVE
12	13
17	42
24	47
28	$\begin{cases} 51 \\ 66 \end{cases}$ *
28	
40	57
61	64
77	70
87	74
Total 374	78
	88
	94
	103
	171
	185
	Total 1203

* 51 and 66 sometimes combined to form a group of 117.

much of the time as possible. In areas with more rain the abundant vegetation supports more baboons, and large troops may be more common in
these areas. For example, in the reserve of the north end of Lake Manyara
(Tanganyika), and in the forested areas adjacent to the Athi River near
Kibwezi (Kenya), we saw approximately one large troop per mile. This
suggests that there were both larger troops and a much higher population
density in these areas, but under conditions where continued observation
was impossible.

The large troops may temporarily subdivide, and the troops of 88, 94,
and 103 at Amboseli, and the troop of 77 at Nairobi, frequently split.
When the troops of 77, 88, and 94 split, all the small infants and their
mothers were in one section of the troop with the largest adult males. On
one occasion troop 171 (Amboseli) was also seen dividing in this way.
When all the individuals in a troop are together, there is a clear distinction between the large, dominant adult males, mothers, and infants
occupying the center of the troop, and the other, peripheral, troop members around them (as described below under ''Troop Structure''). The
temporary divisions seen in these large troops are divided along these
lines. Such a subdivision lasts for only part of the day and the troop
reunites before nightfall. Another type of splitting, in which the troop
divides into two sections with a normal distribution of males, females,
and juveniles in each section, also occurs in some large troops. Troop 103
sometimes split into two troops of 66 and 37, each troop having a center,

a periphery, and all the characteristics of a normal, independent troop. It seems likely that this kind of splitting represents the first stage in the formation of a new troop. Observations on troops 51 and 66 support this. These two troops stayed very close together; if one of the troops arrived at a water hole, the other was likely to appear, and, after using adjacent sleeping trees at night, they often followed the same route away from the trees the next morning. It is tempting to regard this situation as representing a large troop divided one stage further than was the case of troop 103. The reason for regarding 51 and 66 as two troops is that individuals within them did not shift; repeated counts showed that the membership of these two troops was constant, and sometimes they were entirely separate from each other, once for a period of days. It appears that large troops may become unstable, and that divisions occur in troops larger than 70 individuals which are not seen in the small troops. If this division persists, and if the division contains a normal age-sex distribution, a new troop may result.

The division of troops, their large size, and the fact that they met at water holes made counting of troops at Amboseli very difficult. Troop 103, for example, was originally counted as three troops (one of 103, one of 66, and one of 37). Similarly, troops 51 and 66 seemed to form a troop of 117 on some days. A single count made at an Amboseli water hole might include only part of a troop, or a cluster of 400 baboons representing three adjacent troops.

The density of baboons in an area is related to the food supply, but the size of the troop itself bears no such simple relationship. The ranges of the smallest (13) and the largest (185) troops at Amboseli overlapped, and the size of Nairobi troops did not correlate with the different vegetation zones in the park. Social behavior, rather than ecology, seems to determine troop size. Because adult males defend the troop from other animals, troop size is important to the individual's survival. Troop 185 contained over thirty large, adult males, compared to only two in troop 13 and one in the troop of 12 (Nairobi). Like troops of the much smaller vervet monkey (*Cercopithecus aethiops*), a small baboon troop yields to a large troop when they meet at water holes. When food supplies are limited, this gives a large troop an advantage over smaller ones.

TROOP STRUCTURE

A detailed description of the social relationships within baboon troops is given elsewhere. Here we have emphasized those aspects of troop life which are adaptations to life on the ground. Baboons are intensely social, and membership in a troop is a prerequisite for survival. Most of a baboon's life is spent within a few feet of other baboons. Baboon troops are closed social systems, individuals very rarely change to a new troop, and the troop regards any strange baboon with suspicion and hostility.

Within the troop, subgroups are based on age, sex, personal preferences, and dominance. When a troop is resting or feeding quietly, most of the adult members gather into small clusters, grooming each other or just sitting. Juveniles gather into groups of the same age and spend the day in these "play groups," eating, resting, and playing together. The most dominant adult males occupy the center of the troop, with the mothers and their young infants gathered around them, and the groups of young juveniles playing close by. These dominant males, and the small black infants near them, seem to be greatly attractive to the other troop members. During quiet periods the other troop members approach the adult males and the mothers, grooming them or sitting beside them. It is unnecessary for male baboons to herd the troop together; their presence alone insures that the other troop members will not be far away.

Around this nucleus of adult males, mothers, and young juveniles are the more peripheral members of the troop—the less dominant adult males, older juveniles, and pregnant or estrus females. Estrus females and their consorts usually stay at the periphery of the troop. Although the juvenile play groups will not wander far from the troop's center, peripheral adults may leave the troop for short periods. While the center of the troop moves slowly along, the adult and older juvenile (subadult) males and adult females sometimes move rapidly ahead to a new feeding spot. This may separate them from the rest of the troop by a quarter of a mile or more, and they may not rejoin the troop for thirty minutes or an hour. Although peripheral adult males may make such a side trip alone, or in small groups, other troop members will not leave the troop unless accompanied by the males. Healthy "solitary males" observed during the early part of our study later proved to be troop members who had left the troop for a short while.

A baboon troop that is in or under trees seems to have no particular organization, but when the troop moves out onto the open plains a clear order of progression appears. Out in front of the troop move the boldest troop members—the less dominant adult males and the older juvenile males. Following them are other members of the troop's periphery, pregnant and estrus adult females and juveniles. Next, in the center, comes the nucleus of dominant adult males, females with infants, and young juveniles. The rear of the troop is a mirror image of its front, with adults and older juveniles following the nucleus and more adult males at the end. This order of progression is invariably followed when the troop is moving rapidly from one feeding area to another during the day, and to its sleeping trees at dusk. A troop which is coming toward trees from the open plains approaches with particular caution. The tall trees in which baboons sleep are found only where the water table is near the surface, usually along a river or beside a pond. Vegetation is usually dense at the base of these trees, and it is in this undergrowth that predators often spend the day. The arrangement of the troop members when they are moving insures maximum protection for the infants and juveniles in the center of the troop. An approaching predator would first encounter the adult males on the troop's periphery, and then the adult males in the center, before it could reach defenseless troop members in the center.

Because they are in front of the troop by twenty to forty yards, the peripheral adult males are usually the first troop members to encounter a predator and give alarm calls. If a predator is sighted, all the adult males actively defend the troop. On one occasion we saw two dogs run up behind a troop, barking. The females and juveniles hurried ahead, but the males continued walking slowly. After a moment an irregular group of some twenty adult males was between the dogs and the rest of the troop. When a male turned on the dogs, they ran off. On another day we saw three cheetahs approach a troop of baboons. A single adult male stepped toward the cheetahs, gave a loud, defiant bark, and displayed his canine teeth; the cheetahs trotted away. If baboons come upon predators while en route to their sleeping trees, the troop stops and waits while the males in the center move ahead and find an alternate route (the young juveniles and mothers with infants stay behind with the peripheral adult males) Eventually the dominant males return, the original order of progression is re-established, and the troop proceeds along the new route. These behavior patterns assure that the females and young are protected in the troop's center.

The ultimate safety of a baboon troop is in the trees. When the troop is away from trees, the adult males are very important in troop defense. We saw baboons near such predators as cheetahs, dogs, hyenas, and jackals, and usually the baboons seemed unconcerned—the other animals kept well away. Lions, however, will put a baboon troop to flight. From the safety of trees baboons bark and threaten lions but make no resistance to them on the ground. The behavior of baboons when near trees contrasts strikingly with their behavior on the open plains. If the troop is under trees, it will feed on the ground within thirty yards of predators, including lions.

ECOLOGY AND SEX DIFFERENCES

The role of the adult male baboons as defenders of the troop has been described. This behavior is vital to the survival of the troop, and especially to the survival of the most helpless animals—females with new babies, small juveniles, and temporarily sick or injured individuals. Selection has favored the evolution of males which weigh more than twice as much as females, and the advantage to the troop of these large animals is clear, but it is not obvious why it is advantageous for the females to be small. The answer to the degree of sex differences appears to be that this is the optimum distribution of the biomass of the species. If the average adult male weighs approximately 75 pounds and the average adult female 30 pounds, each adult male requires more than twice the food of a female. If the food supply is a major factor in limiting the number of baboons, and if survival is more likely if there are many individuals, and if the roles of male and female are different—then selection will favor a sex difference in average body size which allows the largest number of animals compatible with the different social roles in the troop.

If selection favors males averaging 75 pounds, then it will favor females which are as much smaller as is compatible with their social roles. Since the females must travel the same distances, carry young, engage in sexual and competitive activities, there are limits to the degree of sexual differentiation, but the adaptive value of the difference is clear. For example, a troop of 36 baboons composed of 6 adult males and 12 adult females and their young (18 juveniles and infants) has a biomass of some 1,000 pounds. If the females also weighed 75 pounds each, 6 adult males and 6 adult females would alone total 900 pounds and have only one-half the reproductive potential of 6 adult males and 12 adult females. Because this would halve the number of young, it would greatly reduce the troop's chances of survival. Our data are not sufficiently detailed to analyze the actual distribution of biomass in the troops we observed, but our observations are compatible with the limited data on weights and the numbers of adult animals we saw. Viewing sexual differentiation in size as a function of the optimum distribution of biomass of the troop offers a way of understanding sexual dimorphism fundamentally different from the view which considers only sexual selection, dominance, and intratroop factors. Obviously, all factors should be considered. Adaptation is a complex process and results in compromises between the different selective pressures, but a distribution of biomass which doubles the reproductive potential of a species is so important that other factors may be minimized.

The importance of sex difference in body size is reinforced by social behavior and the structure of the troop. As described earlier, some subadult and adult males are peripheral in the structure of the troop. They tend to be first, or last, when the troop moves. They are the most exposed to predators and are, biologically, the most expendable members of the troop. Interadult male antagonism results in a social order which both protects females and young and reduces feeding competition with females and young. Without altruism, the dominance behavior of a small number of males keeps a feeding space available to subordinate animals.

Juvenile play prepares the adults for their differential roles. Older juvenile females do not engage in the serious mock fighting which characterizes the play of older juvenile males. In this "play" the males learn to fight, and by the time the canine teeth have erupted and the temporal muscles grown to adult size they have had years of fighting practice. Play, social arrangement, and structural sexual dimorphism all supplement each other, producing a pattern in which the females and young are relatively more protected than the large males. Sexual differentiation must be seen as a part of this whole complex social pattern which leads to the survival of troops of baboons.

RANGE

On an average day a baboon troop leaves its sleeping trees at full daylight and moves rapidly to a spot where the animals feed intensively for two or three hours. In Nairobi Park this morning feeding period is often spent in a fig tree (if these are in fruit), along a watercourse, or out on the open plains. During the dry season in the Amboseli Reserve, feeding areas were usually at the edges of water holes. During the middle of the day baboons rest in the shade of bushes or trees, not far from the feeding place of the morning. The late afternoon is another period of relatively intensive feeding. It is often some distance away from the feeding area of the morning, and a different kind of food is usually eaten. If the morning was spent in a fig tree, the afternoon is usually spent eating grass on the plains; if the morning was spent on the plains, the afternoon meal often consists of the pods, buds, and blossoms of acacia trees. During such a day the troop completes an average circuit of about three miles in Nairobi Park, but this distance varies from a few yards on some days to six or seven miles on others. These figures refer to the distance between points on a map. As a troop meanders across a plain, however, the individuals actually walk twice as far as these figures indicate.

During the year a baboon troop moves over an area which probably averages about fifteen square miles in open savanna country, but which may be much smaller (for a small troop or a troop living in forest country). Even where the total animal range is as large as fifteen square miles, only parts of it are used frequently. These areas of frequent use may be called "core areas" . . .

Table 2 shows the size and approximate annual range of the troops in Nairobi Park. Only the annual ranges for the Lone Tree and Songora Ridge troops are complete, but range sizes shown for the other troops probably include about 80 per cent of their annual range. In general, a large troop contains more adult males and covers a wider range. Although

TABLE 2

Annual Range of Nairobi Park Troops

NAME OF TROOP	SIZE	RANGE (IN SQUARE MILES)
Mbagathi River	12	?
Lone Tree	17	9.2
Python Pool	24	7.0 (+)
Athi River	28	3.0 (+)
Songora Ridge	28	15.5
Sosian Valley	40	9.6 (+)
Kapio River	61	?
Kisembe Valley	77	11.7 (+)
Hippo Pool	87	13.8 (+)

both the Athi River and the Songora Ridge troops numbered twenty-eight, the range of the latter is about five times as large as the former. The Athi River troop had only one large adult male; the Songora Ridge troop had six. This gives an approximate measure of the additional range required by a troop with more large males. It also indicates that troops with more males can control a larger range.

Daily routines tend to keep baboon troops apart. Although . . . annual ranges overlap extensively, there is very little overlap of the core areas of adjacent troops. We saw no evidence that troops defend a part of their range as "territory," but in Nairobi Park one troop is seldom seen in the core area of another. The core area or areas of a troop contain sleeping trees, water, resting places, and food sources. A troop uses one core area and one grove of sleeping trees for many weeks at a time but may then shift suddenly to a new area. In 1959 throughout the dry season there were only two sources of water in Nairobi Park which also contained tall trees: the Athi River, which forms the southern boundary of the Park, and a water hole in the core area of the Lone Tree troop. All the troops except Lone Tree had at least one core area along the Athi River, which is the boundary between the park and the Ngong Reserve. At both Nairobi Park and Amboseli baboon troops usually slept in the tall fever trees (*Acacia xanthophloea*) which grow only where the water table is high. Since the plants and fruit trees which baboons use for food also tend to be concentrated near water holes or along rivers, the core areas of a troop include food, water, refuge sites, and sleeping trees. Although a troop usually returns to the same sleeping place after its daily circuit, it also shifts from one core area to another over a period of weeks or months. The existence of alternative core areas serves to reduce contact between adjoining troops, and behavior patterns reinforce this distance. These spacing mechanisms, rather than defense of territorial boundaries, disperse baboon troops in an area.

The population density of baboons in Nairobi Park is about ten per square mile. As a result of social factors and low population density, baboon troops are seldom within sight of each other. When a troop is living on one edge of its range, for example, its neighbor on that side tends to move to a portion of its range well away from other troops. However, where core areas of adjacent troops overlap (along the Athi River), troops may sleep only fifty yards apart without any display of aggression. Only one incident of intertroop aggression was seen when human intervention was not involved. Deliberately bringing two troops together by artificial feeding, however, can cause intertroop threats. The troop with the greatest number of adult males always won in these encounters, although a troop in its core area seemed to be more aggressive than one at the edge of its range.

By contrast to the infrequent encounters between baboon troops in Nairobi Park, troops at Amboseli were seen in close proximity every day. At the end of the dry season at Amboseli (September and October), baboon troops were tightly clustered around water holes. Figure 11–1 shows the location of these troops during this two-month period. The double water hole (center of the map) was used by troops 51, 66, 171, 88, 70, and 57. At this place a 100-yard crescent of vegetation contained two pools 50 yards apart, and it was here that more than 400 baboons from these troops might be seen together. We never saw any fighting between troops, and it soon became clear that there was a pattern to the various troops' use of the surrounding area. Troops 51, 66, and 171 used only the northern pool, and went north and west from the pools during the day (shaded area). The southern pool was used by troops 88 and 70, and probably by 57, and these troops ranged south and east from the pools. The area between the two pools was used by all, except that we have no record of troop 70 there. The shaded portion of Figure 11–1 divides the region around the water holes according to its use by the different troops. The single exception is one observation of troop 171 at the water hole where troop 185 is shown.

Ordinarily this pattern of range utilization segregates the troops into clusters which recognize and tolerate each other at short distances without any sign of nervousness or tension. If a small troop is at a water hole and a large troop which also uses that water holes arrives, the smaller troop feeds slowly away. When troop 171 came once to the water hole usually frequented by 185, however, both troops paid close attention to the other. Adult males clustered where the troops were closest. The gestures, noises, and indications of nervousness were very different from the apparent lack of attention which is characteristic of troops normally frequenting the same water hole. By comparison with the behavior of

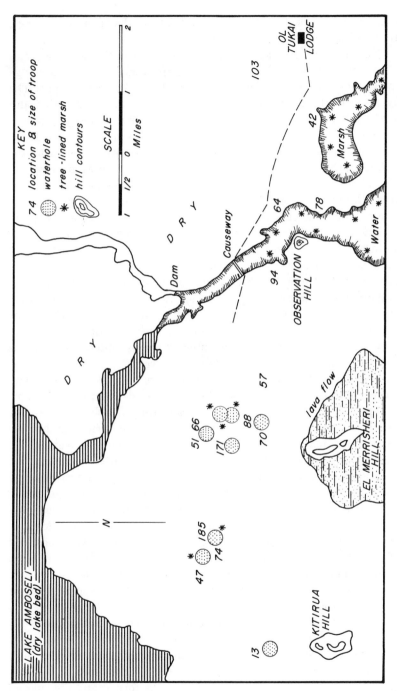

FIGURE 11-1—Size and location of fifteen baboon troops at Amboseli National Reserve during September and October, 1959. (Adapted from DeVore and Washburn by Jacquelyn Hetrick.)

troops in Nairobi Park, troop 171 was probably at the edge of its range, and troop 185 was occupying its core area.

As in Nairobi Park, the baboons at Amboseli slept in the tall fever trees around the water holes and marshes. The importance of trees as refuge from predators is illustrated by the ranges of the Amboseli troops. The marshy area north of the causeway (Fig. 11–1) contained water and plenty of food, but there were no trees there. Despite the heavy competition for the limited food resources during this season, no baboon troop included this treeless area in its range. Lions were often seen near the marsh, but south of the causeway, where lions were seen even more frequently, there were trees, and three large troops (94, 64, and 78) lived in this area. Normally the adult males protect the troop, but against the largest carnivores the only safety is flight into the trees. In areas where there are lions, trees limit the distribution of baboons as much as does the availability of food or water.

In summary, baboon range is based on the existence of refuge sites as well as sources of food and water. These ecological factors control population density, but the interrelations of troops are based on behavior. Troop size, number of adult males in the troop, and frequency of contact between troops determine the outcome of intertroop relations. Territorial defense is not seen, but core areas of different troops tend to space troops apart within ranges which may overlap extensively.

In the evolution of human behavior, hunting is the best clue to the size of the range and the area which is defended from strangers. The pattern of core areas around water, within a larger range, described here for baboons, is analogous to the pattern of land use by primitive hunter-gatherers in savanna country today. The major difference between baboon range and that of human hunters is the vastly larger area which humans, like the other large carnivores, must control. The aggressive protection of the hunting territory by humans also contrasts with the behavior which spaces baboon troops apart. African bushmen and Australian aborigines range over a hunting territory of from 100 to 1200 square miles. A range of this size is far more comparable to the ranges of wolves, wild dogs, and large felines than to the small ranges of the nonhuman primates. Within these large ranges, camp sites near water sources correspond to the core areas of baboon troops. Access to the resources within the core areas of these hunters is rigidly controlled by social custom, religious sanction, and the force of arms. Interband relations between human hunters distinguish between "friendly neighbors" and strangers, a distinction which has an ancient, prelinguistic basis in primate behavior. The most striking difference between the social organization of baboons and human hunter-gatherers is the closed social system of the former and the rules of local exogamy which are usually found in the latter. Although formal rules of exogamy depend upon the presence of language, the exogamous pattern itself may have arisen during the shift to a hunting economy by men of the early and middle Pleistocene.

DIET

A more detailed description of baboon diet is in preparation; the following discussion outlines the range of baboon foods and the relation between food supply and the troop. Baboons, like the macaques of Asia, eat a wide variety of foods. Although the bulk of their diet is vegetable food, they will also eat insects, eggs, and an occasional small mammal. Most of the Nairobi Park, where baboon foods were collected, is grassland with some scattered trees. *The Nairobi Royal National Park Guide Book* contains an excellent brief description of the flora and fauna of the park. Although the western edge of the park is dry semievergreen forest verging on woodland (the range of the Kisembe Valley troop), observations were largely confined to the open grassland country, and the description of baboon diet which follows includes few food items from the forest habitat. A study of the foods eaten by baboons in forest areas would be necessary before the full range of baboon diet in this area could be known.

VEGETABLE FOODS

The diet of baboons living in the savanna of Nairobi Park can be divided into: the vegetable foods which provide forage for them throughout the year, seasonal fruits, insects, and the live animals which they occasionally catch and eat. Grass is the baboon's single most important food. In ten months of observations, not a single day passed in which baboons were not observed eating grass, and for many weeks during the dry season, grasses composed an estimated 90 per cent of their diet. The portion of the grass eaten varies with the season. When the tassels contain seeds, these are "harvested" by pulling the tassel through the closed palm or clenched teeth. Most often, however, baboons pull up the grass shoots in order to eat the thick, lower stem at the base of the culm. Before eating the shoot, the dirt in the root system is carefully brushed away, and the roots themselves bitten off and discarded. By the middle of the dry season, when grass shoots are rare, baboons concentrate on digging up rhizomes —the thick, rootlike runners of the grasses which lie from two to four inches beneath the surface. Even after many weeks or months without rain, these rhizomes are still juicy, providing baboons with considerable water. The ability of baboons to shift to subsurface rhizomes and roots when surface vegetation is dry and sparse is one of their most important adaptations to the grasslands. It enables them to feed in an area which has been denuded of surface vegetation by the many ungulates with whom they share this habitat, and to find sufficient forage during long dry seasons. Digging these rhizomes out of the hard, dry soil with the fingers is a laborious task, and in the dry season baboons spend longer hours getting their food than they do during the rest of the year. The use of a simple digging stick or sharp stone would enormously increase their efficiency in extracting this food from the ground, but no baboon was ever seen trying to use a tool in this or any other way.

There are numerous plants on the Nairobi plains which have large, tuberous roots or bulbs, and the baboons are very adept at finding the tiny stem or leaf which indicates that such a root lies below. It may take as long as twenty minutes for a baboon to uncover a large root, and require a hole as large as 24 inches long, 8 inches wide, and 15 inches deep. Where the water table is high, along the rivers in Nairobi Park and around the water holes at Amboseli Reserve, the lush grasses attract many animal species, including baboons. Not only is the grass more plentiful here during the dry season, but also the earth is softer and more easily dug and many water plants are found which grow nowhere else in the area. Baboons spend the majority of their time feeding in the grass near the water, but they will also wade into the shallow water to eat such plants as rushes and the buds of water lilies.

The baboons' usual diet is further extended by the various bushes, flowering plants, and shrubs of the savanna. In Nairobi Park they were seen eating the berries, buds, blossoms, and seed pods of such plants. Another very important source of food throughout the year is provided by the acacia trees. Probably the buds, blossoms, and beanlike seed pods of all acacias are eaten, but those of the fever trees (*A. xanthophloea*) are particularly important. Not only is this species used almost exclusively as sleeping trees, but when they are in the height of their bloom the baboons also usually feed in them for one or more hours before starting their morning round, returning in the afternoon for another heavy feeding period at dusk. Out on the plains the ant galls on the short whistling-thorn trees (*A. drepanolobium*) are constantly plucked for the ants inside, and extrusions of its sap are eaten as well. Some edible portion— bud, flower, seed pod, sap—of one of the types of acacia tree will be available within a troop's range at almost any time of year, and acacias are second only to grasses in the quantity of food they provide for Nairobi Park baboons. In addition to the plants and trees which provide forage for baboons all year, certain seasonal foods may constitute the bulk of their diet for short periods. The most important source of these seasonal foods in Nairobi Park are fig trees. When large fig trees are in fruit, the baboons may also use them as sleeping trees.

The most important food sources in the park are the grasses, acacia, and fig trees, but despite the frequency with which they feed in these trees, baboons were never seen eating tree leaves. On the southeastern slope of Mt. Kilimanjaro, baboons were observed feeding on the forest floor, while vervets (*Cercopithecus aethiops* and *C. mitis*) fed in the lower branches of adjacent trees. Leaf-eating *Colobus* monkeys occupied the canopy of the same forest. Their ability to find food both on the open plain and in the trees is a distinct advantage for the baboons. Although they compete with a wide variety of ungulates for their food on the plains at Nairobi Park, their only close competitors in the trees are the vervets. Vervets and baboons are commonly seen feeding in adjoining trees in the park and occasionally they occupy the same tree—the baboons on the lower branches and the vervets in the canopy.

In addition to the staple diet, other vegetable foods were frequently eaten when they were available. These included "kei-apples," croton nuts, sisal plants, mushrooms, and the produce of native gardens (potatoes, yams, bananas, beans, maize, peanuts, sugar cane, etc.). Since almost all cultivated plants in this area have been imported from the New World, it is clear that baboons are very eclectic in their food habits.

INSECTS

Baboons eat many types of insects when they can find them, but the climate of Nairobi Park with its dry season, its hot days and cool nights does not support a very heavy insect population. The most common insect eaten in the park is the ant living in the galls of the *Acacia drepanolobium* trees. The amount of ants eaten in this way, however, is very small compared to the grasses and plants eaten during the same feeding period. If the troop is walking slowly through an area strewn with large stones, some of these may be turned over and the ground beneath them examined carefully. Under such stones an occasional beetle, slug, or cricket will be found and is quickly eaten. Rarely, an ant nest is uncovered, and the baboon bends over and licks up the contents of the nest from the earth, licking additional ants from its hands and arms afterward. But the baboons' attitude toward insects is one of mild interest, and no troop was ever seen moving from its pathway to systematically turn over the stones in an area.

Besides the ants in acacia galls, a baboon most frequently eats the grasshoppers which it finds on the branches of the bushes or blades of grass where it is feeding. Young baboons are seldom able to capture grasshoppers, but an adult will move the hand cautiously and deliberately to within one or two feet of the insect, then grasp it very quickly in a movement which is usually successful. Not all insects encountered are eaten.

When a rock is overturned, some beetles and centipedes are ignored while others are carefully selected. Too few instances were observed to be able to say whether such selection was by individual preference, or whether these insects were avoided by all baboons in the park.

Although insect food is minor in the over-all baboon diet, a very heavy infestation of "army worm" caterpillars in the park showed that for short periods insects can become the baboons' most important food. Beginning in early April, during the rainy season, army worms appeared in the park in large numbers. For about ten days the baboons ate little else. Feeding on the worms in a small area were: three baboon troops, totaling 188 animals; several troops of vervet monkeys, perhaps 75 in all; and a group of about 300 Marabou stork (*Leptoptilos crumeniferus*). The different baboon troops fed very near each other, and the other animals, without incident. All were gorging themselves on the caterpillars; several baboons were timed picking up 100 army worms per minute, and continuing at this rate for from 10 to 15 minutes without a break. The eating of insects, in addition to the extensive inventory of vegetable foods, further increases the dietary adaptability of the baboon.

LIVE ANIMALS

On six, perhaps seven, occasions during the twelve months of study in Kenya and the Rhodesias, we saw baboons eating freshly killed animals. Twice they caught and ate half-grown African hares (*Lepus capensis crawshayi*). On the first occasion the male in possession of the hare was being harried not only by two more dominant males in this troop, but by a pair of tawny eagles (*Aquila repax raptor*) as well. The male in possession eluded his harassers and managed to consume most of the hare, the eagles retrieving scraps of viscera and skin. In his haste the baboon dropped the rib cage and a foreleg of the hare, with most of the flesh still attached, *but these pieces were ignored* by the other two baboons chasing him, despite their desire to obtain his catch.

Two or three times baboons were seen eating fledgling birds of some ground-nesting species, probably the crowned plover (*Stephanibyx coronatus*). On several occasions they chased fledglings some yards through the grass without catching them. We never saw baboons finding and eating eggs, but when offered a dozen guinea fowl eggs, they ate these without hesitation. Entire eggs were stuffed into the cheek pouches and the shell broken by the hand pressing the cheek against the teeth and jaws. More significant than the few instances of baboons' eating fledglings are the numerous times when baboons were seen feeding across a plain covered by bird nests without discovering the contents of a single nest. The same animals which are able to detect an underground root from only a tiny dried shoot on the surface will walk beside a bird nest six inches in diameter without noticing it. Furthermore, four species of weaver bird inhabit the park, and their nests are frequently clustered in the acacia branches where the baboons are eating, but no baboon was ever seen investigating such a nest, much less eating its contents. The baboon's attitude toward food is clearly vegetarian. It is common to see a baboon troop completely mingled with a flock of guinea fowl without incident. The only eggs or fledglings which they seem to recognize as food are those which are literally stepped on as the troop searches for vegetable foods on the plains.

On December 14, near the close of the study, two very young Thomson gazelle (*Gazella t. thomsonii*) were caught and eaten by the adult males of a troop. The actual capture of the second gazelle was seen. An adult male baboon grabbed it, brought it above his head, and slammed it to the ground. He immediately tore into the stomach of the gazelle and began eating. Beginning with the most dominant males, five of the six adult males in the troop participated in eating this gazelle, and two hours later only skin, teeth and large bones remained. The viscera were eaten first, followed by the flesh, and finally the thin brain case was bitten open and the contents carefully scooped out with the fingers—bits of skull being pulled through the teeth and licked clean. The incisors, not the canines, were used in biting and tearing at the flesh.

These two Thomson's gazelle were apparently only a few days old, and were hiding in the grass some 150 yards from the herd of 38 with which they were no doubt associated. After the baboon troop moved on, two females from the herd of gazelle (of 35 females, 2 young, and one adult male) came over and paced nervously around the remains of the carcasses. It seems reasonable to assume that the discovery of these two young gazelle took place under circumstances very similar to those involved in the eating of the young hares, that is, that they were discovered accidentally in the grass. In fact, after the first gazelle had been found, and four of the males were pressing its possessor closely, the males passed within five yards of an African hare sitting in plain view. They clearly saw the hare but did not even walk over toward it.

All these cases of flesh eating have one thing in common—they involve the eating of immature animals whose defense is to hide "frozen" in the grass, and in each case their discovery by the baboons seemed fortuitous. Nothing resembling a systematic search of an area or the stalking of prey was ever observed, nor was fresh meat eaten except when it was found alive or taken up immediately by a waiting baboon. Since baboons avoid lion kills when they are away from trees and other carrion is not eaten, the lack of interest shown by the male in the portion of hare which had been dropped (described above) may be due to their avoidance of carrion.

It is also possible that baboons do not recognize as edible any meat which is not alive and easily caught. In either case it seems clear that their attitude toward other animals is not that of a predator, nor do the scores of other species with which they live peacefully so regard them.

The final instance of meat-eating was observed in Amboseli Reserve. While watching baboons in an open area, we heard loud screeches and chattering in a tree where baboons and vervets had been feeding peacefully for the previous hour. When we approached the tree we saw an adult male baboon walking through the branches with a juvenile vervet dangling from his mouth, and the vervet troop had left the tree. The baboon consumed most of the vervet, carrying the carcass in his mouth as he walked toward the troop's sleeping tree at dusk. This observation is in striking contrast to the many occasions when two types of monkey were seen feeding peacefully together. During a brief aggressive interaction between the two species in Nairobi Park, DeVore saw an angry adult male baboon put a troop of vervets to rapid flight, and this case of meat-eating may have been the incidental result of such a situation in the tree at Amboseli. Although Washburn saw baboons chase vervets quite frequently near Victoria Falls, he only once saw a baboon catch one. This was held in the mouth by the female who caught it. She was apparently bewildered by the situation and soon released it unharmed. In much the same way one of the fledglings DeVore saw eaten was actually caught by a juvenile baboon, which seemed puzzled by the object and quickly relinquished it to an adult male (who promptly ate it).

In summary, baboons may be described as very inefficient predators. Meat-eating, to judge by the bewildered state of the female baboon who caught a vervet and of the young juvenile who caught a bird, would appear to be learned by each generation, and meat never becomes an important source of food for the whole troop. Only one baboon other than adult males (an adult female) participated in the eating of meat in any of the instances observed during the study. Accounts of meat-eating in captive baboons are contradictory. Kenya baboons kept near Nairobi Park ate meat readily, but Bolwig found that his captives refused it. In South Africa, where most reports of carnivorous baboons have originated, baboons are only now being systematically studied, and we feel that the importance of meat in the baboon diet has been considerably overstressed. The usual reason given for the habit of meat-eating in South African baboons is that the hardship of drought creates the conditions under which it flourishes, but when the two Thomson's gazelle were eaten in December the park was well into the rainy season, and the vegetable foods baboons ordinarily eat were more abundant than at any other time of year.

It would seem more reasonable to us, on the present evidence, to assume that meat has been a consistent but very minor part of the baboon diet throughout their evolutionary history. In localities where sources of animal protein can be obtained without danger, baboons apparently include these in their regular diet. At Murchison Falls, baboons are often seen digging out and eating crocodile eggs. Hall's description of the foods eaten by baboons along the coast of South Africa is very similar to the inventory of vegetable and insect foods discussed here, except that the South African baboons also eat marine foods such as mussels, crabs, and sand hoppers found along the beach. But baboons are ill fitted anatomically to be carnivores, and too great a dependence on meat eating could have been detrimental to their wide exploitation of the vegetable foods they depend upon today. By their utilization of a wide variety of plant and tree products, baboons have been able to spread over the African continent, and, together with the macaques, to cover most of the tropical Old World.

In the evolution of the human species, meat-eating played a very different role. We have suggested that the earliest hominids may have been living on a diet very like that of the baboons, that is, vegetable foods supplemented by an occasional small animal. The freedom to carry a simple digging implement in the hands would greatly enhance this adaptation. During the dry season in Africa, human hunter-gatherers are also very dependent on the subsurface roots and tubers sought by baboons. A digging stick greatly improves the humans' chance for survival during this period of food shortage, and it may be that the presence of baboon skeletons at Olorgesaille indicates the result of competition between baboons and humans over a limited food supply. It would be an easy step from killing baboons to protect a source of vegetable foods, to killing them for meat.

SCAVENGING

Scavenging has been regarded as an important phase in the evolution of man's carnivorous habits. It seems reasonable that a primate liking eggs, nestling birds, insects, and an occasional small mammal might add to this diet and develop more carnivorous tastes and habits by gleaning meat from kills. This theory seemed reasonable, and we made a particular effort to examine kills and to observe the relations of the baboons to them. Although we saw over a dozen recent kills (including gnu, giraffe, zebra, waterbuck, impala, Grant's gazelle, warthog, Masai cattle, and goat) and have thorough records on some, we were primarily looking at baboons. The subject of scavenging is so important, especially in the interpretation of the deposits in which *Australopithecus* is found, that a much more comprehensive study is needed. However, here are our tentative conclusions.

The scavenging theory is not supported by the evidence, and primates with habits similar to those of baboons could get meat by hunting far more easily than by scavenging. There are several reasons for this. The first is that most kills are made at night and are rapidly and thoroughly eaten. When the hyenas leave at dawn, the vultures locate the remains and clean the last meat from the bones. Some kills are made by day. We saw the remains of a gnu which a pride of ten lions finished in an hour. A pride of four lions (two not fully grown) killed a gnu one afternoon and ate almost all of it in one night. The vultures finished the rest, and the bones were undisturbed for three days. Many bones disappeared on the fourth night. Similarly, we saw two lions eat a warthog, three lions eat a Grant's gazelle, and five cheetahs kill and eat an impala. Only the meat of very large animals is left for long, and Africa is well supplied with highly efficient scavengers which leave little meat to tempt a primate.

Actually there are far fewer kills than might be expected from discussions of scavenging. In the part of the Amboseli Reserve which we studied intensively there were on the order of 100 baboons to one lion. The lions move over large areas, and the chances of a troop coming on a "kill" are very few. We saw a troop around a kill left from the previous night only once in Amboseli. It had been largely eaten, and the baboons appeared to take no interest in it. During nine months of observation in Nairobi Park, baboons were seen to pass near four kills and paid no attention to the few scraps of meat left on them. A Grant's gazelle carcass, presumably a leopard kill, hung in a fig tree where baboons ate and slept, but the baboons apparently ignored it. In addition, they did not attempt to eat fresh carrion when this was found. A further complicating factor is that when there is much meat left, the lions usually stay nearby, and the neighborhood of the kill is very dangerous.

In summary, the chances of a kill within the range of a baboon troop are very small; little meat is likely to be left; and the vicinity of the kill is dangerous. Most of the killing and eating is at night, and primates have neither the sense of smell of the hyenas nor the eyes of the vultures to locate the kill. As noted earlier, the baboons seem uninterested in dead animals. A slight increase in predatory activity against young animals would yield a far greater reward than scavenging, would be much less dangerous, and would represent a smaller change in habit. The use of a stick or stone for digging would increase the baboons' food supply more than any other simple invention. Perhaps in *Australopithecus* we see a form which had such a tool to exploit vegetable foods and which also used this tool as a weapon. If tools were being used at all, their use in the deliberate killing of small animals would be only a small change from the behavior observed in baboons. Once man had become a skilled tool-user in these ways, he could extend tool use to the hunting of large animals, to defense, and to driving carnivores from their kills. Scavenging may have become a source of meat when man had become sufficiently skilled to take the meat away from carnivores, but the hunting of small animals and defenseless young is much more likely to lie at the root of the human hunting habit.

DISCUSSION

In this paper we have tried to stress those aspects of baboon ecology which are of the greatest help in understanding human evolution. Obviously, man is not descended from a baboon, and the behavior of our ancestors may have been very different from that of living baboons. But we think that in a general way the problems faced by the baboon troop may be very similar to those which confronted our ancestors. At the least, comparison of human behavior with that of baboons emphasizes the differences. At the most, such a comparison may give new insights. Many topics have been summarized above, and in this discussion we will call attention only to a few major points.

The size of baboon troops may exceed that of hunter-gatherers, and their population density far exceeds that of primitive man. The human group differs in being exogamous, so that many local groups form the breeding population. We believe that this radically different breeding structure has exerted a profound effect on the latter phases of human evolution and has long been a factor in preventing speciation in man.

The social structure of the baboon troop is important to the survival of the species. Survival depends on the adult males being constantly close to the other troop members. Roles in the troop are divided between the sexes, but these are in the context of a compact troop. With man, the hunters leave the local group, sometimes for days, and then return to their home base. Such a pattern is radically different from anything known in monkeys or apes. Hunting with tools basically changed the social structure of the band, the interrelations of bands, the size and utilization of range, and the relation of man to other animals.

Diet has already been discussed and we will not repeat here, except to point out that our opinion of the importance of scavenging has changed through observation of the actual situation at the kills. It is not enough to speculate that scavenging might have been important. One must estimate how much meat is actually available to a vegetarian, and how dangerous it is to get meat by scavenging.

Finally, we would stress that survival is a complex process, and that all the factors which lead to reproductive success must ultimately be considered. Varied diet, social structure, and anatomy, all are important, but their meaning only becomes clear as they are seen making possible the behavior of a population. Sex differences, peripheral animals, and range —each of these has meaning only in terms of the survival of groups. With the coming of man, every major category is fundamentally altered and evolution begins to be dominated by new selection pressures. Some measure of how different the new directions are may be gained from the study of the ecology of baboons.

12

CHIMPANZEES OF THE GOMBE STREAM RESERVE

Jane Goodall

For a long time, the chimpanzee (pan) *has been accepted as man's closest relative. Almost every known fact about this interesting animal has been gathered from observations in the laboratory or in the zoos. More recently, field studies of chimpanzees in their natural surroundings in central Africa have contributed fresh insight into the primate substrate of human behavior, particularly the behavior of the earliest hominids who were not far removed from ape status themselves.*

However, we should not interpret chimpanzee behavior as directly reflecting the behavior of the earliest men. Chimpanzees are themselves the product of evolutionary processes involving adaptation to special environments, and we, of course, are not descended from any living ape. Nevertheless, field studies of free-ranging groups, such as the following paper by Jane Goodall, enable us not only to appreciate the potentialities

(From *Primate Behavior*, Irven DeVore, editor. Holt, Rinehart and Winston, Inc., 1965, pages 425–473. By permission of the author and the publisher.)

of the infrahuman primate behavioral inventory but also to
see more clearly the actual ways in which the hominids
differ from the apes.

. . . The data on which this chapter is based were obtained during a
total of 24 months (17 months between the end of June 1960 and the
beginning of December 1961, and 7 months from the beginning of June
1962 to the end of December 1962) at the Gombe Stream Chimpanzee
Reserve in Tanganyika. . . .

THE STUDY AREA

The Gombe Steam Reserve supports a semi-isolated population of
P. satyrus (= *t. schweinfurthi*), the eastern or long-haired chimpanzee.
This area was selected for a field study because the country is not the
closed rain forest habitat normal for chimpanzees and thus offers unusually favorable opportunities for observation. It consists of a narrow
mountainous strip stretching for some ten miles along the east shore of
Lake Tanganyika, between Kigoma and Rwanda and Burundi, and
running inland about three miles to the peaks of the mountains of the Rift
escarpment, which rise steeply from the Lake (2334 feet) to heights of
about 5000 feet. Numerous steep-sided valleys and ravines intersect the
mountains, many of which support permanent streams. The dense gallery
rain forests of the valleys and lower slopes give place to more open
deciduous woodland on the upper slopes, and many of the peaks and
ridges are covered only by grass. In the valleys stands of trees reach a
height of up to 80 feet, but the trees of the open woodlands seldom exceed
40 feet. During the rainy season, between October and May, the grass
grows as high as 14 feet, but during the dry season grass fires usually
sweep through the reserve, started by African farmers outside the
boundary.

Temperatures in this area reach 115° in the day and drop below 60°
in the night, and humidity is high during the rainy season. In normal
years this area has about 50 inches of rain. During the wet season, from
October to May, at least an hour's heavy rain fell on most days, and
sometimes it rained for ten hours without stopping.

FIELD STUDY METHODS AND EQUIPMENT

A base camp was established near the lake shore at a central point in
the reserve, and after all areas of the reserve had been investigated, a
main study area of some 15 square miles was selected. I went to the north
or south of this area when chimpanzee groups concentrated there.

From high vantage points in the reserve it is possible to watch chimpanzee movements over areas of up to two miles. The animals cannot be kept in sight all the time, but they can often be located from calls, the movement of branches, and the like. For the first three months of the study I concentrated on becoming familiar with general movements and basic behavior patterns, while also beginning to habituate the chimpanzees to my presence. An average of 12 hours per day was spent in the field, but the actual observation time varied from 0 to 8 hours a day. After the first three months it was unusual for an entire day to pass without my seeing at least one chimpanzee. Fifteen nights were spent near groups of sleeping chimpanzees and they could sometimes be observed in the moonlight.

It was decided from the start that for close-range study it would be necessary to habituate the chimpanzees to the presence of an observer. Observations from places of concealment (from behind tree trunks, tangles of undergrowth, and so on), proved impractical because the sharp eyesight of the chimpanzees normally detected my presence after the first few minutes. Habituation was a lengthy process. At first most of the chimpanzees ran off when they saw me as far away as 500 yards, but this distance gradually lessened, and after 8 months it was possible to approach to within 50 yards of them provided they were in fairly thick cover and up in a tree. (In the open or on the ground they were harder to approach, even at the end of the study.) After 10 months I could approach to within 100 feet of most individuals, and after 14 months the apes carried on their normal activities (feeding, mating, sleeping, and so on) when I was only from 30 to 50 feet away. Three mature males became "tame" and, after 18 months, took food from my hand, making it possible to observe relationships between mature males in detail. As chimpanzees became known individually they were named, and these 3 males were David Greybeard, Goliath, and William. Goliath was the largest and most powerfully built. William was the weakest and most timid.

When a group moved away I never followed (except in the last few months), because the chimpanzees, even when no longer frightened, were usually shy of being observed. Every effort was made to conceal my interest in the activities of the chimpanzees. Often a group that had become uneasy at the proximity of a human was calmed if, for example, I ate leaves or dug a hole. On many occasions when chimpanzees were surprised in a tree they remained there if I walked past, but climbed down and moved away if I stopped to look at them. . . .

DAILY BEHAVIOR PATTERN OF CHIMPANZEES

Chimpanzees in the Gombe Stream area are nomadic in that they usually sleep in a different place each night, and although for the most part they keep within the same general area, they follow no regular circuit in their daily search for food. The distance and direction of this daily wandering varies with the availability of food. Their diet is mainly vegetarian, but chimpanzees in this area have been observed feeding on insects and meat.

They move in small temporary groups, which may consist of any combination of age/sex classes. Lone males and, occasionally, lone females are also encountered. The only group that is stable over a period of months is a mother with her infant and older offspring.

Each night they construct new sleeping platforms or nests, which in this area are always made in trees and never on the ground at night. Individual animals sleep by themselves except for infants, which sleep with their mothers. . . .

POPULATION DENSITY

It was not possible to make an accurate count of the chimpanzee population in the Gombe Stream Reserve, in part because the apes were not restricted to the reserve and in part because of the difficulty of recognizing all individuals encountered, particularly immature animals.

The lake forms a natural boundary to the west and chimpanzee penetration to the north is restricted by native cultivation, but there is nothing to prevent the apes from moving out of the reserve across the southern and eastern boundaries for ten miles or so. I saw five groups actually moving out of the reserve.

Fifteen mature males known individually were continually moving backward and forward across the main study area, and many of them were seen near both the northern and southern boundaries of the reserve. Sixteen known mature females were encountered in various parts of the reserve.

Analysis of the data suggests that there were not less than 32 immature animals. The mature animals not known individually that were seen moving about with known animals were either temporary visitors from outside the reserve or animals which normally remained near the boundaries to the south and east.

At a rough estimate, then, there were no fewer than 60 and no more then 80 individuals normally to be found in the 30 square miles of the reserve. So there were, at a maximum, 2.6 animals per square mile. However, any estimate of the density of the population should take into account the fact that about 25 percent of the reserve is scarcely utilized since it offers little or no food to the chimpanzees. In relation to the area actually used the density of the population is about 3.3 percent. . . .

INDIVIDUAL BEHAVIOR

LOCOMOTION

Chimpanzees usually travel from place to place on the ground, normally in a leisurely fashion, the chimpanzees often helping themselves up steep slopes by hauling on tree trunks or low branches—behavior that I have not observed in other primates. In this area chimpanzees spend between 50 and 70 percent of the day in trees, either feeding or resting, but they seldom move from place to place through the trees, except for short distances during the rainy season. Infant-twos, juveniles, and young adolescents move easily and quickly in trees, but as they attain maturity arboreal locomotion becomes slow and careful unless the animals are frightened or excited.

Bipedal locomotion. Chimpanzees frequently stand upright in order to look over long grass or other vegetation. Sometimes a branch or tree trunk is held with one hand, but often an erect posture is assumed with both arms hanging down at the animal's sides. In addition, they have been observed to walk or run bipedally for distances of as much as 30 yards.

Chimpanzees were observed to walk bipedally when moving through long grass for short distances while looking at an unusual object (such as the observer) or searching for a companion, and when carrying objects in both hands.

Bipedal running often occurs if males are socially excited, as during the branch-waving display, when they may run upright down a steep slope for a few yards before breaking off a branch or when chasing after and threatening baboons or the observer. It also occurs frequently during infant and juvenile play. Bipedal running is often accompanied by arm swinging, the arms being swung forward alternately with a circling movement.

In addition, a ritualized form of bipedal locomotion may occur during greeting and courtship, when a male may stand upright and sway from foot to foot.

Quadrupedal locomotion. When running or walking on four limbs the chimpanzee places the backs of the flexed fingers and the soles of the feet on the ground. When descending a steep slope the arms may be used as crutches and the hind limbs swung through them, a type of locomotion frequently used by early infant-twos, even on level ground. Chimpanzees normally jump a stream quadrupedally, although I have also seen them jump across bipedally as reported by Kortlandt.

When climbing a thick trunk the chimpanzee places its hands on either side with its feet in the normal walking position; it descends in the same way, backwards. When a chimpanzee moves about in a tree the fingers and toes are used for grasping the branches. In order to move from one tree to another, the chimpanzee usually walks out along a branch which bends under its weight until it can reach a lower branch of the other tree, keeping its hold on the original branch until it has secured firm hand and footholds on the new one.

Swinging and leaping. Brachiation for short distances is common. On these occasions, although the overhead branch is the only true support, the chimpanzee frequently grasps small twigs with its feet. It often swings through a tree in the upright position, with equal use of hands and feet.

Young chimpanzees, in play, or adults when excited or frightened, sometimes leap from one branch to another. They may either take off and land quadrupedally or push off with the feet and reach out for another branch with the hands. On two occasions mature males, when excited, took off bipedally and appeared to "dive" down, catching a lower branch with their hands and swinging around under it.

FEEDING BEHAVIOR

Vegetarian feeding. The chimpanzee is primarily a vegetarian. Seventy-three different types of vegetable foods have been collected, consisting of 37 fruits, 21 leaves or leaf buds, 6 blossoms, 4 seeds, 3 stems, and 2 barks. . . .

In this area chimpanzees spend between six and seven hours a day in active feeding. About 90 percent of their food is found growing in trees and they seldom feed intensively on the ground.

They pick large fruits by hand, and usually use their lips to remove small fruits, buds, and blossoms from the stems. The fruits of *Strychnos,* which have hard rinds, are picked off, held in the hand, and banged against the trunk of a tree or against a rock until the rinds crack. Bark, which I saw eaten on only four occasions, was either pulled off in strips and the inner surface scraped with the incisors or the bark was left in place and scraped off directly from the trunk or branch, again with the incisors.

When a chimpanzee starts feeding early in the morning, or after traveling or resting, it eats ravenously, swallowing unripe food, . . . stones and skin. As hunger decreases it shows more discrimination, rejecting unripe foods and expressing the juice from a wad of stones and skin held in its lower lip, which it then spits out. When satiated the chimpanzee frequently sits or reclines, sucking a large wad of this kind for as long as 20 minutes.

Insect eating. In the Gombe Stream Reserve chimpanzees were seen feeding on two types of gall, on two species of ant, and on termites.

Between June and September the larvae of a species of gall fly form small white galls on the leaves of *Chlorophora excelsa*. Chimpanzees pick these off with their lips, and may spend as long as two hours at a stretch feeding in this way. They also eat galls formed by *Paracopium glabricorne* (a lace bug) in buds of *Clerodendrum schweinfurthii*.

Groups of chimpanzees were twice seen feeding on ants, once on a species of arboreal ant that makes a round nest in a tree and once on a species of *Dolaris* that makes an underground nest. The method of eating both species was similar; the chimpanzees poked sticks into the opened nests, left them there for a moment, and then withdrew them covered with ants that they removed with the lips and tongue. Eight sticks that had been used were found to be between 2 and 2½ feet in length, and another was 3½ feet. On three other occasions there was evidence that *Dolaris* ants had been eaten, when sticks with traces of earth adhering to one end were found beside freshly opened nests.

At the beginning of the rains, for a period of as long as nine weeks, the chimpanzees feed for one or two hours daily on a species of termite common in the area. At this time the fertile termites grow wings in preparation for leaving the nest to found new colonies, and their passages are extended to the surface of the termite hill and then sealed lightly over while the insects await good flying conditions. Chimpanzees were observed examining termite hills after a heavy rainstorm several weeks before the termite emigration actually started.

When a chimpanzee sees a sealed-up termite hole it scrapes away the thin layer of soil with index finger or thumb, picks a grass stalk, thin twig, or piece of vine, and pokes this carefully down the hole. It waits for a moment and then withdraws the tool, the end of which is coated with termites, hanging on with their mandibles, and these the chimpanzee picks off with the lips. Either hand may be used in the manipulation of the tool, and while picking off the insects the chimpanzee may support one end of the tool on the back of its other wrist.

The grass or other material selected is not normally longer than about 12 inches. When one end becomes bent the chimpanzee either turns it round and uses the other end or breaks off the bent part. When the tool becomes too short to be of use, a new tool is selected, and if this is too long, the chimpanzee usually breaks a piece off; if a leafy twig or vine is selected, the leaves are stripped off with the lips or fingers.

The chimpanzee also shows discrimination in its choice of materials. A tangle of vines may be briefly examined and rejected if unsuitable. When working at an exceptionally deep hole, one male, after trying with several grasses of the usual length, looked round intently, got up, and went to pick a long piece of vine growing several yards away. An individual often showed a definite preference for one particular type of material for use as a tool on one particular day. Thus, one of the "tame" males picked and used grass stalks on one occasion and on the following day, working in the same place, he used only pieces of vine, even though this entailed climbing about ten feet up a tree to pick them.

On several occasions, when the nearest termite hill was at least 100 feet away and out of sight, a chimpanzee picked a grass stalk, carried it to the termite hill, and used it as a tool. One male carried a grass stalk (in his mouth) for half a mile, while he examined, one after the other, six termite hills, none of which was ready for working.

Meat-eating. Chimpanzees were seen feeding on meat on nine occasions; three times the prey was identified as a monkey (twice the red colobus, *Colobus badius graueri*) and once as a young bushpig (*Potamochoerus koiropotamus sp.*). On four occasions the prey was not identified. Bones (once the toe bones of a monkey) were twice found in chimpanzee feces. On another occasion, the skin of the tail and part of the rump of a monkey was found on a termite hill where two male chimpanzees had been feeding; the skin was still damp and it was presumed that they had left it there. Hunting and killing was seen once only, when the prey was a red colobus. When the chimpanzees were eating the young bushpig referred to above, two adult pigs remained in the vicinity for an hour, chasing a juvenile chimpanzee that climbed to the ground. On one of the occasions when the flesh being eaten was not identified, a female bushbuck remained near the chimpanzees all night and was twice chased by an adult male; it is possible that the chimpanzees were eating its young.

When approached by a chimpanzee, bushbuck bark and run off. Four adult bushpigs moved hurriedly away when surprised by a group of chimpanzees, and one pig bolted when a male chimpanzee disturbed it in a patch of long grass.

On the only occasion when hunting and killing were observed, the prey, a red colobus monkey, was sitting in a tree when an adolescent male chimpanzee climbed a neighboring tree, and remained very still as the monkey looked toward it. A second adolescent male chimpanzee then climbed the tree in which the colobus was sitting, ran quickly along the branch, leapt at the colobus, and caught it with its hands, presumably breaking its neck, as it did not struggle or call out. The other adolescent then leapt into the tree, and five other chimpanzees, including a mature male and a late infant-two, climbed up. The mature male pulled until he had half the carcass. Subsequently I observed that the mother of the infant had acquired a large piece of meat and afterward the other chimpanzees, with the exception of the infant, also managed to get small pieces or scraps. On the other occasions when I saw meat-eating, the prey

FIGURE 12–1—Fishing for termites. This extraordinary photograph shows wild African chimpanzees using stems as tools to fish termites out of a nest. The apes strip leaves from twigs and break off the ends of the twigs when they become bent, thus creating primitive tools. When the stems are withdrawn, insects cling to them. (Photo by Jane Goodall. © National Geographic Society.)

FIGURE 12–2—Once the chimpanzee has withdrawn the stem from the termite mound, all he has to do is munch off the insects. (Photo by Jane Goodall. © National Geographic Society.)

was initially in the possession of a mature male. Each time the other chimpanzees in the group sat close to him, holding out their hands with the begging gesture.

Meat is eaten slowly, the chimpanzee pulling at the flesh with its incisors, and between each bite of meat a mouthful of leaves is always eaten. Small bones, apparently, are crunched up; large ones are gnawed for some time and then dropped.

Two reports from the Kigoma area of human infants being carried off by male chimpanzees are interesting when considered in relation to these observations on meat-eating. In 1957 a baby was seized from its mother's back and carried for some distance; it was already dead when the chimpanzee was driven away by natives. Subsequent medical examination showed that the child had definitely been gnawed by some animal. This incident occurred several miles to the east of the reserve. The second occurrence, however, took place in the reserve; a baby left alone for a few moments was seized by a mature chimpanzee, which was chased and ran off, dropping the child, who had been severely mutilated.

In addition to these two reports I have heard indirectly of a European who maintains that during his tour in the police force in West Africa five babies were carried off by chimpanzees.

Other observations on feeding. Chimpanzees were not observed to eat wild birds' eggs, though one female climbed up a tree to feel carefully in a hollow, and Francolins (*Francolinus hildebrandti*) give the alarm call and fly off when chimpanzees approach. One male ate domestic hens' eggs without hesitation, stuffing several leaves into his mouth with the uncracked egg before eating it. Two other animals, however, persistently ignored eggs offered to them.

On five occasions chimpanzees were observed scraping and eating soil from a cliff face. This behavior was seen only in March and April, although I visited the area regularly throughout the year. Analysis of a sample of the soil showed that a small amount of hilite (sodium chloride) was present.

During the field study a red block of mineral salts that had been put out disappeared, and the following day one of a group of chimpanzees was observed carrying the block of salt. For some 30 minutes it licked the salt while the others in the group sat close and held out their hands with the begging gesture.

A chimpanzee was observed drinking only once; it went to the edge of a stream, put its face down, and sucked up water with its lips for about 30 seconds.

Chimpanzees frequently carry food for short distances. For example, when one is partially satisfied it often makes a collection of fruits or picks a food-laden branch that it then carries, in one hand or in its mouth, to a comfortable branch or, occasionally, to the ground, where it eats at leisure. When a group is on the move one chimpanzee may pick and carry a food branch, pausing from time to time to eat. After feeding intensively on meat for some hours a chimpanzee often moves off with the remains of the carcass in its mouth; one male carried meat for at least half a mile. The block of mineral salts was transported for a distance of at least two miles. The three "tame" males frequently took cloth objects from camp in order to suck at the material. Blankets were either bundled under one arm or held in the hand or foot and dragged along; one heavy blanket was dragged for at least one and one-half miles up a steep mountain.

GROOMING AND NEST-BUILDING

Self-grooming. In captivity old chimpanzees spend more time grooming themselves than young ones do, and the data suggest that this is also true in the wild. Infants were never observed grooming themselves, juveniles only on very few occasions, and adolescents during rest periods. Mature chimpanzees frequently groom themselves for as long as 15 minutes at a time. The areas most commonly groomed are the thighs, arms, chest, and abdomen. Sometimes the chimpanzee parts the hair with both hands and sometimes with one hand and its lips. Flakes of dried skin, grass seeds, and the like are removed with the lips or with the thumb and forefinger.

After rain the chimpanzee helps to dry its coat by shaking, by rubbing its back and shoulders against a tree trunk, or by stroking downward with its hand.

Nest-making behavior. Each chimpanzee builds a new nest every night, with the exception of those infants that sleep with their mothers. Chimpanzees usually sleep in small groups of from two to six individuals, but when two or three such groups are feeding in the same area at dusk they may unite and nest close together. Sometimes, however, a large group will split into two or three small groups at dusk, each nesting some distance from the others. Members of the same group usually construct their nests close together in the same tree or in a group of adjoining trees. One adolescent female left her completed nest when she found the rest of the group was nesting about 60 yards away and made a second one close to the others. A mature male, however, may sleep alone about 100 yards away from a group with which he has been associating, or even quite out of sight or earshot of other chimpanzees.

The area in which nests are made is related to the food available at the time, since chimpanzees normally sleep close to where they have been feeding at dusk. Nests were found in the thick forests and in the more open woodlands, but seldom above 4500 feet, where the vegetation is sparse and offers little or no food.

Chimpanzees in this area do not sleep on the ground at night. The lowest nests were 15 feet from the ground, and the average height was between 30 and 40 feet from the ground.

Almost any type of tree may be utilized, provided it is at least 20 feet high, has a fair amount of foliage and fairly strong branches. At the end of August, 1961, a nest was observed in a palm tree (*Elaesis guineemsis*) for the first time. By the same month in the following year nests in palm trees were conspicuous in all parts of the reserve. Such nests apparently became a "fashion" among the chimpanzee population.

A nest usually takes between one and five minutes to construct, in the following manner. The chimpanzee takes up a central position on a suitable "foundation" (such as a horizontal fork or two adjacent parallel branches), takes hold of a fairly thick branch and bends it down across the foundation to form a crosspiece. This crosspiece is held in place with the feet, and a second branch is bent across it. From four to six main crosspieces are bent in, and then between six and ten smaller branches are bent across to form secondary crosspieces. The branches are bent so that their leafy ends form part of the main structure—if an end projects beyond this the chimpanzee bends it back across the nest. Finally all the small twigs projecting round the nest are bent in and normally a number of additional twigs are picked and laid loose on top of the nest. Occasionally a chimpanzee begins to make a nest, and, after bending in a few branches, abandons it because the material is insufficient or unsuitable.

A nest is usually used for one night only, but on three occasions chimpanzees reused nests that had been previously slept in. On each occasion fresh branches were bent over the existing structure.

In the rainy season nests are frequently made during a rest period in the daytime. Sometimes the chimpanzee simply bends a few leafy twigs across the branch on which it is lying. At other times it makes an elaborate structure, exactly similar to that made for the night. In the dry season when chimpanzees normally rest on the ground, the making of day nests was not observed.

There is evidence that experience gained during the first few years of the chimpanzee's life in the wilds is necessary for the development of nest-building behavior. In the wild the infant has opportunity for watching nest-making, and infants still sleeping with their mothers sometimes make little nests during the day as a form of play activity. An early infant-two was observed to have difficulty in bending in two small twigs, but four infants, estimated at from six months to one year older, were already able to make nests using as many as ten branches.

SLEEPING AND RESTING

Data obtained during 15 nights spent within 20 yards of nesting chimpanzees suggests that they sleep fairly soundly during the night. Whenever they were observed in the moonlight there was little movement. Occasionally, however, when several groups are sleeping within earshot there may be intergroup calling during the night. When asleep the chimpanzee adopts various positions, the most normal being on the side with the knees drawn up close to the body. Sometimes the chimpanzee sleeps on its back with its leg stretched out and, occasionally, on its stomach. The infant sleeps with its head on its mother's shoulder or groin, cradled within one of her arms. The chimpanzee does not normally hold on to branches with hands or feet.

It has been noted that during the rainy season nests may be constructed earlier than they are during the dry season, often as early as two hours before darkness. On these occasions the chimpanzee may continue feeding if food is within reach or it may lie or sit gazing around, or immediately close its eyes and sleep. At dawn the chimpanzee normally urinates and defecates (over the side of the nest), after which it may lie down again relaxed or it may sleep.

Adult chimpanzees rest for at least two hours every day, generally at some time between 9:30 A.M. and 3:00 P.M. Whether they rest on the ground, on a comfortable branch, or on a "day nest," they usually sleep for at least 30 minutes of the rest period. For the remainder of the time they sit or sprawl in relaxed postures, or idly groom each other or themselves. . . .

CONCLUSIONS

It is important to remember that the behavior described in this chapter applies specifically to a chimpanzee population in a rather atypical habitat. One noticeable difference between the Gombe Stream chimpanzees and those of the closed forest habitats, described by Nissen, Kortlandt, and Reynolds, is that the density of the population per square mile appears to be much greater in the latter type of habitat.

Two of the most interesting behavior patterns that were observed during this field study were, first, that these chimpanzees hunt and kill fairly large animals for food and, second, that tool-using is a relatively common practice.

Meat-eating has not, to my knowledge, been recorded from other parts of the chimpanzee's range in Africa, although if it is assumed that human infants are in fact taken for food, the report that five babies were carried off in West Africa suggests that carnivorous behavior may be widespread.

Although meat-eating cannot at present be regarded as common to the chimpanzee species as a whole, the ability to utilize natural objects as tools is undoubtedly a species characteristic of the chimpanzee throughout its range. Merfield describes a group of chimpanzees poking sticks into an underground bees' nest to obtain honey, and Beatty observed a chimpanzee using a stone to break open the kernel of a palm nut. Both these observations were made in West Africa. The Gombe Stream chimpanzees, however, in their ability to modify a twig or stick to make it suitable for a definite purpose, provide the first examples of free-ranging nonhuman primates actually *making* very crude tools.

Finally, I should like to stress that this chapter is based on data obtained in the course of a field study that has not yet been completed at this writing. I hope during the final months in the field not only to obtain many additional facts concerning such behavior as nest-making, feeding, grooming, and so on, but, in particular, to acquire more detailed information concerning the interrelationships between individuals in the complex chimpanzee society.

13

TOOL-USING PERFORMANCES AS INDICATORS OF BEHAVIORAL ADAPTABILITY

K. R. L. Hall

Ever since Benjamin Franklin dubbed man the tool-using animal, man's ability to use and to make tools has been accepted as a major behavioral distinction of the hominids. The distinction has been so sharp that it has been almost impossible to think quantitatively about the changes whereby a non-tool-using form might evolve into a tool-using species. The stress on this human

(From *Current Anthropology*, Vol. 4, December 1963, pages 479–494. By permission of the publisher.)

*characteristic has tended to obscure the widespread occurrence
of tool-making and tool-using among other animals. Seen in
evolutionary perspective, the human capacity for tool-making
appears as a quantitative development from the tool-using
behaviors scattered widely among other mammals.*

*The following article is a review of a considerable part of what is
known at present about the tool-using proclivities of the infrahuman primates as well as of a host of other animals. The late
Dr. Hall was Professor of Psychology at the University of Bristol
in England.*

*Of special interest to the student are the commentaries by
eleven anthropologists, together with Hall's reply, that are
included here following the article. As well as being informative,
these commentaries illustrate the rigorous scrutiny and careful
analysis that are accorded every contribution of anthropologists
by their colleagues and co-workers.*

INTRODUCTION

The use by an animal of an object or of another living organism as a
means of achieving an advantage has been commonly regarded by comparative psychologists as an indication of intelligent adaptability. The
mediating object is required by definition to be something extraneous to
the bodily equipment of the animal, and its use allows the animal to
extend the range of its movements or to increase their efficiency. Phrases
like "functional extension" have been applied to such performances,
whose crucial characteristic is manipulation of something in the environment, in appetitive or aversive behavior or, much more rarely, as part of
an instinctive display or nesting operation.

Many problems arise as to the origin, in ontogeny and phylogeny, of
such performances. It is rarely clear whether a performance is characteristic of a species, or whether individual variations due to local ecological
conditions modify it. Nor is it clear whether a performance, once it has
occurred in an individual given or in a group of animals, can be transmitted to form a "tradition," in the sense of a habit learned and retained, or whether the more likely evolutionary process is selection, on
the basis of the advantage of the performance; in the latter case, the
learning is a matter of trial-and-error application of the tendency,
comparable to the way in which any number of inherited tendencies may
be ecologically employed. Thorpe has examined much of the evidence
along these lines, with particular reference to birds. In the present paper
it is intended to carry the analysis into the realm of nonhuman primate

behavior; some of the well-authenticated studies of other animals will be cited to give the necessary comparative perspective.

On evaluating performances as falling inside or outside the category of tool-using, it will be evident that they vary greatly in their flexibility and apparent behavioral complexity. All performances are conventionally excluded if they involve simply applying a "primary" object, for example, food, to a "secondary" object, such as a rock. Thus, the snail-breaking by thrushes or the dropping of shells by gulls or crows onto a hard surface can be excluded. Included can be performances as manifestly unlike as the carrying of actinians in the claws of crabs and the enlisting of aid among chimpanzees in the cooperative solving of problems beyond the ability of a single chimpanzee, or the inducement of one chimpanzee by another, through food-begging or threat, to bring it food.

TOOL-USING OTHER THAN FOR DEFENSE OR FOOD-SEEKING

The classic example of tool-using in insects, that of the solitary wasp, *Ammophila urnaria,* was reported by Peckham and Peckham; to be sure, Williston had already made similar observations on another species. In each instance, the act consisted of holding a small pebble in the mandibles and using it as a hammer to pound dirt into the nest burrow. The Peckhams commented: "We are claiming a great deal for *Ammophila* when we say that she improvised a tool and made intelligent use of it, for such actions are rare even among higher mammals . . . ." Whether this is to be counted as an "individual" achievement rather than characteristic of a species is not certain, and the problem is not, at this level, of importance except in the way it parallels the situation in "higher" animals. So unexpected and interesting were these observations to the early comparative psychologists that they tended to jump to the conclusion that "intelligent purpose" and "perception of the relation of means to an end" were involved, while McDougall was somewhat more lyrical, saying:

> Are we then to regard each of these two wasps as a lively *bahnbrechende* genius, leading their species onward to the use of tools; individual sports comparable to the man or ape who first took a stone in his hand to crack a nut and so foreshadowed the genius of Nasmyth? I see no other plausible interpretation of the facts.

The best known and most reliably reported instance of tool-using among birds occurs in the Satin bower-bird, *Ptilonorhynchus violaceus.*

This species was said by Chisholm to use a "tool," such as small wads of bark, to aid in the painting of the inside walls of its bower. He commented:

> . . . it had been supposed that these served the office of a brush, but it is now thought more probable that each one acts as a cork, or stopper, to prevent the paint oozing from the tip of the mandibles while the bird is plastering the walls of the bower with the sides of the bill.

Marshall's study provides the behavioral context of these performances in the Satin bower-bird species, as well as a very full description of them:

> . . . many, but not all, adult males begin to plaster their bower with a thick, black, tacky material made from a mixture of charcoal compounded with saliva. With a bark wad held between the tips of the beak, the plaster is forced between the mandibles and so transferred to the inside sticks of the bower.

A similar kind of behavior is reported of some male members of the genus *Chlamydera*: painting their bowers with dry grass mixed with saliva. These performances occur during displays which serve partly to attract females to the display grounds, partly to repel other males, so that pair-formation can occur: "Remarkable as they are the bowers and display paraphernalia of bower-birds are no more than an extension of the territorial and display impulses to be found in other birds," and the whole performance of bower-construction and painting is interpreted by him as the outcome of a "displaced nesting-drive," the male taking no part in nest-building or incubation. Marshall commented that bowerbirds are no more intelligent than other highly developed passerine species, and there is, indeed, no valid reason for supposing they might be simply on the grounds that an elementary act, definable as tool-use, is incorporated into the display. The *rarity* of any such performance among birds or other animals in such a context suggests that it is a special case of behavioral adaptation which has no particular significance in the evolution of "intelligent" tool-using.

Seemingly the only instance in this miscellaneous category known in mammals is that of the Burmese elephant, which, according to Williams, picks up a long stick with its trunk to scratch its body. Although in captivity monkeys and apes are known to cover themselves with sacking or other materials, apparently as protection from cold or wet, no such instances are known from field studies.

TOOL-USING AS A PART OF AGONISTIC BEHAVIOR

Not a single authenticated instance of tool-using as an element in agonistic behavior is known in animals other than that of the monkeys and apes which use a tool in repelling predators or intruders. According to Duerden, the carrying of actinians by the crab *Melia tessellata* may have protective function. The crab travels with the actinians expanded and directed forward, sometimes waving them from side to side; when irritated, it moves its chelipeds toward the source of irritation, thereby placing the actinians in what may be considered the most favorable aggressive or defensive attitudes. It is possible, however, that this function is secondary and incidental, for the crab reacts in the same way whether it is carrying the actinians (as food-getting "instruments") or not.

In considering such evidence as there is of the "agonistic" use of objects by monkeys and apes, trying to analyze the observations in terms of function and context of the act, we should first examine reports on wild animals, in which no training by or imitation of human beings is presumably involved. Some of the sources of information (Table 1) are personal observations of trained field-workers, others, those of naturalists and hunters, and the rest, of unknown source. The two major field studies of baboons include no observations of agonistic object-use. In both of these studies, the investigator's objective was to study the baboons without disturbing them by his presence, and hence, the very situations most likely to elicit agonistic behavior in a group usually were lacking. The unexpected presence of parties of travelers or soldiers in baboon country may produce great agitation in the animals, eliciting a more intensive reaction.

In analyzing the function and context of these "primitive instrumental acts," we shall need to refer chiefly to the few studies in which sufficient detail of observation is available. In general, it is implicit in most early reports that the animals roll stones or drop or throw branches and other objects *with intent* to hit or drive away intruders. Aim or purpose in the act is assumed, and hence the whole act is usually thought of as intelligent or learned rather than instinctive or emotional. Lacking detailed and careful observation, one alternative was that these happenings are the "accidental" result of some agonistic behavior pattern characteristic of the species. Thus, excited macaques may dislodge stones in scrambling up a slope away from an intruder, or members of an arboreal species may chance to break off branches while making threatening gestures. Zuckerman inclined to the view that the many instances of this sort of behavior could be explained as the more or less accidental outcome of emotional displays, and thus did not need to assume the animal's perception of a relationship between such acts and the possible consequence of driving away an intruder.

This explanation seems correctly to emphasize the emotional origin of such acts but probably incorrectly assumes that animals noted for their learning ability would not readily carry out the emotional gesture with a very elementary directedness rather than in a supposedly random fashion.

TABLE 1

*Some Sources of Evidence on the Agonistic Use of Objects
by Monkeys and Apes in the Wild*

SPECIES/GENUS	AUTHOR	BEHAVIOR AND SITUATION RECORDED
Gorilla	Merfield and Miller	When hunted, tearing off branches and flinging in direction of hunters below, "after peering about to locate them accurately"
	Schaller	Various forms of throwing of branches in agonistic display; not reported to be directed at source of disturbance
Orangutan	Wallace	Throwing down of branches and heavy fruits in direction of intruder
	Schaller	Breaking off and hurling branches in direction of observer
Gibbon	Carpenter	Breaking off and dropping dead branches in direction of observer
Howler	Carpenter	Breaking off and dropping dead limbs toward observer also defecation and urination from directly above observer
Red spider	Carpenter	Breaking off and dropping branches close to observer
Cebus	Kaufmann	Dropping nuts and debris onto coatis
Baboons	Brehm, Hornaday, and other sources of unknown reliability	Geladas meeting Hamadryas and rolling stones down upon them; rolling of rocks toward human intruders
Macaques	Kinnaman, quoting another source Hingston Joléaud and other sources of unknown reliability	Deliberate tilting-up and rolling of stones down upon them; rolling of pine cones by Japanese monkeys at passers-by
Patas	Boulenger	Directing "fusillade" of sticks, stones, etc., on river travelers in W. Africa

Analysis of two sets of observations may help to clear the way for a critical evaluation of the status of the behavior involved. Carpenter describes the reactions to man of red spider monkeys in Panama as including the following: (1) barking; (2) frequently, approach; (3) in trees within 40 to 50 feet of the observer, shaking of the branches associated, almost invariably, [with] vigorous scratching: and (4) "breaking off and dropping of branches . . . close . . . to the observer." "This behavior cannot be described as throwing, although the animal may cause the object to fall away from the perpendicular by a sharp twist of its body or a swinging circular movement of its powerful tail."

Sometimes the dropping is delayed for a few seconds, as an observer approaches; feces and urine are also dropped. All are "instrumental acts" carried out with reference to objectives.

This account indicates that: (1) the approach of the monkeys is an aggressive action; (2) the vigorous scratching represents a displacement activity, which is known experimentally to occur in agitated monkeys that, because of caging, are unable to act out their escape or aggressive tendencies more directly; (3) shaking of the branches probably represents a redirection of the aggressive tendency; (4) breaking off and dropping the branches would seem to be a natural carryover of the aggressive movements, no new type of movement being involved; (5) the delay in dropping and the imparting of direction to the branches is "purposive" or "instrumental" in the elementary sense that the consequence of this variation is anticipated as being more rewarding than the consequence of no aiming; in other words, a simple process of operant conditioning is at work, whereby the "aimed" variation is reinforced over the "unaimed."

The objections to such a formulation stem mainly from the lack of information as to the frequency and variability of "directed" performances in these animals. Nevertheless, the learning postulated is of so elementary a kind that all it requires is a very slight modification in the agonistic behavior repertoire apparently characteristic of the species in such circumstances. It is not easy to imagine simpler learning performances, given the usual threat-gesture system of monkeys, for no new act is involved.

For all other species of new and old world monkeys, only a single, very brief statement about the behavior of a *Cebus capucinus* group on Barro Colorado Island has added to our knowledge. During his two-year study of coatis, Kaufmann on one occasion saw the monkeys chase some coatis from a tree, then go on to drop nuts and debris from a *Scheelea* palm onto them. The coatis ignored the shower except to pounce on and eat the ripe nuts that were included. This observation is of particular interest in view of the reputation of *Cebus* in laboratory experiments and because it is the first by a naturalist of behavior of this type involving nonhuman intruders.

Among the apes, Wallace's observations on the orangutan and Schaller's confirmation and elaboration of them suggest a similar pattern. One of Schaller's observations was as follows:

A female with a large infant spent 15 minutes throwing a total of about 30 branches varying in size from twigs to limbs 10 feet long and 3 inches in diameter. Considerable effort was expanded at times in tearing off the larger branches. Limbs were thrown in three ways: (a) she merely held the branch at her side and dropped it limply; (b) she looked down at me and swung the branch like a large pendulum, and at the peak of the arc closest to me she released it; (c) she lifted branches either as high as her chest or above her head with one hand and hurled them down forcefully. Whatever interpretation is given this behavior, there is no doubt that it induced me to jump nimbly at times and that it kept me effectively away from beneath the tree.

Wallace's account concerned the throwing down of branches and of the fruits of the Durian tree by an adult female with young ones near her; and he supposed that the ape's parental instinct may have been specially aroused. However, the essential features of the situations in which this and the resulting behavior occur are similar to those in the red spider monkey account, namely disturbance by a human intruder eliciting agitation and redirection of aggression onto the most readily available objects, and an effective directing of the objects toward the observer.

The explanation already proposed seems to need no revision to include the orangutan data or any other data of similar performances in free-ranging monkeys or apes. This does not imply that such displays always or even usually have a "direction." Schaller's full account of the mountain gorillas' repertoire of gestures in such circumstances does not suggest that branches or leaves are, in the physical sense, aimed at the observer. The amount and kind of learning involved in "aiming" are such that many other mammals below the primates might achieve this behavior very readily *if* they had happened to evolve the sort of manipulatory and agonistic repertoire which seems to be a general simian characteristic. To underline this point, we may briefly consider the agonistic and the feeding repertoire of baboons in the wild. First, baboons frequently turn over stones when searching for food. Second, they may pull violently back and forward on tree branches or rocks while staring at and otherwise threatening an observer. Third, they may hit away, with a swift underarm movement, a noxious or unfamiliar small object or living organism as a sequel to, or component of, a startle behavior sequence. These three aspects of their behavior readily dispose these animals to the simple instrumental act involved in tipping a rock toward an intruder. There would be no mystery if it were shown that baboons or chimpanzees, for example, throw sand, stones or sticks, toward a predator on the same horizontal plane. All that is necessary is that the hitting-away movement be combined with the most elementary of feeding acts, that of grasping some object in the hand and "aiming" it in the same way that a threat-gesture or movement is usually directed *toward* an adversary. Because of the use of objects as missiles has tended to be confused with the use, and even fashioning, of objects as offensive weapons, the complexity of the behavior involved seems to have been greatly exaggerated.

Linking behavior of this kind with that observed to occur spontaneously in captivity adds very little to the over-all picture. Many reports are available of agonistic scooping/throwing in captivity, but all that need be added as commentary is that horizontal aiming is an extension of the threat-display, involving nothing more than the coordination of two acts basic to the repertoire. Brandishing of a stick and using it to beat another animal, as described by Cooper and Harlow in an individual *Cebus fatuellus* and in several chimpanzees, is an interesting elaboration of threat-display against other animals, but the significance of such performances must again be regarded first in their functional context, and only later against the supposed evolutionary background. The kind of brandishing action reported is very similar to that which baboons and other monkeys and apes may engage in throwing a sack or a stick over a food-object.

We are not primarily concerned here with sifting through the varied kinds of evidence and deciding as to their reliability and accuracy. It is not yet possible to make valid comparisons of the various species or, for example, of terrestrial monkeys and anthropoid apes, of old world or of new world types, and the like, with respect to their "ability" to engage in this kind of instrumental behavior. Chimpanzee, capuchin, and baboon may turn out to demonstrate this propensity more readily and more flexibly than other nonhuman primates, but it is all too easy to fit the inadequate observational evidence into whatever evolutionary model one chooses—as Kortlandt and Kooij have done. It is simply the interaction of the processes of learning with the components and sequences of the naturally practiced behavior repertoire that requires a clear and straight-forward analysis. The key to the instrumental learning successes of many types shown in the wild and in captivity by these animals is the exploratory-manipulatory tendency, of a quite general kind, which makes it easy for transfer or generalization to take place from one kind of situation to another, and over a wide range of objects or stimuli. Although we can thus simplify the behavioral analysis in such a way as to show that performances of the kind reported are readily to be expected in these animals, it still remains necessary to consider very carefully the kinds of environmental conditions which elicit or inhibit or just fail to elicit these performances.

TOOL-USING IN EXTENSION OF THE FEEDING REPERTOIRE

The use of an object as a means of obtaining food which the animal cannot reach or which if within its reach, the animal cannot obtain directly is, contrary to the preceding class of performance, reported in birds in several instances, occasionally and rather uncertainly in marine invertebrates, and once only, with two other insufficiently substantiated instances, in subprimate mammals. For monkeys and apes, there is an extensive experimental literature, many observations on animals in capitivity, and extremely few field data that provide evidence for analysis. The data will merely be sampled, as in the previous section, to illustrate points that seem significant for the whole comparative picture. Inevitably, this means paying most attention to the areas where most reliable knowledge is available.

The case of the crab, *Melia tessellata,* and actinian "commensalism," described by Duerden and others, is a curious example of the use of a living organism as a tool to aid the feeding of another. Although Duerden says the crabs do not restrict themselves to one species of anemone and may also, as already noted, hold them forward as a kind of defensive aid, the performance need not be classed as more "intelligent" than other sorts of behavioral adaptation to ecological need in which no tool or accessory is involved.

In birds, there are two sorts of performance which have been much discussed, namely, the string-pulling achievements of *Parus* and other passerines, and the use of a cactus-spine or twig as an extension of the bill to probe out insects or larvae in the so-called Galapagos woodpecker-finch, *Cactospiza pallida.* The former type of behavior clearly has some parallel in the probable factors involved here and in similar perform-ances of primates. There may be an "inherited tendency" to pull upon and manipulate with beak and foot grasses, hair, bents, and other long flexible materials, in the course of nestbuilding or perhaps in obtaining certain sorts of food. This factor and practice can be supposed to account for the ease with which some of these birds seem immediately to tackle the task of pulling in a string on the end of which a bait is attached. We may note that the direct pulling-in of a string or stick to the end of which the food-object is attached seems to be a task requiring very little modification of existing repertoire other than trial-and-error application.

The tool-using performances of the woodpecker-finch are usually con-sidered a remarkable example of behavioral adaptation to fit it into the special ecological circumstances of the Galapagos Islands bird popula-tion. According to Lack, this primarily insectivorous finch resembles a woodpecker in that it climbs up and down vertical trunks and branches in search of its food. But whereas the woodpecker, having excavated in a branch with its beak, inserts its long tongue into the crack to get the insect out, the finch has evolved the alternative method of picking up a cactus spine or twig, holding it lengthwise in its beak and poking it up the crack, dropping the twig to seize the insect in its beak as it emerges. It has been seen to reject a twig if it proved too short or too pliable, and sometimes the bird carries a spine or twig about with it, poking it into cracks or crannies as it searches one tree after another. Bowman added further observations on this behavior. He saw it most frequently in the dry season in the arid zone, where almost every bird of the species was seen carrying a cactus spine in its bill. He also reported two cases of what appeared to be attempts of the bird to adjust the size and shape of its probe to fit the cranny or crack in which it was searching:

> One such bird was holding a spine about six inches long. Only about two inches of the spine protruded from the tip of the bill, the remainder passed along one side of the face and neck. Apparently the bird realized that the stick was excessively long, for it made an unsuccessful attempt to twist off approximately three inches of the spine by holding it with the feet.

He quotes an observation made by Mr. Kastdalen in 1956:

> I was looking at a finch the other day, and he convinced me that the stick habit is intelligent and not instinctive. One of them was working in a hole . . . which seemed to be full of bugs, so he had to drop its stick several times to catch the bugs. Each time it went for a new stick, but after a few times it came with a forked stick, and tried to get it into the hole a couple of times, but in vain. Then he saw what was wrong and turned the stick around and broke it off at the fork, and started working.

Ignoring the terminological points about the bird's "realizing" what it was doing and the distinction between "intelligent" and "instinctive," it is evident that something definable as "tool-making," that is, an attempting to work upon the tool-object, is here involved. However, it is likely that nothing more worthy of note is involved in such an attempt than what is routine in nest-constructing activities.

While it is indeed remarkable that this finch should have evolved a behavioral adaptation supposedly more appropriate at the primate level of evolution, the chief significance of such a performance, in the comparative behavior framework, is perhaps to emphasize the fact that *tool-using as such,* and even tool-making, taken outside of the total behavioral context in which it occurs, is not a criterion of adaptability that should be assigned any special weight. If in rare cases a species of crab or bird evolves a behavioral, rather than a physical, adaptation to deal with some ecological condition, this may be interesting evidence of the versatility of evolutionary processes but involves no more complex type of *learning* than, one may suppose, the sort of trial-and-error adjustments which these "remarkable" species have in common with other crabs and other birds.

Among subprimate mammals, we have already cited Williams' report of elephants using sticks to scratch their bodies, and he also describes how "Many young elephants develop the naughty habit of plugging up the wooden bell they wear hung around their necks with good stodgy mud or clay so that the clappers cannot ring, in order to steal silently into a grove of cultivated bananas at night.'' While the performances of elephants in captivity indicate that their potential in tool-using is probably greater than that of any other nonprimate animal, there is no systematic evidence of the variety of their performances in the wild. It can merely be noted in passing, however, that the way in which they pull down or push over trees to get at foliage otherwise beyond their reach is an ''instrumental act'' at least on a par for behavioral complexity with patterned string or string-pulling performances. It is also, for the elephant, a much more economical way of feeding than would be say, its attempt to knock off fruit or leaves by brandishing a stick in its trunk.

Apart from elephants, another class of mammal that may be found to use tools as a feeding aid in the wild are bears. The readiness with which they stand on hindlegs and use their paws in manipulations would predispose them to develop such skills where need arises, and Harington interestingly reviews the evidence that polar bears dislodge or pick up and cast down blocks of ice onto the heads of sleeping walruses. The only subprimate mammal for which there are reliable reports is the sea otter, *Enhydra lutris*. Studies made of its feeding habits show that in the Aleutians as well as in California, mollusks form a substantial part of the diet. In California, abalones are also commonly brought up and eaten, but it is not known whether rocks are used to aid in the process of removing these large shellfish from their sites. Fisher was the first to give a detailed account of this animal's use of a stone as a tool:

> It is a not uncommon thing to hear a sharp clicking sound and then to locate its point of origin . . . This sound is always made by an otter that is trying to crack open something with a very hard stonelike shell. The object that the otter has in its paws is too small to see—possibly it is some mollusk. The object is held with both paws and with full arm action from well over the head, it is brought down hard on a piece of rock that rests on the otter's chest. These pieces of stone are brought to the surface at the same time as the food. It may take several severe blows before the object is cracked enough for the otter to get the food out. These rocks are not small but appear to be almost as large as the large abalones. When the otters roll over they hold both the rock and the food on their chests. This clicking sound is so distinct that it can be heard for some distance above the noise of the waters.

Murie confirmed this observation on the California animals, and Hall and Schaller have obtained quantitative data on this performance; they reported that it is usually mussels that are banged against the rock anvil, although occasionally other animals, such as spiny lobsters, may be pounded in this way. Krear, who spent from late July until mid-December 1957 on Amchitka in the western Aleutians, watching sea otters most of the time, observed only one young animal traveling with its mother that used a rock as a tool: "The immature was observed on three occasions to bring rocks to the surface, and on these he would pound and crack his food items, most of which were little blue mussels." It is probable that the mussels in the Aleutians did not require tool-use of the sort so frequently seen off the California coast, but that the propensity for such performances is readily available, as is strongly indicated by Kenyon's account of how an adult otter, captured in the Aleutians, used rocks as anvils on which to pound clams.

The sea otter data suggest very little at present as to the origin, variability, and other characteristics of this behavior. So far as is known, no developmental observations are available, other than the one instance quoted. It is also likely that the pup acquires the habit by observing the behavior of its mother, for it swims for many weeks very close to her, takes food from her chest, and is occasionally offered food by her. It is thus highly probable that the pup must learn its discriminations of food objects and of behavior appropriate to deal with them by observing the corresponding behavior in the mother. The fundamental dependency relationship is such that "following," both perceptually and in the locomotor and manipulatory senses, is necessary for the pup's survival. This is generally true of mammals and is mentioned here only because it may help to explain the origin of the habit.

Considering now the nonhuman primates, detailed evidence from field studies indicates that only one, the chimpanzee, uses tools; this it does in reference to a probably minor feeding behavior, probing termites out of holes with twigs. Beatty reported that chimpanzees in Liberia break open palm nuts by hammering them with rocks, and Merfield and Miller described how chimpanzees poke long twigs into the entrance holes of the ground nests of bees and withdraw the twigs coated with honey. The distance at which this observation was made was 50 yards, using binoculars. Pitman mentioned seeing a free-living gorilla using a stick to obtain fruit otherwise out of its reach, but Schaller had no record of such behavior in 12 months of field study.

This lack of evidence of tool-using comes as a surprise to the many investigators familiar with the ease with which other species of great ape and several species of monkey learn spontaneously in captivity, as well as with progressive training procedures, to use sticks, sacks, boxes, or even live rats to haul in food objects otherwise out of reach. *Cebus capucinus* and perhaps other *Cebus* species appear to be particularly adept in this respect, while individuals of the *Papio ursinus* species show a similar kind of aptitude. The surprise of the laboratory investigators is due to the apparent discrepancy between the *potential* that these animals have for such performances when given situations designed to elicit them in captivity and their failure to make use of the potential as an aid in increasing their dietary repertoire in the wild. Two of the main factors accounting for this discrepancy are: (1) Systematic field evidence is still far too scanty for us to know how great the discrepancy is; for example, very little is known of the details of the feeding habits of free-ranging *Cebus*. (2) The discrepancy is not a behaviorally significant one but is rather due to a misconception as to the degree of transfer or generalization involved when the wild-born animal is given the usual run of instrumentation tasks in captivity This point requires a brief elaboration.

If we take as an example the natural feeding behavior of the baboon and the more or less continuous processes of exploration and manipulation of objects that go with it, some of which have already been mentioned, we find that the animal is practicing, either in play or in actual feeding, a variety of skills which are readily generalized in the experimental situation. The young ones carry sticks or branches in their mouths or in one hand and do not use them in feeding. All of them at some time or other break dead branches from bushes in searching for food, as when, for example, they are searching for larvae or ants' nests. They push over slabs of rock, and they tend to investigate almost any strange manipulable object that lies in their path. They pull upon telegraph wires, open the doors and windows of unoccupied huts and cars, and so on. In short, they show a generalized tendency to fiddle with and try out objects that may or may not be instrumental in obtaining food. These animals appear to have a surplus of exploratory-manipulatory energy for which there may seem to be no immediate ecological need. However, it is perfectly feasible to suppose that it is just this kind of generalized activity which has enabled baboons to be sufficiently adaptable to survive over large areas of Africa in a very wide variety of habitats, for example, allowing them to be omnivorous in some regions (although they are classed as predominantly vegetarian in all areas where the diet has been adequately scheduled, according to Washburn and DeVore and Hall). Thus, given the behavior repertoire the baboon is known to possess, the learning involved in obtaining food that is out of reach would appear to be of a rudimentary kind.

Similar evidence as to the maturation of the necessary manipulatory coordinations and as to the effective role of natural and instrumental practice has been put forward for the chimpanzee, and there is no need to review it. One comment of Schiller's is particularly appropriate, however, because it indicates how, in chimpanzees and other species, the "emotional" repertoire of gesture may be readily utilized in differing contexts:

> That a chimpanzee breaks off a branch if excited has nothing to do with his desire to get the food [in an experimental situation]. Once he has the stick in

his hand, he will use it sooner or later. Such a sequence can easily be reinforced in a couple of trials, then it appears to be a coherent, continuous pattern.

GENERAL EVALUATION

Tool-using performances have tended to be treated as though they represented some kind of behavioral homology at the different levels of organism in which they have been recorded. This view seems to be incorrect, however, because it seems evident that the application of a common term to so varied an assortment of performances has led to the glossing over of fundamental differences in adaptive significance. While the criterion of tool-using is no longer used by anthropologists to signalize a supposedly critical stage in the transition of ape to human, it is still not unreasonably inferred that tool-using was an important behavioral adaptation somewhere in primate evolution, and that the *making* of tools derived from a prevalence in tool-using far in excess of that now discernible in any living nonhuman primate. For anthropologists, behavioral evidence of living nonhuman primates in the wild is thus of interest to the extent that it indicates "transitional" ingredients of essentially hominid characteristics such as the carnivorous tendency and tool-using.

In the general framework of animal evolution, we have seen that instances definable as tool-using occur in highly specialized ecological settings, as in the woodpecker-finch, crab-actinian commensalism, and probably the *Ammophila*. These are basically behavioral adaptations that are probably produced by trial-and-error learning, like that commonly found in almost all living organisms. These adaptations do not appear to give their possessors any selective advantage over other species which have evolved alternative forms of adaptation. Rather, they simply enable their possessors to survive at a certain population level in their ecological niches. In other words, such performances are only worthy of special note because of their entirely superficial, indeed one might almost say fortuitous, resemblance to human tool-using. The case of the string-pulling performances of some passerines is of the same order. While one allows that birds of the *Parus* genus, as an example, show a certain aptitude in this kind of problem, as in others, such as pecking open milk bottle tops, no one, but for the human analogy, would probably be disposed on this ground to give this species a specially high rating for adaptability. As others have clearly indicated, birds may evolve certain rather restricted propensities enabling them to learn through what one might call a special aptitude. The natural practice of food-seeking and nest-construction may fit into the scheme. A performance classifiable as tool-using may in fact be less significant as an adaptability indicator than one which cannot strictly be so considered, such as the performances of thrushes, gulls, or crows in breaking open hard food-objects.

The observations of the sea otter were reviewed at length to refute the view that its performance indicated that a new process had appeared at the *Mammalian* level of evolution. The apparent uniqueness of this performance and its occurrence in the context of a particular marine ecological situation for which the animal shows other peculiar behavioral and physical adaptations, such as lying on the back when feeding, indicate that there is no reason to judge this animal's performances as of any greater evolutionary significance than those for which other marine mammals, such as seals and dolphins, are noted.

In the evaluation of what is known about the nonhuman primates' performances and potentialities, we have to consider two main types of tool-using: that in the service of agonistic behavior and that in obtaining food. It is in the former category that by far the most evidence is available, suggesting that "instrumental acts" with some degree of direction or purpose are quite a widespread and general characteristic in monkeys and apes, as a straightforward function of fear-threat motivation and manipulatory endowment. And indeed it seems, as the quotation from Schiller indicated, that we have here a behavioral adaptation of a fairly general and simple kind which evolved primarily in the context of agonistic tendencies toward opponents that inhibit direct attack. Associating this with the fact that no such instances have been reliably reported in any other class of animal, one can infer that this is the fundamental behavioral situation from which all other instances of primate tool-using have been derived. There is, in most monkeys at any rate, an arousal of fairly strong agonistic tendencies in any food-to-be-gained situation in which they are frustrated. They tend easily, in such circumstances, to show displacement activities or redirections of aggression, and their tool-using attempts often consist of throwing actions which are hardly distinguishable from threat-gestures. It will be only through systematic developmental studies of young primates that we shall be able to trace the course of these performances and to study the relationship between frustration responses and the emergence of tool-use in general.

SUMMARY

Tool-using performances in animals have often been considered important indicators of relative intelligence, but no comparative analysis of their probable origin and place within the total ecological and behavioral setting has been available. The usual definition has tended to emphasize features that performances at different phyletic levels have in common, while glossing over the underlying and even overt differences.

The many examples in the literature are sampled with reference to the use of tools: (1) in agonistic behavior; (2) in extending the feeding habits of a species; and (3) in courtship display (Satin bowerbirds), nest-hole construction (*Ammophila* spp.), and, possibly, body care (elephants).

Examples of the second category include what appear to be special behavioral adaptations that are functionally equivalent to physical extensions or modifications, as in the case of the crab-actinian relationship in *Melia tessellata,* the Galapagos woodpecker-finch, *Cactospiza pallida,* and possibly also in the sea otter, *Enhydra lutris.* To varying degrees, the tool-using adaptation has importance in the life of the species. In the crab and the finch, it seems to involve a basic feeding adjustment, while in the sea otter it is reportedly used only with respect to one major item of food, mollusks, and it may be much more prevalent in the southern limits of distribution than in the north. Among nonhuman primates in the wild, tool-using of this sort is rare, not being known in baboons and macaques, and only reliably reported, among the anthropoid apes, in the chimpanzee which appears to use a food-getting tool to obtain a supplementary rather than a staple item of diet.

Examples of the first category occur only in nonhuman primates. In systematic field studies in the wild, "primitive instrumental acts" of breaking off and casting down branches, twigs, or leaves in the direction of the observer have been reported of howlers and red spider monkeys, gibbons, and orang-utans. Gorillas include throwing gestures in their complex and apparently stereotyped displays when disturbed, but no "directing" toward the source of disturbance has been noted. Terrestrial monkeys of the *Macaca* and *Papio* genera have been reported to push or roll stones towards intruders. There are, however, no detailed field observations of this behavior, and, if it occurs, it is probably elicited in groups of monkeys that are highly disturbed and unused to human intrusion and would not be seen under the noninterference conditions in which the field observer usually tries to work.

Controversy over the reliability of the evidence on tool-using, particularly in nonhuman primates, and over the explanation of such instances as are irrefutable, seems to stem from the following: (1) a tendency to overestimate the significance of such performances as indicators of behavioral adaptability, largely because of the urge to discover equivalences to stages in human evolution; (2) a failure to analyze in detail the context and function of such performances. It is suggested that the "primitive instrumental acts" involve only an elementary form of operant conditioning imposed upon the agonistic repertoire of the species, and that "direction" of aim with objects is no more surprising than the fact that threat gestures without objects are normally aimed at an intruder.

The discrepancy, commented upon by laboratory investigators, between the apparent ease with which many monkeys and apes use tools to gain food in captivity situations and their apparent failure to use this propensity to advantage in the wild, has no real significance. Possibly the "primitive instrumental acts" provide the primary emotional bases from which any kind of tool-using arises, the transfer to other situations, such as food-getting, being conditioned by the way in which the animals manipulate objects not directly related to food.

The present evaluation of the comparative data has, as its purpose, the clarification of the confusion caused by inadequacy of behavioral evidence and by the biasing of such evidence to fit some evolutionary scheme. The hypothesis that the "emotional" use of tool objects by monkeys and apes may provide the lead to an understanding of the origins, in phylogeny and ontogeny, of such performances in human beings is suggested by the fact that no comparable agonistic performances are known in any other class of animal. On the other hand, tool-using as a feeding adaptation occurs in several different types of animal but has so far proved very rare in monkeys and apes.

ABSTRACT

Use of an object by animals as a functional extension of their limbs in order to obtain food or to facilitate some other goal-seeking activity has quite commonly been reported as an especially significant indicator of intelligence or complex learning ability.

The present review has selected well-authenticated examples of tool-using behavior from different types of animal, such as wasps, crabs, birds, subprimate mammals, and nonhuman primates, and examined the context of their occurrence and the apparent complexity of performance involved. These performances have been concerned with: (a) attainment of food; (b) offensive or defensive use against predators or intruders; (c) miscellaneous functions such as self-grooming, courtship, nest-building. Categories (a) and (b) contain by far the most instances, and (c) has very few indeed.

The problem, in attempting a comparative analysis of such instances, is to evaluate the performance within the whole context of the animal's capacities and the way these are expressed in various ecological settings. The evidence cited is primarily from naturalistic studies, that from restrictive settings, such as zoo or laboratory, being adduced only in emphasizing discrepancies. As an example, baboons have, so far, not been seen to demonstrate tool-using in the wild in their food-seeking behavior, but they do so readily when given the opportunity in captivity. They thus have a potential which their natural surroundings perhaps only rarely bring into action, whereas chimpanzees demonstrate their capacity for this kind of performance in diverse ways both in the wild and in captivity.

Certain performances by nonprimate animals, such as the Galapagos woodpecker-finch or the California sea otter, indicate that tool-using of a very effective, though presumably restricted, kind can evolve in animals having a narrow habitat range, and in whom, therefore, other significant aspects of adaptability may be missing. Further, from assessing the many instances of category (b) and the very few instances of category (a) in wild monkeys and apes, it was tentatively suggested that the emotional offensive-defensive type of tool-using might have had primacy in evolution over that of food-getting and the other miscellaneous instances. A review of this sort, with a suggestion of this kind, is put forward anyway chiefly as an attempt at clarification which may lead to much further detailed studies, experimental and naturalistic, of the animals in question.

As always in describing complex behavior and in deriving models or inferences from the description, the profusion and confusion of terminology are difficult to sort out neatly or clearly. But the objective of this review will have been achieved if, in deliberately avoiding the use of controversial terms, it has been possible to show the need for a fresh research approach to the comparative study of behavioral adaptability in animals with a view to working out much more satisfactorily than at present the bearing that such evidence may have upon fundamental questions of human evolution.

COMMENTS

By R. J. ANDREW

New Haven, Conn., U.S.A. 5.20.63

My comments will be brief, since I agree with all the principal points made by Prof. Hall. It seems clear that our main attention should be concentrated on the use of tools by primates in the field. There is very little information to be obtained concerning the evolution of tool-use by studies in which primates are trained by investigators to use tools.

However, even in the absence of such field data, it is possible to investigate in captive animals the normal range of motor patterns used by a species in grasping or manipulating the objects with the hands. As Schiller emphasized, the number of such patterns is far fewer even in the chimpanzee than might be expected. A recent study by Bishop in my laboratory has shown that only one grasping gesture is used by the Lemuroidea and only one (a different one) by the Lorisoidea, the second being adapted to catching insects. Unlike the Ceboidea or Cercopithecoidea their power and precision grips are the same. Current work in our program of comparative studies of primate behaviour suggests that a single manipulative pattern may function in several different contexts and so be exposed to widely differing selection pressures. One interesting example is the pattern of grasping an object with both hands, and then rotating the hands outwards so that they separate distally. This, when used in grooming, serves to part the hair and make the skin accessible to the lips and teeth. When used in grasping an object, it has two functions. In the case of a solid unyielding object it results in the object being turned, since one of the hands ceases to oppose the other and relaxes for long enough to allow some rotation. A series of such movements permits the animal to investigate the object from all sides. In the case of a soft object the opposing rotation of the two hands may break the object. It is as yet impossible to decide in what context this pattern probably first appeared. It is present in both Cercopithecoidea and Ceboidea from *Saimiri* up.

In the more advanced members of both groups, further grasping and manipulatory patterns appear. In the present article, the hitting away of objects by baboons was mentioned. In *Papio hamadryas* a two-handed backward and forward scrubbing of objects on the ground passes with increasing rejection of the object into more lateral movements in which the object is held in one hand and may finally be flung away. Besides finding a variety of uses in foraging the first type of movement is used in punishing young animals. In *Cebus* one-handed banging of an object against the substrate may occur as well.

A more comprehensive knowledge of the distribution and relative ease of elicitation of such manipulative patterns may make it possible to say something definite concerning the ecological determinants of their evolution. This in turn would be relevant to the problem of the origin of tools, in that the first use of tools by human ancestors must have been greatly affected by the range of manipulative patterns which they possessed. However, the data collected by Hall on the use of tools by animals other than primates suggests that the use of tools in the human line, and their almost complete absence in other primates was not due primarily to very advanced manipulative abilities, or even intelligence in our ancestors. It appears that the use of tools can appear without either if the selective pressures for this are strong enough. (A similar argument can be made concerning the origin of vocal mimicking.) It may therefore be most profitable to look for a major ecological difference between the human line and other primates. Cooperative hunting of moderate to large-sized prey is perhaps the difference most commonly suggested. The dropping or throwing of objects in defense by primates has been very fully discussed in the present article, and it is no novel suggestion that such behavior might have been critical in the first development of tools.

By C. R. CARPENTER

Oak Park, Pa., U.S.A. 5.24.63

The interesting paper by Hall describes *special* performances of animals in natural environments which may indicate *special* behavioral adaptability. The evidence arrayed and the inferences stated oppose attributing tool-using to animals, including nonhuman primates living in the wild. The conclusions, also, oppose explanations which include "intelligence" and "purpose." Learning of "simple" kinds including trial-and-error and "operant conditioning" are judged adequate to explain "primitive instrumental acts." If these statements are correct, then a more descriptive title than the one selected might have been used.

The general definition given of a category of behavior, modified as follows, could be useful: *The use by an animal of an object, or of another living organism, as a means of achieving an advantage indicates adaptability.* Such a definition and inference could include defined acts, defined objects, conditions and other organisms, and the consequence of behavioral events.

I should have liked to have had Hall's definition of tools and tool-using and to know whether or not he accepts the concept that tool-making could be defined as the shaping or molding of material or object to serve repetitively a set of functions. Also, I would have appreciated knowing what is implied by "primitive instrumental acts." The aggressive-defensive acts of howlers, spider and cebus monkeys, gibbons and orangs breaking limbs or branches and timing their fall relative to a moving object, person, or another animal are rather complex even though "primitive."

The nonhuman primates for which there are reliable observations of breaking, holding, somewhat directing, and releasing objects in aggressive-defensive situations are all *arboreal* types. For them height, availability of obtainable and droppable objects, gravity, and perhaps, other factors provide conditions for the occurrence of the described behavioral patterns. Tree-shaking occurs in rhesus monkeys but *not* the breaking off and dropping of objects with reference to sources of disturbances.

How does Hall classify and interpret the *bridging behavior* observed in howler and spider monkeys? When an adult, usually a female but sometimes a male, spans a space, remains suspended, and permits a young animal to cross over it, is this too a "primitive instrumental act?"

Hall seems to have accomplished his objective of raising serious doubt that the evidence supports the hypothesis that behavior which corresponds closely to tool-using, occurs in animals including the nonhuman primates. However, it does seem that many animals and nonhuman primates exhibit *naturalistic* behavior patterns which are *instrumental in achieving goal states*. The explanations and functions of these classes of behavior surely are not as simple as Hall seems at times to imply.

By Radomír Čihák

Prague, Czechoslovakia. 5.25.63

This interesting paper approaches the problems of so-called tool-using in animals from the standpoint of behavior studies. From the viewpoint of an anatomist studying the development of the human hand in ontogenesis and phylogenesis, I might comment on several points of common biological interest, and then add a comparison with our results of developmental studies of the primate hand.

(1) I have to agree with the author's conclusions that problems exist in comparing similar actions in different animals of the same phylum or in animals of different phyletic position.

(2) All these problems depend upon the exactness of definition of the terms, *tool, tool-using* and *tool-making*. If the definition of the tool-using performance is to be extended to include all actions of animals— in whatever sense—where we find the use of an object foreign to the

body of the animal in question; this multiplies the examples of tool-using animals.

(3) The author states:

> Tool-using performances have tended to be treated as though they represented some kind of behavioral homology at the different levels of organism in which they have been recorded. This would not seem to be the case at all, because it seems evident that the application of a common term of classification for so varied an assortment has led to the glossing over of fundamental differences in adaptive significance.

The term "behavioral homology" presents difficulties. In morphology the term "homology" indicates body structure in different animals that are of the same relation, principal pattern in the body, and of the *same origin*. For other structures of similar form, but of different origin— the term *analogous* is the only correct one. Hence the observations quoted sometimes concern similar actions of animals at different phyletic levels, i.e., of animals whose structures of the central nervous system, e.g., in insect and mammal, are not homologous at all. The actions described may be similar to the action of tool-using man; this does not mean that it *is* tool-using. Hence, if we extend this terminology to the classification of behavior—the results are *behavioral analogies* at different phyletic levels.

(4) The author states that not tool-*using* but tool-*making* signalizes the critical stage in the transition from ape to human; but it ought to be pointed out that tool-making, as *"shaping an object in an imaginary future eventuality,"* is the real boundary between ape and man. The real *tool* is the obviously shaped and obviously used object. Based upon this view we would probably be right in saying that there is no tool-*using* in animals at all; but that there are many examples of using stones, branches, or other objects during reproduction, nesting, feeding, excitation, etc. From the physiological viewpoint, these processes are chains of unconditioned or, sometimes, conditioned reflexes connected with food, reproduction, etc., developed during the phylogenesis of the species concerned as adaptations to the environment. These processes are the same in their physiological base in all species, including non-human primates.

(5) For some observations greater accuracy, probably followed by a new and reconsidered explanation is necessary; for other observations (elephants plugging their bells so that the clappers cannot ring, or polar bears casting blocks of ice onto the heads of walruses), fundamental revision of the facts registered in the literature is desirable. Many zoological observations tend to express the behavior of animals in anthropomorphistic fashion.

(6) There are several problems concerning apes: Köhler's experi-

ments indicate the ability to use bamboo poles in order to obtain fruit which is out of the animals' reach. This use of a pole may occur in a complicated manner, but it is always initiated by seeing the food desired. In Hall's paper, contrary to experimental conditions, apes are reported as using objects during excitation with the implication that this is the probable mode of origin of tool-using in man's phylogenetic past. This may be right, but with the reservation, concerning the above-expressed differences in the definition of the tool, tool-using, and tool-making.

The physiological condition of the brain of tool-using and tool-making man is different from any living nonhuman primate. It is necessary to point out that both recent apes and recent men are ends of *divergent* developmental branches of primates. This divergence is determined by the whole complex of erect posture, the development of the central nervous system, together with tool-using and tool-making hands, and the begining of social life of early human ancestors.

The differences between recent apes and recent men *even occur in the anatomical pattern of the human hand*. According to our latest studies, differences in situation of muscular layers develop during human ontogenesis. The fusion of two superimposed muscular layers forming the dorsal interossei (i.e., muscles executing fine movements of the fingers) occurs. Complete loss of the so-called layer of contrahentes muscles in its ulnar sector is characteristic only of man. On the other hand, recent anthropomorphic apes possess two muscular layers (functioning as flexors) in place of man's dorsal interossei, and at least the rudiments of the whole contrahentes muscles layer.

(7) In concluding my comment I should like to express my opinion that it is impossible to explain the development of tool-using in man solely from the comparative behavior evidence; i.e., from the standpoint of a single research field. I see the necessity of joining several standpoints; namely, developmental morphology, the comparative studies of physiology of the central nervous system based upon exact experiments, and consideration of mutual influences of social factors and tool-using in early evolution. From an integration of these multiple complex standpoints, it might be useful to try, retrospectively, to explain various observations of primate behavior and thereby gain more positive results.

BY R. DALE GIVENS

Richmond, Kentucky, U.S.A. 6.3.63

Since I am in essential agreement with K. R. L. Hall, there are only a few comments I wish to make:

(1) It may be hoped that additional research will clarify even more

the nature of tool-using in nonhuman animals since the picture presented here is still far from clear, complete, or well documented. This, however, is due more to the lack of data than to any fault of the author. Still, it seems somewhat premature to attempt to explain incipient tool-using behavior as "only an elementary form of operant conditioning imposed upon the agonistic repertoire of the species." Nor would such an explanation, if verified, make tool-using phenomena any less important as a behavioral form of adaptation, as Hall seems to imply.

(2) Hall considers the "use" of one chimpanzee by another to obtain a goal, such as, perhaps, food, as a case of tool-using. Classifying social interaction of this type as tool-using seems to me to assign too much to the latter concept and to confuse two totally different phenomena. If we follow Hall in this, we would have to call most social relationships, including those found among man, tool-using.

(3) In view of a recent news report of rudimentary tool-making behavior among chimpanzees in the wild, it would appear that Hall's position requires modification. If the Jane Morris-Goodall findings reported in *Newsweek* are accurate, the behavior displayed, that of moistening the end of a stick with saliva to attract termites, can hardly be explained in terms of an extension of agonistic behavior; it is directly oriented toward food procurement. What Morris-Goodall's report and the present paper both indicate, however, is that the gap between early man and the higher primates is not much greater in regard to mental capabilities than it was already known to be for biological characteristics. Leslie White notwithstanding, the distinction between the mentality of human and nonhuman primates is a matter of degree and not a difference in kind.

By Harry F. Harlow

Madison, Wisconsin, U.S.A. 6.10.63

I totally and highly approve of the article.

By Gordon W. Hewes

Boulder, Colorado, U.S.A. 6.10.63

Chance calls attention to the role of the repertory of innate motor patterns in much of the seemingly insightful problem-solving observed in apes and monkeys, though insight cannot be wholly excluded. Primate tool-using probably began in manipulatory behavior not directed toward any external goal. Rewarded manipulation, if repeatedly successful in a given environment—enhancing food supply or increasing security from enemies—could be expected to spread by social imitation to the rest of the local population. Hall does not refer to the Japanese macaque studies where behaviors analogous to invention and diffusion of tool-using have been observed. Higher primates can learn vicariously by observation of the actions of other individuals as anyone who has worked with them can testify. Endowed with this capacity to a very high degree, primates are "pre-adapted" to persistent, functional tool-using where environmental conditions make it biologically rewarding.

Monkeys approach some of the conditions of tool-preparation and tool-handling in their inspection, peeling, stripping, and other preliminary steps in the eating of wild plant foods. Such behavior is far more deliberate, and far more flexible than the nut-gnawing of squirrels, and is best seen when the monkey is confronted with an unfamiliar plant which may have edible parts. Wild monkeys distinguish carefully between food and containers, as in Kawamura's report of macaques extracting wheat grains from paper envelopes. A stumptail macaque at the University of Colorado drinks from cups, opens paper boxes, and removes wrappings from any stray packages suspected of having edible contents.

Cord-pulling is also part of the common motor repertory of monkeys. It is evidently easier to pull a cord or stick toward the body to secure a desired object than to get at it by pushing something outward, away from the body. Such preferences in basic motor patterns have undoubtedly affected the evolution of primate tool-using. The primate hand is used regularly with precision not only for food preparation, and feeding, but also grooming. Hall does not mention grooming, nor has this been stressed by other writers on the subject of the emergence of tool-using in primates. Macaques in grooming usually steady the body-part being worked on with one hand, while dextrously probing with the fingers of the other to the base of each hair or clump of hairs, opposing the ball of the thumb to the terminal phalange of the index finger. Transfer of the motor habits and psychological drive toward grooming, to the surface treatment of tool-objects—from decortication of twigs to the systematic removal of surface irregularities on chipped stone implements, and eventually even to tasks such as weeding, does not seem too far-fetched.

Carrying of food, infants, and objects usable as tools has also probably been important. My own ideas as to the relation between Hominid bipedalism and tool-using differ from those who see a direct relationship between incipient tool-using and bipedal locomotion.

Washing of food, and other "manipulations" of water, have certain analogies to tool-using. The invention of sweet-potato washing by a Japanese macaque, and its subsequent acceptance as a cultural trait in the entire troop is well known. Our captive macaques regularly soak or dunk their hard biscuits before eating them. This would seem to be a step beyond merely peeling or husking, in the direction of more elaborate forms of food-preparation. On the topic of the "tool" use of water, I have observed gorillas at the Cheyenne Mountain Zoo, U.S.A., using their fingers to direct a stream of water from their water-fountains toward spectators, and with great accuracy. The spectators are safely behind plate glass. Chimpanzees in the same zoo fill their mouths with water and send spurts toward onlookers, in this case unprotected by glass. Under suitable environmental conditions, apes will use brushes and paints to achieve far more than random splashes of color. Although these behaviors do not occur in nature, they illustrate the kind of tool-using potential which is present in infrahuman primates. Hall notes that captive apes sometimes drape themselves with sacking, etc., but that comparable behavior has not been observed in the wild; however, Schaller shows in a sketch a wild infant gorilla who had decked himself in a "green hat" of lobelia frond.

Hall's major contribution to the study of tool-using among non-human primates is that it can arise spontaneously in agonistic behavior, as when apes throw sticks or branches toward intruding humans. But it is hard to believe that this action would do more than temporarily annoy a hungry carnivore. Its effectiveness might lie in another kind of situation: Hall observes that monkeys exhibit very strong aggressive responses when competitors prevent them from getting at food immediately present. If their competitors were members of their own troop, the usual dominance signals would be employed rather than stick-hurling. If however the competing eaters were, say, vultures working on a carcass, stick-throwing and stone-throwing by outraged and hungry primates might be the most effective way of driving the birds away. To be sure, modern apes and monkeys do not steal carrion away from vultures, but there are enough references to occasional meat-eating, hunting or killing of small, slow game, and even to winter hare-hunting (by members of one troop of Japanese macaques) to suggest that under some ecological conditions, even existing ape or monkey species might be capable of a more carnivorous regime than they are accustomed to. Scavenging of carcasses left by predators, as I suggested would have provided for more agonistic missile-hurling as well as for increased transportation of food-burdens to places of greater safety.

Napier shows a chimpanzee preparing a thin stick or reed as a probe to extract termites from their nest. This is Napier's second stage of tool-using, in which the tool is modified. His first step is the *ad hoc* use of a convenient stick or stone, and his third stage is the making of tools to a pattern. Hall does not sufficiently distinguish between the state of mind of aggressive stick-throwing and the deliberate selection and modification of a natural object as exemplified by this chimpanzee termite-extractor. It is the former, deliberate selection of a tool—as in the stones on the living floors in Olduvai Gorge, or the bones, etc. in the breccias of Makapansgat, rather than in the breaking off of a branch to annoy an intruder that sustained tool-using probably—got its start. In connection with bones, captive macaques are capable of a considerable amount of bone-modification by slow gnawing. With no more goal than to obtain the maximum amount of marrow and chewable cartilage, our captive macaque can work a bone down to unusual and unnatural shape. This suggests that once a carnivorous habit had been stabilized, primate bone-handlers would be forever reshaping them through gnawing. The continuing human nervous habit of chewing the ends of implements is perhaps not altogether irrelevant. An object serving both as a tool and as something to chew on has a greater chance of being reused.

Recent field studies of apes and monkeys have made it clear that their present living conditions do not impel them to much if any high-quality tool-using. However, it is not altogether impossible that before the rise to dominance of the genus *Homo,* some groups of apes ancestral to modern apes may have occupied environments in which more tool-using could have occurred, in ways contributing to their survival. This would parallel the situation of certain recent human groups which have been forced into marginal, stoneless alluvial regions, where the entire lithic tradition has been abandoned (to be sure, other kinds of tools have persisted).

I disagree with Hall's suggestion that the ease with which captive apes and monkeys acquire the use of tools together with their failure to exhibit this propensity in the wild "has no real significance." To me this is the most significant point of the whole discussion. Conditions of captivity provide tool-using opportunities for these primates while their natural habitats do not. We regularly use tools not because of our impressively larger brains and adept hands, but because we have been trained in cultural environments, in this respect analogous to the conditions of captivity for apes and monkeys. Feral human beings drawn from modern *Homo sapiens* populations, and living in the restricted, toolless environments of gorillas and chimpanzees, or of baboons, would probably do hardly any better than these animals in developing tools and weapons. Our superior brains might accelerate the process of tool-development by a factor of two or three, so that an Acheulean technology could be achieved in two or three hundred thousand years instead of a million years or more.

What we must explain then is the initial environmental "push," sufficient to stimulate tool-using among suitably endowed primates, and to sustain it through social learning from generation to generation. Stick-hurling in anger appears less promising than the reported palmnut cracking with rocks reported from Liberia. I see the conditions for take-off, in a changed food-habit, plus the adoption of relatively permanent bases of operation—rockshelters or living-floors. Dart has stressed the importance of osteodontokeratic litter in stimulating tool-using; such accumulations of bones, horns, and teeth could arise from scavenging as well as from hunting, at least to begin with. Present forest environ-ments used by anthropoid apes do not provide for semi-permanent sanc-tuaries where trash suitable for tools could accumulate, though the Kwangsi Gigantopithecines evidently lived in caves. Aimless tool-han-dling could be stimulated by residence in a trash-filled cave or shelter, but practical use of tools requires something more—most likely food in a form which must be crushed, pounded, cut, or broken before it can be consumed; the carcasses of medium to large sized animals represent such a food. The reconstruction of the ecological status of the primordial Hominids is most urgent.

To conclude, Hall's paper has stimulated me to suggest some large-scale and undoubtedly expensive experiments, utilizing apes and mon-keys in naturalistic environments, but not necessarily in environments identical to their present habitats. In such environments, the animals would be provisioned with foods requiring special preparation—palm-nuts to be cracked with stones, carcasses to be dissected, or even small, slow game animals to be hunted and killed with regularity. We might even try out Washburn's suggestion of supplying baboons with digging sticks, in a range in which such tools would significantly increase their food supply. If the initiation of such behaviors in nonhuman primates required some deliberate training of selected individuals, this would violate no basic canon of scientific experimentation. If we are interested in the ramifications—technological as well as sociological—of regular tool-using in nonhuman primates, we need not wait for fifty thousand years for some ape to discover a simple tool-technique by himself.

I have not commented on Hall's examples of non-primate tool-using, illuminating as they are, since I think our understanding of the emer-gence of human tool-using and tool-making is most likely to come from studies of primate behavior.

By Harry J. Jerison

Yellow Springs, Ohio, U.S.A. 6.12.63

When animal behavior is treated in purely evolutionary terms and limited to naturalistic field observations, there is an inherent obstacle in the way of scaling the behavior to provide a measure of adaptability. This is due to the assumption implicit in evolutionary analysis that the present state of nature represents a peak of excellence for the measure, or, stated another way, that a given pattern of behavior that is observed in the field is the best that has been achieved for the adaptive niche within which the behavior occurs. It seems to me that Hall's analysis of tool-using as a measure of adaptability illustrates the problem very well. If I read him correctly, he finds that tool-using, when it occurs in the field, is a rare behavioral adaptation to selection pressures associated with particular niches in the environment, and that the very category, "tool-using," is no more than an anthropomorphically derived identity for behaviors that may differ radically in their bases.

In presenting his interesting and in many ways original review of tool-using, Hall has eliminated this superficial category of behavior from serious consideration as a measure of adaptability. Yet it seems fair to ask him to state his views on the nature of appropriate measures, and, if possible, to suggest some examples of behavior categories that would provide such measures. Is it true, as I have just suggested, that the species-specific nature of much of the behavior that can be observed in the field limits the potential of such behavior for comparative purposes? I think a persuasive argument can be made for this position. Hall's review suggests that, at least in some primates, novel tool-using behavior patterns appear in the unusual environments of laboratories and zoos, and is not the frequency of novel and adequate responses to new situations one of the definitions of adaptability? One might therefore study adaptability profitably in laboratory settings where novel responses, including tool-using, might provide an appropriate comparative measure.

This is a treacherous position, too. I recall my own dismay when working with a very well-trained Java monkey (*Macaca irus*) that had to reach through a window and press a lever to avoid or escape a shock after an easily detected signal was presented. Pressing a lever is a classic "instrumental" act in the psychological laboratory, and it is clearly a bit of tool-using—or is it? In this case I found that when the clearly visible lever was moved back about 2 cm, this was enough to disrupt the animal completely. The monkey went through all of its usual response movements, but it missed the lever every time, because it failed to correct for the new lever distance. One must conclude that at least some "tool-using" in the laboratory as well as in the field is the result of the interaction of stereotyped (even if learned) movements with movable objects.

These comments are less on tool-using, which is apparently a weak descriptive category for animal behavior, than on the problem of defining and measuring adaptability. I would appreciate additional discussion of this problem.

By Arthur J. Riopelle

Covington, La., U.S.A. 6.11.63

Tool-using by animals has fascinated behavioral scientists for many years. Particularly perplexing has been an apparent comparability of behavior in even widely divergent orders of animals. This is nicely illustrated in this paper by Hall who juxtaposes examples from wasps, crabs, birds, elephants, monkeys, and apes. Historically, explanations of this apparent common trait have emphasized either instinct or intelligence. In one case the task is to explain how high up the phyletic chain one sees evidence for instinctive behavior and in the other case how much intelligence and insight is possessed by primitive animals. The popularity of these alternate views has fluctuated from decade to decade, depending on the dramatic strength of the latest data in favor of one viewpoint or the other and with the temper of observations in related sciences.

Similarities and parallels can often be found in different behaviors and in the approaches to the study of them, and the conceptualization of the proper approach in one may be helpful in the other. Imitation and observational learning are cases in point. (Interesting enough, observational learning, too, has engaged Hall's attention.)

The kinds of behavior that may be classified as imitative are as diverse as the kinds called tool-using. Many factors likely are involved, including the identification of the native elemental responses, the diversity of responses available, the situation surrounding the response, and the motivation and learning components.

Thorndike in 1898 stated the task for studying imitation: "Now if a bird really gets a sound in his mind from hearing it and sets out forthwith to imitate as mocking birds are said at times to do, it is a mystery and deserves the closest study. If a bird, out of a lot of random noises that it makes, chooses those for repetition which are like sounds he has heard, it is a mystery *why,* though not in the previous case a mystery how, he does it."

Hall's paper identifies similar components of the problem of tool-using. All species, because of innate response capabilities, are predisposed to execute certain kinds of responses rather than others. (Here Hall is more restrictive than Thorndike.) Out of the responses that are made, some lead to reinforcement, satisfaction, and gratification, whereas others do not. Those reinforced will tend to be repeated. Thus Hall has taken Thorndike's less mysterious route to search for an explanation of the behavior he and others have observed.

Hall's report, like Thorndike's before him, is perhaps less of an explanation of tool-using behavior than an identification of the significant components of it. It, naturally, goes beyond Thorndike in its use of concepts, such as displacement activity, which were not available in 1898. It is to be hoped, therefore, that Hall's report will stimulate experimental work on tool-using behavior just as Thorndike's did for imitation.

There is another emphasis in the paper which deserves mention, and that is the breadth of the sources of literature cited. Tool-using is evidently that kind of animal activity which brings together scientists of differing orientation and thus serves as a vehicle for the transport of ideas among them. One cannot help but observe that such communication broadens our sciences and sharpens our concepts. Hall's study will further this process.

BY J. P. SCOTT

Bar Harbor, Maine, U.S.A. 6.5.63

This is an excellent review of the subject and points out the fact that it is difficult to draw a line anywhere in the animal kingdom which will strictly separate human from nonhuman behavior. The following remarks are intended as addenda rather than criticism.

A distinction should be made between instances where tool-using is a part of the regular behavioral repertoire of a species, and cases where such behavior can be learned and passed along from individual to individual by some form of cultural inheritance, the latter being the more human attribute. However, simple observation does not reveal which of these two alternate explanations of behavior applies to any particular case. The use of stones in cracking mussel shells by the sea otter might belong in either category until it is possible to experiment with animals which have not had an opportunity to learn from their own kind.

A great many animals are capable of instrumental learning; i.e., of performing certain acts, obtaining a result which is rewarding to them, and consequently learning to repeat the activity. No high degree of intelligence or capacity for symbolic logic is necessary. The likelihood of learning to use tools under these circumstances is largely dependent upon the species' ability to manipulate objects.

Instrumental learning may have a variety of motivations besides the two basic ones suggested by Hall in connection with agonistic and ingestive behavior. Captive chimpanzees at Yerkes Laboratories used to squirt water and throw feces at passing spectators with considerable accuracy. While the motivation may have been agonistic, it may also have resulted from the simple pleasure of watching the spectators jump and yell.

In general, Hall has shown that tool-using is not a unique human capacity. Rather, human societies excel, but are not unique, in their capacity to communicate tool-using by cultural means. In our search for the beginnings of cultural heredity in other forms, we should not neglect the opposite side of the coin, that human behavior may include a basic repertory of patterns whose development is largely under biological control.

By S. L. WASHBURN

Berkeley, California, U.S.A. 5.22.63

This paper clarifies a confused subject and offers what may well prove to be a major contribution to the understanding of human evolution. The clear separation of objects used in emotional-display behavior from those used in feeding is new and important. I would like to comment briefly on how this supplements available notions on the origins of human tool-using.

In both chimpanzee and gorilla the emotional-display throwing occurs when the animals are bipedal and on the ground. In particular the chimpanzee may break off a branch and swing it vigorously as part of the display (Morris-Goodall). The animal does not try to strike the creature against whom the display is directed, but this might easily happen. Here then is a situation in which apes might repeatedly discover the effectiveness of striking with an object. As a part of the aggressive display the branch is effective whether it strikes another animal or not. Here is a relatively common situation in which the utility of a tool, both offensively and defensively, might be learned. I have always wondered about the first steps in the evolution of a weapon. Unless a stick is well selected and skillfully used an ape's teeth are far more effective. The agonistic-display origin of weapons solves this dilemma because, if the display fails, the ape still may fight or flee. The selection pressure maintaining the large teeth would not be relaxed until after the swinging-branch display had evolved into effective behavior. If young apes incorporated this bipedal, object-using display into their play repertoire, a background for skillful adult use would be laid.

I see no conflict between the "emotional" use of objects theory and continuing to stress the importance of even minor tool use in extending feeding habits. Surely the more different reasons objects are manipulated, the more likely it is that new uses will be found and skills developed. Future field observations and experiments, guided by Hall's clarification, may give us a much deeper understanding of the possible origins of human tool-making.

By J. S. Weiner

London. 5.16.63

Hall draws attention to and discusses the apparent paucity of evidence of "tool-using" activities by nonhuman primates in the wild in contrast to the many instances recorded for captive animals. One of the two factors he puts forward to account for this discrepancy is simply that the systematic field evidence is missing and he mentions specifically here the ignorance of details on the feeding habits of *Cebus*. I claim no first-hand or special knowledge of this topic, but it seems to me that in the case of *Cebus fatuellus* the evidence for similar tool-using activities in the wild and in captivity is not so undocumented as Hall suggests. I had occasion to describe some of the "hammering" activities of *Cebus fatuellus* at the Primate Symposium in London when making some comments on a film supplied by G. M. Vevers to show the use of a tool by a Capuchin monkey. I was interested to find fairly detailed references to rather similar activity in descriptions given by Romanes and by Osman Hill for both captive and wild monkeys. I would add that instances of this sort of tool-using in the wild, and of others mentioned by Hall, do not in any way refute the generalization for which I think he has made a very strong case, namely that the basis of the handling of various objects is to be found in the transfer of the "emotional" repertoire of gesture to a different context. The importance of the *Cebus* example would be that it marks a particular case of such a transfer.

REPLY

By K. R. L. Hall

Several very interesting points are made in these comments, and I shall select a few for more detailed discussion.

First, the question of terminology used in describing these, and other, performances is a recurrently difficult and important one. Čihák queries the use of "homology" in the present context, but I think it is here appropriate because the point I was trying to emphasize was, to para-phrase Jerison's very clear expression of it, that tool-using has been a classificatory term for similar appearing performances the underlying bases of which may be radically different, but that the term has often been used with the *implication* of common origin. Analogies, therefore, they indeed are, but homologies they have been implied to be.

Carpenter deals with the terms used in describing the nature and status of the performances, and in drawing inferences from their description. Possibly "elementary" or "simple" would be less equivocal qualifiers of some of the instrumental acts under discussion, but I used the term "primitive" in this context because, so far as I recall, it was the one Carpenter himself has used in describing branch-breaking or some other such emotional gesture. As to the status of these acts, it is still surely correct to apply the simplest kind of model that fits the evidence, and there is no denial of the possibility of purpose or insight or some other "higher" conception being involved in some cases. The status of performances such as those of chimpanzees in using tools for food-getting is certainly more intelligent, and less emotional, than the display acts which these and other nonhuman primates show in the offensive–defensive kind of situation. But, as the theme of the paper tries to indicate, these more complex performances may be shown to derive, both ontogenetically and phylogenetically, from the simple emotional ones, in the kind of way Washburn has interestingly envisaged weapon-use might have developed.

A second major that seems to me to arise out of several comments is the need for thorough comparative studies of behavior ontogeny. Scott indicates that such studies would be essential to substantiate, or otherwise, the suggestion that emotional gestures precede and form the basis for transfer to the more complex skills sometimes shown in food-getting. Scott also points out that only experimental studies could really distinguish between the status of tool-using performances by different types of animal, and these, I think, would have to be mainly developmental, and carried out under varying conditions that would test the limits of the animals' capacities.

Thirdly, and leading directly on from this, is the important point which Riopelle and Hewes discuss—how the skill involved in tool-using may be transmitted within a group, or from group to group in a population area. Hewes mentions the Japanese work on habit transmission in their macaque groups, and, in my review elsewhere of this and other field and experimental data on imitation in monkeys and apes I thought that it was difficult clearly to show that anything more was occurring than a focusing of one animal's attention upon some object in the environment which, at least temporarily, it was ignoring. It seemed to me very doubtful whether anything new in the repertoire of skills of the observing animal ever has been convincingly shown to occur, and yet, at the same time, I feel that this whole fascinating problem of imitation needs perhaps a rather different research approach, particularly by exploring very thoroughly what it is that really goes on in the constant interactions of infant and mother and age-mates in the natural group situation of the animal. In watching sea otter pups with their mothers, one cannot fail to be impressed by the closeness of the relation and by the continual

FIGURE 13–1—Young lowland gorilla, "Albert." Note the quadrupedal stance, and the way in which forelimbs are used for support. (San Diego Zoo Photograph)

FIGURE 13–2—Chimpanzee, "Esther." This chimpanzee is rather old; note the grey whiskers. In the female the brow ridges are less heavy than in the male. (San Diego Zoo Photograph)

opportunity for the pup to observe what the mother is doing in her search for and manipulation of food objects. But with Scott I see no way of getting at the core of the problem except by experimental study.

A fourth point, concerning the nature of adaptability, is very well brought out in the comments of Andrew and Jerison. Jerison seems to me to go right to the heart of perhaps the major issue in modern comparative behavior studies in posing the question of how to define and measure adaptability. In terms of tool-using, chimpanzees seems easily to excel baboons. In terms of ability to make use of widely differing habitats and climatic zones, baboons, and perhaps vervets, are more successful than chimpanzees. Likewise, the sea otters might be considered the marine counterpart of the chimpanzee, and no doubt there is a Mustelid equivalent to baboons. In terms of laboratory measures, it seems clear that far too much emphasis has been placed upon performance scores which are not related to the sort of adaptability shown by the animal in the wild. Although there is obvious interest in seeing how an animal deals with a novel situation, it seems to me most likely that the animal studies that will give significant leads towards understanding some of the factors in human evolution will be planned to work out how the stresses of differing social and ecological settings affect the development of behavior. All this goes around the topic of tool-using, but I think it may put tool-using in the right perspective as possibly only a minor clue too close a look at which has stopped us seeing some of the major ones.

SELECTED READINGS

DeVore, Irven, ed., 1965, *Primate Behavior: Field Studies of Monkeys and Apes.* New York: Holt, Rinehart and Winston, Inc.

Eimerl, Sarel, and Irven DeVore, 1965, *The Primates,* from *Life Nature Library.* New York: Time Inc.

Frisch, J. E., 1959, "Research on Primate Behavior in Japan," *American Anthropologist,* 61:584–596.

Hayes, Cathy, 1951, *The Ape in Our Home.* New York: Harper & Row.

Imanishi, Kinji, 1960, "Social Organization of Subhuman Primates in Their Natural Habitat," *Current Anthropology,* 1:393–408.

Reynolds, V., 1965, "Some Behavioral Comparisons between the Chimpanzee and the Mountain Gorilla in the Wild," *American Anthropologist,* 67:691–706.

Schaller, George B., 1963, *The Mountain Gorilla: Ecology and Behavior.* Chicago: University of Chicago Press.

Schultz, A. H., 1950, "The Specializations of Man and His Place among

Catarrhine Primates," *Cold Spring Harbor Symposia on Quantitative Biology,* 15:37–53.

Southwick, C. H., ed., 1963, *Primate Social Behavior.* Princeton, N.J.: Van Nostrand.

Washburn, S. L., and I. DeVore, 1961, "The Social Life of Baboons," *Scientific American,* 204:62–71.

PART FIVE

INTERPRETING
FOSSIL
MAN

New fossils keep turning up, and new ways of making inferences from the fossil record are always being developed. Our view of human evolution alters from one decade to the next, and we should not be surprised or troubled by the different interpretations synthesized at different times. If, despite the collection of new data and the development of new theories, the generalizations remain the same, then our endeavors are not really scientific at all.

The following articles reflect the kind of interpretation currently placed on the course of human evolution, based on the facts and observations accumulated thus far. Simons summarizes the story of prehuman evolution. Mayr, as a zoologist, offers a classification of human fossils that reflects evolutionary relationships. Oakley discusses archeological data that illuminate the course of human evolution. Robinson compares and contrasts the fossils of the earliest known hominids, the australopithecines. Le Gros Clark identifies the chief points at issue among paleontologists today, and Weidenreich reminds us of the dangers attendant upon reading too much from a fossil record that consists essentially of skulls.

The views represented in this section remind us forcibly that careful observation of fossils themselves is more important than ever. Despite the proliferation of theories about human evolution, the newer physical anthropology continues to depend on a close reading of the fossil record.

14

THE EARLY RELATIVES
OF MAN

Elwyn L. Simons

*Over the last three generations, a great debate has raged among
students of evolution as to which primate stock man can claim
as ancestral. Is man descended immediately from the apes? Did
the line leading to man separate at the monkey stage? Or, is
man descended from the tarsiers? Did the separation of the
hominid line take place 1 million years ago? 10 million years ago?
70 million years ago?*

*Recently evidence regarding human descent has made clear
that man is descended from an ape, probably some kind of
African ape.[1]*

*With this great clarification in the theory of human evolution,
what is now needed are more fossils that will show the precise
course of evolution between our apelike ancestors and ourselves. In this article, Simons describes the recent fossil finds
that illuminate this evolutionary sequence. His study emphasizes
that careful analysis of the bones themselves is absolutely
necessary to understand what happened in evolution.*

A major feature of biological evolution during the past 70 million years
has been the rapid rise to a position of dominance among the earth's
land-dwelling vertebrates of the placental mammals (mammals other
than marsupials such as the kangaroo and primitive egg-laying species
such as the platypus). A major feature, in turn, of the evolution of the
placental mammals has been the emergence of the primàtes: the mammalian order that includes man, the apes and monkeys. And a major event
in the evolution of the primates was the appearance 12 million to 14

(From *Scientific American*, Vol. 211, July 1964, pages 50–62. Reprinted
with permission. Copyright © 1964 by Scientific American, Inc. All rights
reserved. Available separately @ 20¢ as offprint No. 622 from W. H. Free-
man and Company, 660 Market Street, San Francisco, California.)
[1] See Simpson, *Science*, 152:472–478.

million years ago of animals, distinct from their ape contemporaries, that apparently gave rise to man.

Much of the evidence of the origin of man is new, but by no means all of it. For many years students of human evolution have broadly agreed that man's earliest ancestor would be found among the apelike primates that flourished during Miocene and early Pliocene times, roughly from 12 million to 24 million years ago [Figure 14–2]. As long ago as the 1920's William K. Gregory of the American Museum of Natural History, after studying the limited number of jaw fragments and teeth then available, flatly pronounced man to be ''a late Tertiary offshoot of the *Dryopithe-cus-Sivapithecus* group, or at least of apes that closely resembled those genera in the construction of jaw and dentition.''

Until recently students of primate evolution have had little more evidence to work with than Gregory and his contemporaries did. Within the past 15 years, however, a number of significant new finds have been made—some of them in existing fossil collections. The early primates are now represented by many complete or nearly complete skulls, some nearly complete skeletons, a number of limb bones, and even the bones of hands and feet. In age these specimens extend across almost the entire Cenozoic era, from its beginning in the Paleocene epoch some 63 million years ago up to the Pliocene, which ended roughly two million years ago.

Sometimes a single jaw can tell a remarkably detailed evolutionary story, but there are no greater paleontological treasures than reasonably complete skulls and skeletons. Many such specimens have become available in recent years, but they do not lie in the exact line of man's ancestry. They are nonetheless important to the evolutionary history of all the primates. Both by their relative completeness and by their wide distribution in time they reveal new details concerning the main stages through which the primates probably passed during their evolutionary development.

To describe these stages is one of the two objectives of this article. The other objective is to summarize what is known about the relation of the early primates to the primate order's more advanced lineages, including man's own family: the Hominidae. The accomplishment of these objectives show that the weight of today's knowledge fortifies Gregory's declaration of the 1920's.

SUBDIVIDING THE PRIMATES

Ideally zoological classification uses standard suffixes to guide the student through the maze of descending divisions: from class to order and thence—by way of suborders, infraorders, superfamilies, families, subfamilies, and the like—to a particular genus and species. The grammar of primate taxonomy is not this simple. Two factors are responsible. First, there is no international agreement as to how the order of primates should be subdivided. Second, generations of literary usage preceding man's first awareness of evolution have made all nouns derived from the Greek *anthropos* or the Latin *homo* virtually synonymous.

Nonetheless, an ability to read these taxonomic signposts is vital to an understanding not only of the relations among the 50-odd genera of living primates but also of the positions assigned to various extinct primates. This is because modern classification interrelates organisms in a pattern that reflects their evolutionary relations. In tracing the subdivisions that lead to man, for example, the first major branching divides the whole group of living primates into two suborders. [See Fig. 14–1.] The less advanced primates are assigned to the Prosimii; they are the various tree shrews, the many kinds of lemurs, the less abundant lorises, and the solitary genus of tarsiers. The earliest known fossil primates belong exclusively to this suborder. The line to man, however, runs through successive divisions of the second primate suborder.

This suborder, consisting of the more advanced primates, is the Anthropoidea. It is divided into two infraorders. The less advanced anthropoids, including all the primates native to the New World, are the Platyrrhini. "Platyrrhine," which literally means "broadnosed," refers to the wide spacing of the nostrils that is characteristic of the New World anthropoids.

The more advanced anthropoids are the Catarrhini. They include all other living anthropoids: the Old World monkeys, the apes, and man himself. "Catarrhine" is opposed to "platyrrhine"; it literally means "hooknosed" but refers to a close spacing of the nostrils. The catarrhine infraorder is in turn divided into two superfamilies: the Cercopithecoidea and the Hominoidea. The first of these means "apes with tails"; it embraces the two subfamilies and 13 genera of living Old World monkeys.

The second catarrhine superfamily, the Hominoidea, embraces the subdivisions that finally separate the genus *Homo* from the rest of the living primates. The hominoids are split three ways: the families Hylobatidae, Pongidae, and Hominidae. The first of these takes its name from *Hylobates,* the gibbon of South Asia, and includes both this hominoid primate and the closely related siamang of Sumatra. The family Pongidae embraces the three genera of great apes: *Pongo,* the orangutan; *Pan,* the chimpanzee, and *Gorilla,* whose scientific name is the same as the common.

Of the family Hominidae, however complex its subfamilies and genera may or may not once have been, there survives today only the single genus *Homo* and its single species *Homo sapiens*. Man, then, is the sole living representative of the hominid family within the hominoid superfamily of the catarrhine infraorder of anthropoids. Or, to reverse the

ORDER	SUBORDER	INFRAORDER	SUPERFAMILY	FAMILY	SUBFAMILY	*GENUS*	COMMON NAME
PRIMATES	PROSIMII	LEMURIFORMES	TUPAIOIDEA	TUPAIIDAE	TUPAIINAE	*TUPAIA* *DENDROGALE* *UROGALE*	COMMON TREE SHREW SMOOTH-TAILED TREE SHREW PHILIPPINE TREE SHREW
					PTILOCERCINAE	*PTILOCERCUS*	PEN-TAILED TREE SHREW
			LEMUROIDEA	LEMURIDAE	LEMURINAE	*LEMUR* *HAPALEMUR* *LEPILEMUR*	COMMON LEMUR GENTLE LEMUR SPORTIVE LEMUR
					CHEIROGALEINAE	*CHEIROGALEUS* *MICROCEBUS*	MOUSE LEMUR DWARF LEMUR
				INDRIDAE		*INDRI* *LICHANOTUS* *PROPITHECUS*	INDRIS AVAHI SIFAKA
				DAUBENTONIIDAE		*DAUBENTONIA*	AYE-AYE
		LORISIFORMES	LORISOIDEA	LORISIDAE		*LORIS* *NYCTICEBUS* *ARCTOCEBUS* *PERODICTICUS*	SLENDER LORIS SLOW LORIS ANGWANTIBO POTTO
				GALAGIDAE		*GALAGO*	BUSH BABY
		TARSIIFORMES	TARSISOIDEA	TARSIIDAE		*TARSIUS*	TARSIER
	ANTHROPOIDEA	PLATYRRHINI	CEBOIDEA	CALLITHRICIDAE		*CALLITHRIX* *LEONTOCEBUS*	PLUMED AND PYGMY MARMOSET TAMARIN
				CEBIDAE	CALLIMICONINAE	*CALLIMICO*	GOELDI'S MARMOSET
					AOTINAE	*AOTES* *CALLICEBUS*	DOUROUCOULI TITI
					PITHECINAE	*PITHECIA* *CHIROPOTES* *CACAJO*	SAKI SAKI UAKARI
					ALOUATTINAE	*ALOUATTA*	HOWLER
					CEBINAE	*CEBUS* *SAIMIRI*	CAPUCHIN SQUIRREL MONKEY
					ATELINAE	*ATELES* *BRACHYTELES* *LAGOTHRIX*	SPIDER MONKEY WOOLLY SPIDER MONKEY WOOLLY MONKEY
		CATARRHINI	CERCOPITHECOIDEA	CERCOPITHECIDAE	CERCOPITHECINAE	*MACACA* *CYNOPITHECUS* *CERCOCEBUS* *PAPIO* *THEROPITHECUS* *CERCOPITHECUS* *ERYTHROCEBUS*	MACAQUE BLACK APE MANGABEY BABOON, DRILL GELADA GUENON PATAS MONKEY.
					COLOMBINAE	*PRESBYTIS* *PYGATHRIX* *RHINOPITHECUS* *SIMIAS* *NASALIS* *COLOBUS*	COMMON LANGUR DOUC LANGUR SNUB-NOSED LANGUR PAGI ISLAND LANGUR PROBOSCIS MONKEY GUERAZA
			HOMINOIDEA	HYLOBATIDAE		*HYLOBATES* *SYMPHALANGUS*	GIBBON SIAMANG
				PONGIDAE		*PONGO* *PAN* *GORILLA*	ORANGUTAN CHIMPANZEE GORILLA
				HOMINIDAE		*HOMO*	MAN

FIGURE 14-1—Taxonomy of the living primates ranks the order's 52 genera (*scientific and common names at far right*) according to divisions of higher grade. There is no universal agreement on how this should be done. For example, the two infraorders of anthropoids in this system are held by many investigators to be suborders and thus equal in rank with the Prosimii. It is generally agreed, however, that man belongs among the catarrhines and, within that group, is a member of the hominoid superfamily (as are all the apes) and the hominid family, in which he is the only living species of the genus *Homo*. (Adapted by Jacquelyn Hetrick.)

order of classification, among the 33 or so living genera of Anthropoidea whose names are accepted as valid there are only six genera of hominoids and a single hominid genus.

A PALEOCENE TREE DWELLER

The Age of Mammals was ushered in some 63 million years ago by a brief geological epoch: the Paleocene. Lasting perhaps five million years, the Paleocene was followed by the much longer Eocene epoch, which occupied roughly the next 22 million years. Both periods seem to have been characterized by warm temperatures that permitted tropical and subtropical forests to extend much farther north and south of the Equator than is the case today. These forests were inhabited by a diverse and abundant population of primates. The fossil record shows that species belonging to nearly 60 genera of prosimians, the bulk of them grouped in eight families, inhabited the Northern Hemisphere during Paleocene and Eocene times.

Three of these eight prosimian families are characterized by elongated front teeth, presumably adapted for chiseling and gnawing, as are the rather similar teeth of today's rodents and rabbits. It seems reasonable to suppose that these early primates started their evolutionary careers in competition for some kind of nibblers' and gnawers' niche in the warm forests. They were not successful; before the middle of the Eocene all three chisel-toothed prosimian families had become extinct. Perhaps they were put out of business by the rodents, which became abundant as these prosimians were dying out.

The skeletal remains of a member of one of these extinct families were recently found by D. E. Russell of the French national museum of natural history in late Paleocene strata near Cernay-lez Reims in France. This early fossil primate belongs to the genus *Plesiadapis,* and the Cernay discovery includes a remarkably complete skull and a relatively complete series of limb and foot bones. An incomplete *Plesiadapis* skeleton is also known from Paleocene deposits in Colorado, and there are numerous jaws, jaw fragments and teeth from many other North American sites. These discoveries in opposite hemispheres, incidentally, make *Plesiadapis* the only genus of primate other than man's own that has inhabited both the Old and the New World.

Species of *Plesiadapis* varied in size from about the size of a squirrel to the size of a housecat. In life they probably looked as much like rodents as they did like primates. The patterns of the crowns of *Plesiadapis'* check teeth, however, resemble such patterns in lemur-like fossil primates of the Eocene epoch, and the structure of its limb bones links it with such living prosimians as the lemurs of the island of Madagascar (now the Malagasy Republic).

Plesiadapis is nonetheless distinctive. Its skull has a small braincase and a long snout. Its enlarged and forward-slanting incisors are widely separated from its cheek teeth. This arrangement is characteristic of the rodents, and although *Plesiadapis* appears too late to be an ancestor of the rodents, some workers have suggested that the order of rodents may be descended from animals not very different from it.

Plesiadapis exhibits two other traits that set the genus apart from almost all later primates. First, most if not all of its fingers and toes ended in long claws that were flattened at the sides. Among living primates only the tree shrews have a claw on each digit; all other species have either a combination of nails and claws or nails exclusively. Moreover, the claws of living primates are small compared with those of *Plesiadapis*. Regardless of their size, these claws probably served the same function as claws do among living tree shrews, helping this ancient aboreal primate to scramble up and down the trunks of trees.

The second peculiar trait, possibly one of lesser significance, is a resemblance between the structure of the middle ear of *Plesiadapis* and that of a nonprimate: the colugo, or "flying lemur," which still inhabits southeast Asia. The first thing to be said of the colugos, as George Gaylord Simpson has put it, is that they "are not lemurs and cannot fly." Colugos are so unusual that taxonomists have been obliged to place them in a mammalian order—the Dermoptera—all their own. The size of a squirrel or larger, with broad flaps of skin for gliding that run from its forelimbs to the tip of its tail, the colugo shows little outward resemblance to any other living mammal. It has been conjectured that the colugos are ultimately related to both the primates and the bats. The resemblance in ear structure is not the only similarity between the living colugos and the long-extinct *Plesiadapis:* the colugo's digits also bear sizable claws. Both of these similarities, however, could have been acquired independently rather than from a common ancestor.

Although early in time and cosmopolitan in range, *Plesiadapis* is clearly too specialized a primate to be the ancestor of later prosimians. This sterile offshoot of the family tree is significant to primate history on other grounds. First, the relative completeness of its remains makes *Plesiadapis* the most thoroughly known primate of the Paleocene. Second, many details of its skeletal form serve to link its order with that of the even earlier placental mammals—the Insectivora, from which the primates arose.

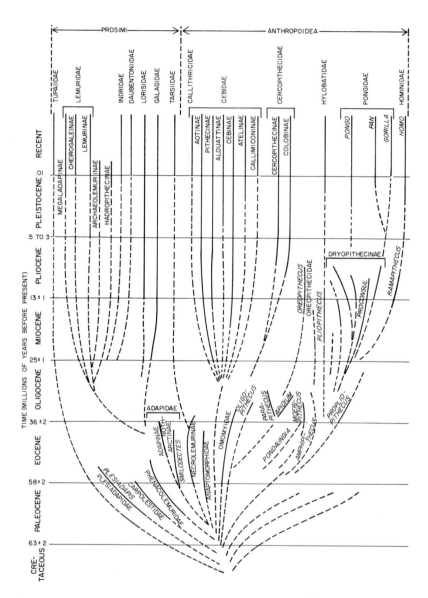

FIGURE 14–2—Phylogeny of all the primates traces the evolution of the
order from its beginnings sometime before the middle of the Paleocene.
The first to appear were prosimian families that stemmed from a basic
stock of small and sometimes arboreal mammals called Insectivora (whose
living kin includes the shrews and moles). The chart's broken lines show
hypothetical evolutionary relations. In the interval between Eocene and
Miocene times these relations are particularly uncertain. Solid lines show
the periods when species of the groups named are known to have flourished.
(Adapted by Jacquelyn Hetrick.)

EOCENE EVOLUTIONARY ADVANCES

The next fossil primates of which there are nearly complete remains come from North American strata of the middle Eocene. The best-known examples are species of two related lemur-like genera: *Notharctus* and *Smilodectes*. The degree to which these prosimians have advanced beyond *Plesiadapis* demonstrates the rapid evolution of primates as much as 50 million years ago. Many incomplete specimens of *Notharctus* were exhaustively studied in the 1920's by Gregory. Since then an even more complete skeleton of one species—probably *Notharctus tenebrosus*—has come to light in the paleontological research collection of Yale University. Although the skull is missing, the rest of the skeleton represents one of the two most complete individual primates yet recovered from fossil beds of such early date. C. Lewis Gazin of the Smithsonian Institution has recently recovered several complete skulls and many other bones of *Smilodectes gracilis* in southwestern Wyoming. The abundance of this new material has permitted the assembly of a skeleton and a restoration of *Smilodectes'* probable appearance.

These New World primates resemble living lemurs both in their proportions and in their general structure. In contrast to the small-brained, snouty, side-eyed *Plesiadapis*, the skull of *Smilodectes* shows an enlargement of the front portion of the brain and a shifting of eye positions forward so that individual fields of vision can overlap in front. These features of the head, taken together with the animal's rather long hind limbs, suggest that in life *Smilodectes* looked rather like one of today's Malagasy lemurs, the sifaka.

It is most unlikely, however, that either *Smilodectes* or *Notharctus* contributed to the ancestry of living lemurs. This honor can more probably be conferred on some member of a European genus, such as *Protoadapis* or *Adapis*, of equal Eocene age, if indeed the ancestors of modern lemurs were not already in Africa by this time. *Adapis* has the distinction of being the first fossil primate genus ever described. The French paleontologist Baron Cuvier did so in 1822, although he originally thought *Adapis* was a hoofed mammal or a small pachyderm and not a primate at all. Unfortunately none of these possible Old World precursors of living lemurs is sufficiently represented by fossils to provide the kind of detailed skeletal information we possess for their New World contemporaries.

This is also the case for a roughly contemporary European prosimian: *Necrolemur*, known from skulls and limb bones found in the Quercy deposits of France and by extrapolation from parts of a related species recovered in Germany. In *Necrolemur* the evolutionary advances represented by *Notharctus* and *Smilodectes* have been extended. Enlargement of the forebrain and a further facial foreshortening are apparent. A forward shift of the eye position—with the consequent overlapping of visual fields and potential for depth perception—should have equipped *Necrolemur* for an active arboreal life in the Eocene forests. Actually this early primate, although it is probably not ancestral to any living prosimian, shows a much closer affinity for the comparatively advanced tarsier of southeast Asia than for the more primitive Malagasy lemurs.

The evolutionary progress made by prosimians during the Eocene, both in North America and in Europe, is obvious. Yet not a single fossil primate of the Eocene epoch from either continent appears to be an acceptable ancestor for the great infraorder of the catarrhines, embracing all the living higher Old World primates, man included. One cannot help wondering what developments may have been taking place in Africa and Asia during the Eocene's span of more than 22 million years. In both regions the record is almost mute. In Asia the only known primate fossils dating to this epoch are a few equivocal bits and pieces from China and some fragments from a late Eocene formation in Burma. From the Eocene of Africa there are not only no primates but also no small mammals of any kind.

One of the Burmese fragments is a section of lower jaw containing three premolar teeth and one molar, described in 1938 by Edwin H. Col-

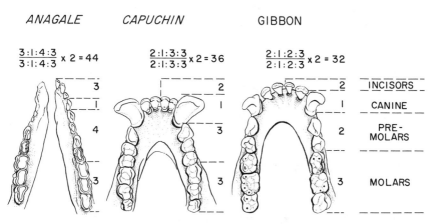

FIGURE 14–3—Higher primates have fewer teeth than the original placental total of 44 (see the lower jaw of *Anagale*, left). The platyrrhine primates have lost an incisor and a premolar on each side of both jaws, and some have even lost molars. Thus the New World cebids have 36 teeth (capuchin monkey, center). All the catarrhines have lost one more premolar all around, so the Old World monkeys, apes, and man have only 32 teeth (gibbon, right). (Adapted by Jacquelyn Hetrick.)

bert of the American Museum of Natural History, who named the new species *Amphipithecus mogaungensis*. A brief lesson in primate teeth is necessary to understand its significance. The lesson is painless; it merely involves counting. The facts are these: Regardless of tooth size or shape all adult catarrhines—Old World monkeys, apes and man—have the same "dental formula." In each half of a jaw—upper and lower alike—are found from front to back two incisors, a single canine, two premolars and three molars. In anatomical shorthand the fact is written:

$$\frac{2 : 1 : 2 : 3}{2 : 1 : 2 : 3} \times 2 = 32.$$

Because of its three premolar teeth *Amphipithecus* is dentally more primitive than any catarrhine, fossil or living. It may have had such a dental formula as

$$\frac{2 : 1 : 3 : 3}{2 : 1 : 3 : 3} \times 2.$$

This is typical of some living lemurs and of many platyrrhines—the marmosets and monkeys of the New World. Yet in other characteristics the *Amphipithecus* jaw is advanced rather than primitive. The horizontal ramus—that portion of the jaw that holds the teeth—is deep and massive, as is also true in many fossil and living apes. The fossil premolars, and the molar as well, are similar to the corresponding teeth in *Oligopithecus,* a newly discovered catarrhine from the Oligocene of Egypt.

The other Burmese fossil consists of both rear portions of a lower jaw, discovered together with a segment of upper jaw containing two molar teeth. G. E. Pilgrim of the Indian Geological Survey gave this find the name *Pondaungia cotteri* in 1927. The two molars almost equally resemble those of prosimians on the one hand and of some Old World higher primates on the other. The material is so fragmentary, however, that some scholars have even questioned *Pondaungia*'s inclusion in the primate order. If neither *Amphipithecus* nor *Pondaungia* were known, it would seem almost certain that the Old World anthropoids had arisen in Africa. Further collecting in the Burmese Eocene formation that contained both Pilgrim's and Colbert's fossils is required before final judgment of their significance can be made.

By the end of the Eocene the primates had been differentiating for almost 30 million years. This is a long time. Yet only one result is known with certainty: a number of primates, lemur-like and tarsier-like, had evolved in the Old World, some of which must have contributed to the ancestry of today's lower primates, the Prosimii. Not until the close of the Eocene do some puzzling fossil fragments from Burma offer a hint of what must have been a major, even though still undocumented, evolutionary development in the Old World Tropics. This development can be postulated with confidence, in spite of a paucity of evidence, because early in the following epoch—the Oligocene—fossil Anthropoidea appear in substantial numbers and varieties. It is highly improbable that these Oligocene primates could have evolved, in terms of geologic time, almost overnight. So far our knowledge of their geographical distribution is exceedingly limited: all their remains discovered to date have come from a single formation in the desert badlands of the Egyptian province of the Fayum.

THE CATARRHINE EMERGENCE

A hundred miles inland from the Mediterranean coast and some 60 miles southwest of Cairo a brackish lake stands at the edge of a series of escarpments and desert benches that are almost devoid of plant and animal life. At the end of the Eocene epoch the shore of the Mediterranean extended this far inland, and rivers flowed into the shallow sea through dense tropical forests. The rise and fall of sea and land is clearly revealed by alternating river-deposited strata and layers of marine limestone. In the middle of these escarpments, running from southwest to northeast between the lake and a lava-capped ridge called Gebel el Quatrani, is a fossil-rich stratum of sandy early Oligocene sediments that first yielded primate remains in the early 1900's.

Primates were not the only inhabitants of this forested Oligocene shoreline. Crocodiles and gavials swam in the sluggish streams. Tiny rodents and various relatives of today's hyrax lived in the underbrush, as did hog- and ox-sized cousins of the modern elephant. The largest animal of the fauna was a four-horned herbivore about the size and shape of today's white rhinoceros.

Until the recent Yale Paleontological Expedition the primate inventory from the Fayum totaled seven pieces of fossilized bone: one skull fragment (picked up by a professional collector in 1908 and sent to the American Museum of Natural History), one heel bone, three fragmentary portions of jawbone and two nearly complete lower jaws. This may not seem a particularly rich haul, but studies over the years have shown that these seven fossils represent at least four distinct genera and species of Oligocene primates.

By the end of the Yale Expedition's fourth season this past winter more than 100 individual primate specimens had been added to the

Fayum inventory. Although many of these finds consist of single teeth, there are also more than two dozen lower jaws, a skull fragment and some limb bones. Thus far the Fayum beds have not yielded any skulls or other skeletal remains of the kind that provide so much detailed information on Paleocene and Eocene prosimians. What has been found, however, reveals a great deal. As one example, an incomplete lower jaw was discovered in 1961 by a member of the expedition, Donald E. Savage of the University of California at Berkeley. This fragment permits the establishment of a new primate genus, which I have named *Oligopithecus*. The molar teeth of the "type" species of the genus indicate that it may well be on or near the evolutionary line that gave rise to the superfamily of living Old World monkeys: the cercopithecoids.

The other Old World primate superfamily—the hominoids—also appear to be well represented among the Fayum fossils. Possible ancestors for one family of living hominoids—the gibbons and siamangs—are present: the well-preserved jaw of a gibbon-like animal, as yet undescribed, was turned up by the Yale Expedition in 1963. In this connection it should be noted that the study of all the Fayum fossils belonging to the genus *Propliopithecus*—for many years regarded as an ancestor of the gibbon—indicates that it probably represents a more generalized hominoid ancestor instead. This small Oligocene primate may well prove to be on or near the line of evolutionary development that led to the living pongids and to man.

THE MIOCENE HOMINOIDS

Throughout the entire 11-million-year span of the Oligocene the fossil fauna of Europe does not include a single primate. In the following epoch—the Miocene, which had its beginning some 24 to 26 million years ago—primates reappear in the European fossil record. A few years after Cuvier named *Adapis* the paleontologist-antiquarian Édouard Lartet reported a primate lower jaw from Miocene strata at Sansan in France. This fossil was the basis for establishing the genus *Pliopithecus*. Since then dozens of other *Pliopithecus* specimens have been uncovered in formations of Miocene and Pliocene age, in both Europe and Africa. The best of these *Pliopithecus* finds to date—a skull, including facial portions, and most of a skeleton—was made in a Miocene deposit near the Czechoslovakian town of Neudorf an der March in 1957. . . .

Many millions of years younger than the gibbon-like hominoids of the Fayum, *Pliopithecus* presumably represents a further advance in the lineage that leads to the living gibbons. Yet this Miocene hominoid shows quite generalized characteristics. The arms of today's gibbons are considerably longer than their legs; *Pliopithecus,* in contrast, has hind limbs and forelimbs of nearly equal length. In fact, where comparisons are possible, *Pliopithecus* is not radically different from other roughly contemporary but not as fully preserved Miocene hominoids. Study of its skeleton tells us much about what the early hominoids were like.

A near contemporary of *Pliopithecus* is *Dryopithecus,* the animal mentioned by Gregory as one candidate for a position ancestral to man. *Dryopithecus* was also also named by Lartet; he described a lower jaw in 1856, almost 20 years after his discovery of *Pliopithecus.* Since that time many other fossil fragments of *Dryopithecus*—but no complete skulls or skeletons—have been found in strata of Miocene and even Pliocene age in Europe. In the late 1950's fossil teeth assignable to *Dryopithecus* were uncovered in brown-coal deposits in southwestern China, indicating that the range of these hominoids extended across Europe to the Far East.

Because the fossil inventory for *Dryopithecus* consists mainly of individual teeth and teeth in incomplete jawbones, the reader will find useful some additional facts about primate dentition. These facts concern shape rather than number. First, although the crowns, or chewing surfaces, of any primate's molars may be ground flat by years of wear, each crown normally shows several bumps called cusps. Typically there are four cusps to a crown, one at each corner of the tooth. Second, all members of one of the two higher Old World primate superfamilies—the cercopithecoid monkeys—exhibit a unique cusp pattern. On the first and second upper and lower molars ridges of enamel project toward each other from the front pair of cusps; there are similar ridges between the back pair of cusps. Before the crown has been worn down there is often a gap in the middle of the ridge, but worn or unworn these molars are unmistakable.

The hominoids, on the other hand, have their own distinctive cusp pattern. The lower molars normally have five cusps rather than four, and the pattern of valleys that separate these bumps of enamel somewhat resembles the letter Y, with the bottom of the Y facing inward. The pattern is called Y-5. The evolutionary significance of the pattern lies in the fact that the lower molars of *Dryopithecus* and of early men typically exhibit a Y-5 pattern. Thus Y-5 is a hereditary characteristic that has persisted among the hominoids for at least 24 million years.

Because the *Dryopithecus* fossil remains in Europe and the Far East are fragmentary, they reveal almost nothing about the skull and skeleton of this hominoid. Fortunately discoveries in Africa have altered the situation. There, thanks to the untiring efforts of L. S. B. Leakey and his colleagues, a substantial inventory of Miocene primate fossil remains has been accumulated, most of them from Rusinga Island in Lake Vic-

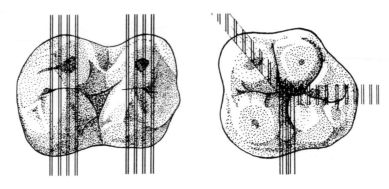

FIGURE 14–4—Shape of molar teeth serves to split the catarrhines into two groups. The crowns of Old World monkeys' molars have a cusp at each corner (baboon, left): both front and rear pairs of cusps are connected by ridges. The crowns of apes' and man's lower molars normally have five cusps (chimpanzee, right), and the "valleys" between the cusps resemble the letter Y. This Y-5 pattern first appeared some 24 million years ago. (Adapted by Jacquelyn Hetrick.)

toria and the nearby shores of the lake. As a result several species of African proto-ape, apparently ranging from the size of a gibbon to that of a gorilla, have been described.

In spite of this variety in size, all these species are assigned to the single genus *Proconsul*. The name *Proconsul* is an "inside" British joke: the "pro" is simply "before" but "Consul" was the pet name of a chimpanzee that had long been a beloved resident of the London Zoo. All jokes apart, the name implies an evolutionary position for these African hominoids close to the ancestry of living chimpanzees and quite possibly to the ancestry of gorillas as well.

Among the *Proconsul* species the fossil remains that are most nearly complete belong to the gibbon-sized *Proconsul africanus*. They include parts of two skulls—almost complete in the facial portions—and some limb bones, including parts of a foot and a forelimb with a hand. The picture that emerges from the study of this material is that of an advanced catarrhine, showing some monkey-like traits of hand, skull, and brain but hominoid and even partially hominid characteristics of face, jaws, and dentition. The foot and forelimb are also more suggestive of some ape-like adaptations—including an incipient ability to swing by the arms from tree branch to tree branch—than they are of either arboreal or ground-dwelling Old World monkeys.

Recent taxonomic investigations show that species of the genus *Proconsul*, with their relative abundance of skeletal remains, should almost certainly be lumped together with the genus *Dryopithecus*. What such an assignment would mean, in effect, is that all these Miocene-Pliocene hominoids—not only Eurasian but African as well—belong to a single cosmopolitan genus. This might have been recognized 30 years ago except for a series of mischances. A. T. Hopwood of the British Museum (Natural History), who named *Proconsul* in 1933, stated that the lower jaws and teeth of *Proconsul* and *Dryopithecus* could not be distinguished as belonging to separate genera. He found the opposite to be true of the upper teeth, but it happens that the particular specimen of *Dryopithecus* upper teeth he chose for comparison was not of that genus at all: it belonged to another primate, *Ramapithecus*. When W. E. Le Gros Clark of the University of Oxford and Leakey later enlarged the definition of *Proconsul*, they still drew the primary upper-dental distinctions from the same specimen, which was not recognized as *Ramapithecus* until 1963. *Proconsul* and *Ramapithecus* are not the same genus. *Proconsul* and *Dryopithecus*, in all probability, are.

THE PUZZLE OF THE COAL MAN

In any listing of the more complete early primates the Italian species *Oreopithecus bambolii*, sometimes irreverently known as the Abominable Coal Man, cannot be omitted. Its first bits and pieces were discovered almost 100 years ago. Since then *Oreopithecus* remains have been found in abundance in the brown-coal beds of central Italy, a formation that is variously assigned to late Miocene or early Pliocene times. In 1956 Johannes Hürzeler of the natural history museum in Basel assembled a number of new *Oreopithecus* specimens, and in 1958 Hürzeler was instrumental in the recovery of a nearly complete skeleton from a coal mine at Grosseto in Italy. This superb fossil is still being examined by specialists from various nations.

Evidently these Miocene-Pliocene primates were of substantial size— some four feet tall and probably weighing more than 80 pounds. Among the living primates the closest in size would be a female chimpanzee. Because its face is short and flat instead of showing an elongated snout, and because studies of its pelvis and limb bones suggest the possibility of an erect walking posture, *Oreopithecus* has received some notoriety as a possible direct precursor of the hominid family. Intensive study of the 1958 specimen, however, has led a number of workers to rather different conclusions.

One of the surprising things about *Oreopithecus* was first noted by Gregory in the 1920's: the cheek teeth of its lower jaw strongly resemble the corresponding teeth of *Apidium*, one of the four primates named from the original Fayum finds of the early 1900's. The surprise is that

Apidium dates to the Oligocene, some 20 to 25 million years earlier than *Oreopithecus*. This remarkable dental coincidence might easily have remained no more than a curiosity if the Yale Expedition had not recovered a number of additional *Apidium* teeth—this time the cheek teeth from upper jaws. The study of these teeth is not yet complete, but it is already evident that the newfound *Apidium* uppers correspond as well to the equivalent *Oreopithecus* uppers as the lowers do to the lowers. Such a similarity strongly suggests that, in spite of their separation in time, the ancient *Apidium* and the comparatively modern *Oreopithecus* are representatives of a single group of now extinct Old World higher primates. *Apidium* cannot be directly ancestral to *Oreopithecus*, however, because it lacks one pair of incisors that are still present in *Oreopithecus*. Although in the evolutionary sense this group is not far removed from the pongid-hominid stem, it seems to have developed its own distinctive characteristics by early Oligocene times.

A DRYOPITHECINE FROM INDIA

Having come to the end of Miocene times, with a scant 12 million to 14 million years remaining in which to discover a human forebear, we must re-examine Gregory's declaration. One of his candidates, *Dryopithecus*, has now been shown to be a long-lived and cosmopolitan genus, one of an abundant dryopithecine group to which in all probability the African species of *Proconsul* belong. What about *Sivapithecus*, Gregory's other nominee for a position as a hominid ancestor?

The Siwalik Hills of northwestern India and adjacent Pakistan have been known to paleontologists since the first half of the 19th century for their fossil-rich deposits of Miocene and Pliocene age. It was from these strata that Pilgrim, who described the Burmese borderline primate *Pondaungia*, uncovered and named *Sivapithecus* in 1910. Later, in the 1930's, G. Edward Lewis collected fossils for the Yale-Cambridge North India Expedition from these same beds and discovered a number of primate jaw fragments and teeth. In due course they were assigned to several separate primate genera, including some additional examples of Pilgrim's *Sivapithecus*.

Recent re-examination of *Sivapithecus* species suggests that they are not markedly different from *Dryopithecus*. Like *Proconsul*, they may well deserve nothing more than subgeneric status among the cosmopolitan dryopithecines. This would mean that not only Africa and Eurasia but also India supported separate populations of a single hominoid genus during Miocene and the earliest of Pliocene times—a span of at least 15 million years. However confused and confusing dryopithecine taxonomy and evolutionary relations are at present, the inescapable fact remains that throughout this entire span of time this is the only group of primates known in any Old World continent that can be considered close to the source of the hominid family line.

Because of the dryopithecines' very broad distribution throughout the Old World, the precise time and location of the primates' evolutionary advance from hominoid animals to specifically hominid ones may always remain uncertain. Yet a tentative guess is possible.

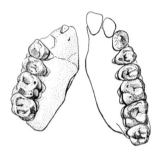 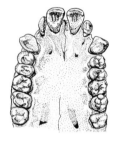 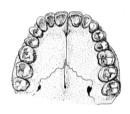

FIGURE 14–5—Upper jaw of *Ramapithecus,* in a comparative reconstruction at left, is compared with that of an orangutan (center) and a man (right). In each comparison the jaws have been made the same size. The U-shaped arc formed by the ape's teeth contrasts sharply with the curved arc in *Ramapithecus,* which is closer to the human curve. This, as well as the manlike ratio in comparative size of front and cheek teeth and the modest canine, are grounds for considering *Ramapithecus* man's earliest known hominid ancestor. (Adapted by Jacquelyn Hetrick.)

Another of the fossil primates Lewis collected in the Siwalik Hills was *Ramapithecus.* The type species of *Ramapithecus* is founded on a portion of a right upper jaw and is named *Ramapithecus brevirostris.* The fossil includes the first two molars, both premolars, the socket of the canine tooth, the root of the lateral incisor and the socket of the central incisor. When it and other fossils of *Ramapithecus* are used to reconstruct an entire upper jaw, complete with palate, the result is surprisingly human in appearance. [See Fig. 14–5.] The proportions of the jaw indicate a foreshortened face. The size ratio between front teeth and cheek teeth is about the same as it is in man. (The front teeth of living apes are relatively large.) Estimating from the size of its socket, the canine tooth was not much larger than the first premolar—another hominid characteristic, opposed to the enlarged canines of the pongids. The arc formed by the teeth is curved as in man, rather than being parabolic, or U-shaped, as in the apes.

FROM RELATIVE TO ANCESTOR

Just such traits as these, intermediate between the dryopithecines and hominids, had led Lewis in 1934 to suggest that *Ramapithecus* might well belong to the Hominidae. This suggestion was challenged in the years immediately following. In my opinion, however, both the re-examination of the type species and the identification of new material reinforce Lewis' original conclusion. Taxonomic decisions of this sort are not made lightly, and to draw a large conclusion from limited fossil evidence is always uncomfortable. Thus it was particularly gratifying to learn of Leakey's recovery, in 1962, of the jaws of a similar hominid near Fort Ternan in southwestern Kenya.

Leakey has assigned this fossil to the species *Kenyapithecus wickeri*. Like the remains of Lewis' *Ramapithecus brevirostris,* it preserves much of the upper dentition. Included are the first two molars on both sides, an intact second premolar and the stub of a first premolar. The socket for one canine is intact; a canine tooth and a central incisor were found separately. Potassium-argon dating of the specimen yields an absolute age of about 14 million years, a time near the boundary between the Miocene and the Pliocene.

The significance of the Fort Ternan find lies in the fact that *Kenyapithecus* not only has an abundance of close anatomical links with *Ramapithecus* but also exhibits no pertinent differences. In this new specimen, a continent removed in space from *Ramapithecus,* are found the same foreshortened face, dental curve and small canine tooth—each a hominid trait. The conclusion is now almost inescapable: in late Miocene to early Pliocene times both in Africa and India an advanced hominoid species was differentiating from more conservative pongid stock and developing important hominid characteristics in the process. Pending additional discoveries it may be wiser not to insist that the transition from ape to man is now being documented from the fossil record, but this certainly seems to be a strong possibility.

15

THE TAXONOMIC
EVALUATION
OF FOSSIL HOMINIDS

Ernst Mayr

*Zoologists have often criticized the cavalier manner in which
paleoanthropologists have named and renamed human fossils
without regard to the principles of zoological nomenclature. They
object to the stress anthropologists have placed on minor
differences in classifying fossils and in building genera and
species of fossil man. Population geneticists have leveled their
barbs at the ways in which anthropologists have disregarded
population models in making classifications. It has been claimed
that attempts have been made to construct relationships without
taking into consideration either variation within populations or
the polymorphic and polytypic character of most human
populations.*

*Ernst Mayr is a zoologist who has specialized in the evolution of
birds. Like many other zoologists in recent years, he has begun
applying his experience to problems of human evolution and
fossil classification. In this article, he suggests a taxonomy for
fossil hominids that is more in line with zoological thinking about
classification.*

INTRODUCTION

The concepts and methods on which the classification of hominid taxa
is based do not differ in principle from those used for other zoological
taxa. Indeed, the classification of living human populations or of samples

(From *Classification and Human Evolution*, Sherwood L. Washburn, editor,
pages 332–345. Copyright © 1963 by Wenner-Gren Foundation for Anthropological Research, Inc. First published 1963 by Aldine Publishing Company, 64 East Van Buren Street, Chicago 5, Illinois. By permission of the
author and the publisher.)

of fossil hominids is a branch of animal taxonomy. It can only lead to confusion if different standards and terminologies are adopted in the two fields. The reasons for the adoption of a single, uniform language for both fields, and the nature of this language, have been excellently stated by G. G. Simpson [in the symposium *Classification and Human Evolution*]. . . .

There is, perhaps, one practical difference between animal and hominid taxonomy. Hominid remains are of such significance that even rather incomplete specimens may be of vital importance. An attempt must sometimes be made to evaluate fragments that a student of dinosaurs or fossil bovids would simply ignore. But, of course, even a rather complete specimen is only a very inadequate representation of the population to which it belongs, and most specimens are separated by large intervals of space and time. Yet, it is the task of the taxonomist to derive from these specimens an internally consistent classification.

The non-taxonomist must be fully aware of two aspects of such a classification: first, that it is usually by no means the only possible classification to be based on the available evidence, so that a taxonomist with a different viewpoint might arrive at a different classification; and second, that every classification based on inadequate material is provisional. A single new discovery may change the picture rather drastically and lead to a considerable revision.

The material of taxonomy consists of zoological objects. These objects are individuals or parts of individuals who, in nature, were members of populations. Our ultimate objective, then, is the classification of populations as represented by the available samples.

OBJECTS VERSUS POPULATIONS

The statement that we must classify populations rather than objects sounds almost like a platitude. . . . Yet, it is not so many years ago that the study of fossil man was in the hands of strict morphologists who arranged specimens in morphological series and based their classification almost entirely on an interpretation of similarities and differences without regard to any other factor. He who classifies specimens as representatives of populations knows that populations have a concrete distribution in space and time and that this provides a source of information that is not available to the strict morphologist. Any classification that is inconsistent with the known distribution of populations is of lowered validity.

THE APPLICATION OF TAXONOMIC PRINCIPLES IN CONCRETE CASES

There have been several previous attempts to apply the principles of systematic zoology to some of the open problems of hominid classification. A great deal of new evidence has since accumulated and there has been some further clarification of our concepts. The time would seem proper for a new look at some of these problems.

SUBSPECIES OR SPECIES

The decision whether to rank a given taxon in the category "subspecies" or in the category "species" is often exceedingly difficult in the absence of conclusive evidence. This is as true in the classification of living populations (geographical isolates) as it is for fossils. A typical example as far as the hominids are concerned is the ranking of Neanderthal Man. I have found three interpretations of Neanderthal in the literature.

(1) "Neanderthal Man is a more primitive ancestral stage through which *sapiens* has passed." This we might call the classical hypothesis, defended particularly during the period when the interpretation of human evolution was based primarily on the evaluation of morphological series. This classical hypothesis had to be abandoned when it was found to be in conflict with the distribution of classical and primitive Neanderthals and of *sapiens* in space and time.

(2) "Neanderthal is an aberrant separate species, a contemporary of early *sapiens* but reproductively isolated from him."

(3) "Neanderthal is a subspecies, a geographic race, of early *sapiens*."

What evidence is there that would permit us to come to a decision as to the relative merits of alternatives (2) and (3)? We must begin by defining rigidly what a species is and what a subspecies [is]. As clearly stated by Simpson and Mayr, degree of morphological difference per se is not a decisive primary criterion. A species is reproductively isolated from other species coexisting in time and space, while a subspecies is a geographic subdivision of a species actually or potentially (in the case of geographical isolates) in gene exchange with other similar subdivisions of the species.

The difficulty in applying these concepts to fossil material is obvious.

It can be established only by inference whether two fossil taxa formed a single reproductive community or two reproductively isolated ones. In order to draw the correct inference, we must ask certain questions:

Does the distribution of Neanderthal and *sapiens* indicate that they were reproductively isolated? Not so many years ago Neanderthal was considered by many as a Würm "eskimo," but he is now known to have had an enormous distribution, extending south as far as Gibraltar and North Africa and east as far as Iran and Turkestan. There is no evidence (but see below) that Neanderthal coexisted with *sapiens* anywhere in this wide area. Where did *sapiens* live during the Riss-Würm Interglacial and during the first Würm stadial? No one knows. Ethiopia, India and southeast Asia have been suggested, but these will remain wild guesses until some properly dated new finds are made. All we know is that at the time of the first Würm interstadial Cro-Magnon Man suddenly appeared in Europe and overran it in a relatively short time.

THE SAPIENS PROBLEM

There has been much talk in the past of the "Neanderthal problem." Now, since the average morphological differences between the classical Neanderthal of the first Würm stadial and the earlier Neanderthals of the Riss-Würm Interglacial have been worked out, and since the distribution of Neanderthal has been mapped, *sapiens sapiens* has become the real problem. Where did he originate and how long did it take for pre-*sapiens* to change into *sapiens*? Where did this change occur?

All we really know is that *s. sapiens*, as Cro-Magnon, suddenly appeared in Europe. Sufficient remains from the preceding period of unmixed Neanderthal in Europe and adjacent parts of Africa and Asia (and a complete absence of any blade culture) prove conclusively that *s. sapiens* did not originate in Europe. The rather wide distribution of types with a strong supraorbital torus (e.g., Rhodesia, Solo-Java) suggests that *s. sapiens* must have originated in a localized area. The sharpness of distinction between Neanderthal and *s. sapiens* (except at Mt. Carmel) further indicates that Neanderthal, as a whole, did not gradually change into *sapiens*, but was replaced by an invader.

There is a suspicion that evolutionary change can occur the faster (up to certain limits), the smaller and more isolated the evolving population is. If *s. sapiens* lost his supraorbital torus very quickly (and the various other characters it has before becoming *sapiens*) then it can be postulated with a good deal of assurance that *sapiens* evolved in a rather small, peripheral, and presumably well isolated population. Even if we assume that the rate of change was slow and the evolving population large, we must still assume that *sapiens* was rather isolated. Otherwise, one would expect to find more evidence for intergradation with late Neanderthal.

It is obvious that the available evidence is meager. Let us assume, however, for the sake of the argument, that Neanderthal and *sapiens* were strictly allopatric, that is, that they replaced each other geographically. Zoologists have interpreted allopatry in the past usually as evidence for conspecificity, because subspecies are always allopatric. We are now a little more cautious because we have discovered in recent years a number of cases where closely related species are allopatric because competitive intolerance seems to preclude their geographical coexistence. The rapidity with which Neanderthal disappeared at the time Cro-Magnon Man appeared on the scene would seem to strengthen the claim for competitive intolerance and consequently for species status of these two entities. Yet, here is clearly a case where it is perhaps not legitimate to apply zoological generalizations to man. The Australian Aborigines and most of the North American Indians disappeared equally or perhaps even more rapidly, and yet no one except for a few racists would consider them different species.

We are thus forced to fall back on the two time-honored criteria of species status, degree of morphological difference and presence or absence of interbreeding. Our inference on the taxonomic ranking of Neanderthal will be based largely on these two sets of criteria, supplemented by a third, available only for man.

1. Degree of Morphological Difference

The amount of difference between the skulls of Neanderthal and *sapiens* is most impressive. There are no two races of modern man that are nearly as different as classical Neanderthal and *sapiens*. And yet one has a feeling that the differences are mostly of a rather superficial nature, such as the size of the supraorbital and occipital torus and the general shape of the skull. The cranial capacity, on the other hand, is remarkably similar in the two forms. The gap between Neanderthal and *sapiens* is to some extent bridged by two populations, Rhodesian Man and Solo Man, which are widely separated geographically from Neanderthal. Although sharing the large supraorbital torus with Neanderthal, these two other populations differ in many details of skull shape and cranial capacity from Neanderthal as well as from *s. sapiens*. Whether or not these peripheral African and Asiatic types acquired their Neanderthaloid features independently, can be established only after a far more thorough study and the investigation of additional material. It seems quite improbable that they are directly related to Neanderthal. In view of their small cranial capacity they may have to be classified with *H. erectus*.

As it now stands, one must admit that the inference to be drawn from the degree of morphological difference between Neanderthal and *sapiens* is inconclusive.

2. INTERBREEDING BETWEEN NEANDERTHAL AND *Sapiens*

Cro-Magnon Man, on his arrival in western Europe, seems to have been remarkably free from admixture with the immediately preceding Neanderthal. There is, however, some evidence of mixture in the material from the two caves of Mt. Carmel in Palestine. Both caves were inhabited early in the Würm glaciation. The older cave (Tabun) was inhabited by almost typical Neanderthals with a slight admixture of modern characters, the younger cave (Skhul) by an essentially *sapiens* population but with distinct Neanderthaloid characters. The date is too late to consider these populations to have belonged to the ancestral stock that gave rise both to Neanderthal and modern man. It seems to me that the differences between Tabun and Skhul are too great to permit us to consider them as samples from a single population coming from the area of geographical intergradation between Neanderthal and modern man, although this could be true for the Skhul population. Hybridization between invading Cro-Magnon Man and Neanderthal remnants is perhaps a more plausible interpretation for the Skhul population, while there is no good reason not to consider Tabun essentially an eastern Neanderthal, particularly in view of its similarity to the Shanidar specimens.

Repeated re-examinations of the Mt. Carmel material have thus substantiated the long-standing claims that this material is evidence for interbreeding between Neanderthal and *sapiens*.

3. THE CULTURAL EVIDENCE

As our knowledge of human and hominid artifacts increases, it becomes necessary to include this source of evidence in our considerations. My own personal knowledge of this field is exceedingly slight, but when I look at the implements assigned to Neanderthal and those assigned to Cro-Magnon, I feel the differences are so small that I can not make myself believe they were produced by two different biological species. I realize that the history of human or hominid artifacts goes back much further than we used to think, yet this is not in conflict with my hunch that there was no opportunity for the simultaneous existence of two separate hominid species of advanced tool-makers.

I would like to add some incidental comments on tools and human evolution. The history of peoples and tribes is full of incidences of a secondary cultural deterioration, *vide* the Mayas and their modern descendants! Most of the modern native populations with rudimentary material cultures (e.g., certain New Guinea mountain natives) are almost surely the descendants of culturally more advanced ancestors. This must be kept in mind when paleolithic cultures from Africa and western Eurasia are compared with those of southern and eastern Asia. Stone tools and the hunting of large mammals seem to be closely correlated. Could such peoples have lost their tool cultures after they had emigrated into areas poor in large game? Could this be the reason for the absence of stone tools in Javan *Homo erectus*?

Conclusion. The facts that are so far available do not permit a clear-cut decision on the question whether Neanderthal was a subspecies or a separate species. It seems to me, however, that on the whole they are in better agreement with the subspecies hypothesis. It would seem best for the time being to postulate that Neanderthal (*sensu stricto*) was a northern and western subspecies of *Homo sapiens* (*sensu lato*), which was an incipient species but probably never reached species level prior to its extinction.

POLYTYPIC SPECIES AND EVOLUTION

All attempts to trace hominid phylogeny still deal with typological models. "*Australopithecus* gave rise to *Homo erectus*," etc. In reality there were widespread polytypic species with more advanced and more conservative races. One or several of the advanced races gave rise to the next higher grade. It may happen in such a case that the descendant species lives simultaneously (but allopatrically) with the more conservative races of the ancestral species. This is often interpreted to indicate that the ancestral species could not have given rise to the descendant species. *True,* as far as the ancestral species in a typological sense is concerned, but *not* true for the ancestral species as a polytypic whole.

The concept of most polytypic species being descendants of ancestral polytypic species creates at once two formidable difficulties. One of these is caused by unequal rates of evolution of the different races. Let us say that there was an ancestral species 1 with races 1a, 1b, 1c and 1d. Race 1a evolved into species 2, absorbing in the process much of race 1b, and now forms races 2a and 2b. Race 1c became extinct and race 1d persisted in a relic area without changing very drastically. We now have 2 (a and b) and 1 (d) existing at the same time level, even though they represent different evolutionary stages (morphological grades). It is thinkable, for instance, that Heidelberg Man was the first population of *Homo erectus* to reach the *sapiens* level, and that as *Homo sapiens heidelbergensis* it was contemporary with *Homo erectus* of Java and China. (This is purely a thought model, as long as only a single mandible of Heidelberg Man is available.) It is possible that *Homo erectus* persisted in Africa as *rhodesiensis* and in Java as *soloensis* at a time when European populations clearly had reached *Homo sapiens* level. Such a possibility is by no means remote, in view of the many polytypic species of recent animals in which some races are highly advanced and others very primitive.

I am calling attention to this situation to prevent too far a swing of the pendulum. The late Weidenreich arranged fossil hominids into morphological series strictly on the basis of morphology without regard to distribution in space and time (*e.g.*, Neanderthal—Steinheim—*H. sapiens*). Some modern authors tend to swing to the other extreme by classifying fossil hominids entirely on the basis of geological dating without paying any attention to morphology. The unequal rates of evolutionary change in widely dispersed and partially isolated races of polytypic species make it, however, necessary to take morphology and distribution equally into consideration. Even though *Homo sapiens* unquestionably descended from *Homo erectus,* it is quite possible, indeed probable, that some races of *Homo erectus* still persisted when other parts of the earth were already populated by *Homo sapiens.*

The same argument is even more true for genera. The fact that *Homo* and *Australopithecus* have been found to be contemporaries does not in the least invalidate the generally accepted assumption that *Homo* passed through an *Australopithecus* stage. The Australopithecines consisted of several species (or genera, if we recognize the generic distinction of *Paranthropus*) and each of these species, in turn, was polytypic. Only a segment of this assemblage gave rise to *Homo.* Much of the remainder persisted contemporaneously with *Homo,* for a longer or shorter period, without rising above the Australopithecine grade. The modern concepts of taxonomy and speciation do not require an archetypal transformation (*in toto*) of *Australopithecus* into *Homo.*

The second great difficulty caused by the evolution of polytypic species is a consequence of the first one. It is the difficulty to determine what part (which races) of the ancestral species has contributed to the gene pool of the descendant species. This in turn depends on the amount of gene flow between the races of the ancestral species while it passed from the level of species 1 to the level of species 2. The amount of gene flow is determined by the nature of the interaction between populations in zones of contact. Unfortunately, the situation in the near-human hominids (*Homo erectus* level) was probably different from both the anthropoid condition and the condition in modern man. A number of possibilities are evident in an area of contact between races:

(1) Avoidance
(2) Extermination of one by the other
(3) Killing of the men and absorption of the women
(4) Free interbreeding

There is much evidence that all four processes have occurred and it becomes necessary to determine their relative importance in individual cases. The Congo pygmies, the bushmen, and various negritoid pygmies in the eastern tropics illustrate avoidance by retreating into inferior environments. The Tasmanians and some Indian tribes illustrate extermination. The white invaders in North America and Australia absorbed extremely few genes of the native peoples. The frequently made assertion that invaders kill off the men and take the women is often contradicted by the facts. The sharpness of the difference between classical western European Neanderthal and invading Cro-Magnon indicates to me that Cro-Magnon did not absorb many Neanderthal genes (some contrary opinions notwithstanding). Language and cultural differences must have militated at the *Homo erectus* level against too active a gene exchange between different races. The distinctness of the negro, mongoloid, and caucasian races supports this assumption. Gene flow obviously occurred, but against considerable obstacles.

SYMPATRIC SPECIES OF HOMINIDS

When one reads the older anthropological literature with its rich proliferation of generic names, one has the impression of large numbers of species of fossil man and other hominids coexisting with each other. When these finds were properly placed into a multi-dimensional framework of space and time, the extreme rarity of the coexistence of two hominids became at once apparent. We have already discussed the case of Neanderthal and *sapiens,* but there are others in the Middle and early Pleistocene.

At the *Homo erectus* level, we have Java Man and Pekin Man, originally described as two different genera, but so strikingly similar that most current authors agree in treating them as subspecies. Ternifine Man in North Africa may be another representative of this same polytypic species. The existing material is, however, rather fragmentary. A further contemporary is Heidelberg Man, whose massive mandible contains teeth that appear smaller and more ''modern'' than those of a typical *erectus.* Was this a second species or merely a deviant peripheral isolate? This can only be settled by additional discoveries.

In Africa we find incontrovertible evidence of contemporaneity of several species of hominids. *Australopithecus* and *Paranthropus* apparently differed considerably in their adaptations. Perhaps this is the reason why they are not found together in most South African deposits. Yet the degree of difference between them and the time span of their occurrence leaves no doubt that they must have been contemporaries. Here, then, we have a clear case of the contemporaneity of two species of hominids. The fragments of the small hominid (*Telanthropus*) found at Swartkrans with *A. robustus,* which may belong to an Australopithecine or *Homo,* supply additional proof for the coexistence of two hominids in South Africa. In Java, in the Djetis layers, there is also the possibility of the coexistence of two hominids, "*Meganthropus*" and *Homo erectus.*

By far the most exciting instance of the coexistence of two hominids is that established by Leakey in East Africa. In layer 1 of Olduvai "*Zinjanthropus,*" an unmistakable Australopithecine of the *Paranthropus* type, is associated with remains of an advanced hominid, "co-Zinjanthropus," that—when better known—may well turn out to be closer to *Homo* than to *Australopithecus.* Whether the tools of this layer were made by both hominids or only the more advanced, can be determined only when the two types are found unassociated at other sites. This will also influence the decision on the identity of the maker of the Sterkfontein tools in South Africa.

The picture that emerges from all these new discoveries is that only one species of hominids seems to have been in existence during the Upper Pleistocene, but that there is much evidence from the Middle and Lower Pleistocene of several independent lines. Some of these gave rise to descendant types, others became extinct. The coexisting types were, so far as known, rather distinct from each other. This is what one would expect on the basis of *a priori* ecological considerations. The principle of "competitive exclusion" would prevent sympatry if there were not considerable ecological divergence. *Australopithecus* and *Paranthropus,* or *Zinjanthropus* and the associated hominid, "co-Zinjanthropus," were able to coexist only because they utilized the resources of the environment differently. Whether one of them was more of a hunter, the other more of a gatherer (or hunted), whether one was more carnivorous, the other more of a vegetarian, whether one was more of a forest creature, the other a savanna inhabitant, all this still remains to be investigated, when better evidence becomes available.

It is important to emphasize that nothing helped more to make us aware of these problems and to assist in the reconstruction of evolutionary pathways than an improvement of the classification of fossil hominids both on the generic and on the specific levels. It is here that the application of principles of zoological taxonomy has been particularly fruitful. Indeed, the earlier morphologists never appreciated the biological significance of the problem of coexistence or replacement of closely related species.

GENERIC PROBLEMS

The category "genus" presents even greater difficulties than that of the species. There is no non-arbitrary yardstick available for the genus as reproductive isolation is for the species. The genus is normally a collective category, consisting of a group of species believed to be more closely related to each other than they are to other species. Yet, every large genus includes several groups of species that are more closely related to each other than to species of other species groups within the same genus. For instance, in the genus *Drosophila* the species belonging to the *virilis* group are more closely related to each other than to those belonging to the *repleta* group, yet both are included in *Drosophila*. They are not separated in different genera because the species groups have not yet reached the degree of evolutionary divergence usually associated with generic rank. As Simpson has pointed out, the genus usually has also a definite biological significance, indicating or signifying occupation of a somewhat different adaptive niche. Again, this is not an ironclad criterion because even every species occupies a somewhat different niche, and sometimes different genera may occupy the same adaptive zone.

It is particularly important to emphasize again and again that the function of the generic and the specific names in the scientific binomen are different. The specific name stresses the singularity of the species and its unique distinctness. The generic name emphasizes not a greater degree of difference but rather the belonging-together of the species included in the genus. To place every species in a separate genus, as was done by so many of the physical anthropologists of former generations, completely stultifies the advantages of binomial nomenclature. As Simpson has stated correctly . . . the recognition of a monotypic genus is justified only when a single isolated known species is so distinctive that there is a high probability that it belongs to a generic group with no other known ancestral, collateral or descendant species. The isolated nature of *bamboli,* the type species of *Oreopithecus,* justifies the recognition of this monotypic genus.

Of the literally scores of generic names proposed for fossil hominids, very few deserve recognition. More and more students admit, for instance, that the degree of difference between *Homo erectus* and *H. sapiens* is not sufficient to justify the recognition of *Pithecanthropus.*

There are a number of reasons why it would seem unwise to recognize the genus *Pithecanthropus* in formal taxonomy. First of all, *Homo* would then become a monotypic genus and *Pithecanthropus* contain at most two or three species. This is contrary to the concept of the genus as a collective category. More importantly, the name *Pithecanthropus* was first applied to an actual fossil hominid when only a skull cap was known and the reconstruction envisioned a far more anthropoid creature than *erectus* really is. When the teeth and other body parts were discovered (or accepted, like the femur) it was realized that the total difference between *erectus* and *sapiens* was really rather small and certainly less than is normally required for the recognition of a zoological genus. The recognition of *Pithecanthropus* as a genus would lead to an undesirable heterogeneity of the genus category.

The genus *Australopithecus* has already many of the essential characters of *Homo*, such as a largely upright posture, bicuspid premolars, and reduced canines. For this reason I suggested previously that "not even *Australopithecus* has unequivocal claims for generic separation." I now agree with those authors who have since pointed out not only that the upright locomotion was still incomplete and inefficient, but also that the tremendous evolution of the brain since *Australopithecus* permitted man to enter a new niche so completely different that generic separation is fully justified. The extraordinary brain evolution between *Australopithecus* and *Homo* justifies the generic separation of these two taxa, no matter how similar they might be in many other morphological characters. Here, as in other cases, it is important not merely to count characters but to weight them.

Whether or not one wants to recognize only a single genus for all the known Australopithecines or admit a second genus, *Paranthropus*, is largely a matter of taste. The species (*robustus*) found at Swartkrans and Kromdraai is larger and seems to have more pronounced sexual dimorphism than *A. africanus*. Incisors and canines are relatively small, while the molars are very large and there are pronounced bony crests on the skull, particularly in adult males. These differences are no greater than among species in other groups of mammals. *Zinjanthropus* in East Africa seems to belong to the more massive *Paranthropus* group. The two Australopithecines (*africanus* and *robustus*) seem to represent the same "grade" as far as brain evolution is concerned, but the differences in their dental equipment and facial muscles indicate that they may have occupied different food niches. It may well depend on future finds whether or not we want to recognize *Paranthropus*. The more genuinely different genera of hominids are discovered, the more important it may become to emphasize the close relationship of *Australopithecus* and *Paranthropus* by combining them in a single genus. It depends in each case to what extent one wants to stress relationships. We have a similar situation among the pongids. I have pointed out earlier that gorilla and chimpanzee seem to me so much nearer to each other than either is to man or to the orang or to the gibbons, that degree of relationship would seem to be expressed better if the gorilla were included in the genus *Pan* rather than to be recognized as a separate genus. The decision on generic status is as always based on somewhat arbitrary and subjective criteria. One cannot prove that gorilla and chimpanzee belong to the same genus, but neither can one prove that they belong to different genera.

DIAGNOSTIC CHARACTERS

The collective nature of the categories above the species level show clearly why it is often so difficult to provide an unequivocal diagnosis for taxa belonging to the higher categories. Those who think that "the characters make the genus" have little difficulty in characterizing differences between species and calling them generic differences. It is much easier to characterize the species "chimpanzee" and the species "gorilla" than to find diagnostic characters that clearly distinguish the chimpanzee-gorilla group from man, the orang and the gibbons. Higher categories often can be diagnosed only by a combination of characters, not by a single diagnostic character. The definition of the genus *Homo* presented in this volume is an example of such a combinational diagnosis.

The problem of the relation between taxonomic ranking and diagnostic characters will become increasingly acute as new Pliocene and Miocene fossils are found. Nothing would be more short-sighted than to base the classification of such finds on isolated "diagnostic" characters. We must ask ourselves each time whether relationship will be expressed better by including such new taxa in previously established ones, or by separating them as new taxa. If we combine them with previously established taxa, that is, if we include them in previously recognized genera, subfamilies, or families, we may have to modify the diagnosis of such taxa. We must always remember that the categories above the species are collective categories and subjectively delimited. The pronouncement made by Linnaeus, "It is the genus that gives the characters, and not the characters that make the genus," is true not only for the genus but for the categories at the family level. Diagnostic characters are a convenient tool of the working taxonomist, [and] should never become a strait jacket.

NOMENCLATURE AND COMMUNICATION

Superimposed on all the taxonomic difficulties are some purely nomenclatural ones. Simpson . . . has already pointed out that it is altogether inadmissible to change a scientific name because it is considered inappropriate. A scientific name is, so to speak, merely a formula and its etymological meaning is quite irrelevant. What is important is to avoid arbitrary changes, because the words of a language lose all usefulness if they are shifted around or replaced by new ones. If an anthropologist wants to play around with names, let him concentrate on the vernacular names. No one will care whether he talks of Heidelberg Man or Man of Mauer, or of Pekin Man rather than Man of Choukoutien.

As soon as an anthropologist employs zoological nomenclature that has very definite rules, he must obey these rules. In particular, I would like to call the attention of anthropologists to Article 35b of the Rules of Zoological Nomenclature, which states that the names of families and subfamilies must be based on the name of an included genus. Since there is no genus Euhomo, there can be no family name Euhominidae. If a subfamily is recognized for the Australopithecines, it can only be Australopithecinae. Not only is this system the only valid one, but it also has the advantage of being simple and unambiguous. I should hope that such confusing terms as Praehominidae would soon disappear from the literature.

Those who gives names to fossil Hominidae might also be more careful in the choice of specific names. To have several *africanus* and *robustus* in this family is confusing, particularly during this period of rearranging of genera. It would not seem an impossible demand that only such new specific names be given that had not been given previously to other species in the family Hominidae.

THE CLASSIFICATION OF
THE MISSING LINK

Nothing characterized the early study of human evolution as much as the search for the missing link. When one looks at early reconstructions of the missing link, one realizes how strongly the concept was dominated by the ancient idea of the *scala naturae*. If evolution were limited to a single lineage, as thought for instance by Lamarck, the missing link would simply be the halfway stage between the anthropoids and man. Now as we realize that there is no single line of descent but a richly branching phylogenetic tree, the search for the missing link has become somewhat illusory. It is now evident that there is not just one missing link but a whole series of missing links. There is first the species which was at the branching point between the Pongidae and the Hominidae. On the hominid branch there were those species that first acquired such essentially human traits as making tools, making fire, and possessing speech. There is the first species to be referred to the genus *Homo,* and there is the species that acquired a brain capacity about halfway between the anthropoids and modern man. We may already have representatives satisfying most of these qualifications, and rather than searching for *the* missing link we are now beginning to classify kinds of missing links.

It is now clear that we must distinguish between two essential phenomena. There is on one hand the phylogenetic branching of the hominid line from the pongid line. Yet even after this branching had taken place, which presumably was sometime during the Miocene, there was no sign of Man on the new hominid line. The hominids throughout the Miocene and Pliocene were still apes, and even the Australopithecines of the early Middle Pleistocene can hardly be classified as human. It does appear that *Homo erectus* qualifies better as representative of the stage between prehuman hominids and Man than any other form. It is almost certainly the stage at which the hominids became Man.

THE HIGHER CATEGORIES

The Pleistocene hominids present no problem at the family level. They all clearly belong to the Hominidae. Whether or not to separate the Australopithecines in a subfamily Australopithecinae is essentially a matter of taste. Matters are more difficult when it comes to Pliocene and Miocene fossils. Not only are most of them known from insufficient fragments, but the criteria on which to base the decision pongid or hominid become increasingly elusive as we go back in time. Furthermore, there is considerable probability of the existence of additional equivalent branches of anthropoids or near-anthropoids which have since become extinct. *Oreopithecus* seems to represent such a branch.

The evidence concerning the branching-off point of the hominid from the pongid line seems on first sight contradictory. Schultz finds that all the great apes agree with each other in very numerous characters of general morphology, in which they differ from Man. Yet, the African apes (*Pan* sensu lato) are closer to Man than to orang or gibbon in hemoglobin structure, in serum proteins and in chromosomal morphology. What can be the explanation of this apparent conflict in the evidence? Perhaps the simplest interpretation would be to assume that Man's shift into the niche of the bipedal, tool-making, and speech-using hominid necessitated a drastic reconstruction of his morphology, but that this reconstruction did not, in turn, require a complete revamping of his biochemical system. Different characters and character complexes thus diverged at very different rates. If one assumes this to be correct, one will conclude that the *Homo*-line branched from the *Pan*-line well after the line of their common ancestor had separated from the orang (*Pongo*)-line.

Full awareness of mosaic evolution is particularly important for the correct placing of early hominid fossils. As Le Gros Clark and I have emphasized, the Hominidae are a classical example of mosaic evolution. Every character or set of characters evolved at a different rate. Even *Australopithecus* is still essentially anthropoid in some character while having considerably advanced toward the hominid condition in other characters, for instance with respect to upright posture and the general shape of the tooth row. We must furthermore be aware of the fact that evolution is not necessarily irreversible and that temporary specializations may secondarily be lost again. The Pliocene forms *Ramapithecus* from India and *Kenyapithecus* from Africa may well belong to the hominid line. Even more difficult is the allocation of Miocene genera. To place them correctly one may have to use "prophetic characters" (a preevolutionary term of Agassiz), that is, characters which foreshadow future evolutionary trends. It is quite certain that the Miocene hominoids lacked some of the characteristic specializations of both the pongid and the hominid lines. They were not the extreme brachiators that some of the modern pongids are, nor had they reached the completness of upright posture and the special features of dentition of the later hominids. Such seemingly irrelevant characters as the shape of tooth cusps may be more revealing in such forms than the relative size of the canines or the development of a simian shelf. The recent arguments about *Oreopithecus* show how difficult it is to reach an objective evaluation of the evidence.

CONCLUSIONS

Fossil hominids are samples of formerly existing populations distributed in space and time. Their classification must be consistent with the generalizations derived from the study of polytypic species in animals. Whenever the anthropologist uses the terminology of subspecies, species, and genera, such terminology must be consistent with the meaning of these categories as developed in modern systematics. Application of the principles of systematics has helped to clarify the formerly bewildering diversity of morphological types. Pleistocene hominids display much geographic variation, but the number of full species coexisting at any one time is not known to have exceeded two. The relatively wide distribution of some of the fossil hominids indicates that there has been a considerable amount of gene flow as early as the lowest Middle Pleistocene.

16

SKILL
AS A HUMAN POSSESSION

Kenneth P. Oakley

In the following article, Kenneth P. Oakley, an archeologist,
summarizes the relation between human structural evolution and
the evolution of tool-making. The fragmentary nature of the
fossil hominid record and the implications that can be drawn
from the discovery of stone tools at archeological sites are
synthesized into a picture of the way the human capacity for
tool-making and tool-using developed.

I. EVOLUTION OF SKILL
IN PRIMATES

To trace the origin and development of skilled behavior in man, it is
necessary to consider the history of the primates. The earliest were the
Prosimii. These evolved from tiny insectivores similar to those found in
Cretaceous rocks in Mongolia. By the middle Eocene, when sub-tropical
conditions were widespread, there were prosimians in almost all parts of
the world. In many ways they resembled their modern survivors, the tree-
shrews, lemurs, and tarsier. Like them, they probably lived mainly on
insects and fruit. In common with other primitive mammals they had
five movable digits on each limb. These were well adapted to climbing
trees and grasping branches. Among the more advanced types the first
digit acquired unusual mobility, so that it could be opposed to the others.
This both enhanced grasping power and facilitated the catching of small
insects and the plucking of fruits with the forelimbs. Thus the forelimbs

(From Kenneth P. Oakley, *History of Technology*, The Clarendon Press,
Oxford, 1957, Vol. 1, pages 6–13, 15–16, and 18–34. By permission of the
author and the publisher.)

began to assume many functions which in four-footed animals are usually performed by jaws and teeth. In other words, hands were being born out of habit.

Ground-dwelling mammals explore their environment and test the objects they encounter by smell; but as soon as any of them leave the ground and take to climbing, flying, or swimming other senses become more important. Being small and defenseless, the ancestors of the primates probably took to an arboreal life for security and for new sources of food. But life in the trees made its own demands; it put a premium on increased acuity of sight, touch, and hearing—particularly sight, which rapidly displaced smell as the master sense. Many early prosimians were probably, like the tarsier, nocturnal feeders: a habit dependent on special powers of vision.

In very primitive prosimians, the eyes are at the side of the head, divided by a snout. In due course the eyes shifted to a forward-facing position, so that both could be focused on the same near point; the brain thus perceived a stereoscopic picture, that is, one having depth and solidity. The spectral tarsier (*Tarsius*), surviving in the Indo-Malay archipelago, is a "living fossil" representing this stage in the evolution of the higher primates. Its eyes are enormous, and their field of vision is not divided by a snout.

Certain Eocene prosimians were ancestral to the higher primates (monkeys, apes, and men). They exhibited an increase in size, more particularly in brainsize. The portion of the brain associated with co-ordination of impressions of the senses other than smell—namely, the greater part of the cortex of the cerebrum—is relatively much more extensive and also more highly organized in structure in monkeys than in the prosimians. In the evolution of apes and men the cerebral cortex continued to increase in size, with the result that it became infolded, forming a complex pattern of convolutions and fissures.

Comparing the exploratory behavior of a typically terrestrial animal with that of a monkey, the enormous difference in their powers of sensory appreciation becomes obvious. A dog or an earth-bound insectivore, such as a hedgehog, tests an unusual object by sniffing it; a monkey fingers it while examining it visually. As a primary result of adaptation to life in the trees, the hand in the higher primates became not only a grasping organ but an important sense organ. The development of close cerebral co-ordination between touch and sight made possible the skilled manual activities of man.

Among early primates, concomitance of acute vision and prehensile powers gave a scope for intelligence, which was, however, limited in relation to manipulative skill by the restrictions of arboreal life. There is no reason to suppose that forest monkeys of today are any more intelligent

FIGURE 16–1—Modification of pelvic girdle for upright gait. Chimpanzee and reconstruction of an australopithecine. (Adapted by Jacquelyn Hetrick.)

than their Oligocene ancestors of 40 million years ago. The only further openings for development of intelligence were through abandonment of arboreal habits and adaptation to life on the ground, with retention of the nimbly prehensile hands of arboreal creatures. Prosimians at the end of the Oligocene evolved in three directions. One line, the New World monkeys, acquired extreme agility in the trees by developing prehensile tails. A second line, the Old World monkeys, mostly restricted to forests, retained the tail but only as a balancer—or even lost it. A few species became ground-dwellers, but were limited by undue specialization of the feet.

The third line included the ancestors of apes and men. The early members were probably not very different from *Proconsul,* which lived in East Africa early in the Miocene. They were unspecialized, monkey-like creatures, no doubt capable of tree-life and occasionally of swinging by their arms from bough to bough (brachiation), but also able to run along the ground, and even to rear up and scuttle on two legs. Subsequent evolution in this group proceeded along two divergent lines. In one line, leading to the specialized forest-bound apes of today, brachiation became firmly established as the main mode of locomotion. The arms lengthened, and the hands were specialized for hooking on branches. The other line, leading to man, had the advantage of remaining relatively unspecialized. Our monkey-like ancestors were probably used to tree-life, but in regions where woodland was interspersed by grassland they had to move in the open, and they acquired the habit of walking on two legs. This set.the hands free to carry young and to collect food. These early *Hominidae*, which were probably clearly differentiated from the apes or *Pongidae* before the end of the Miocene, developed two interrelated specializations: first, the pelvic girdle was modified for the upright gait, and secondly, the foot lost prehensile power and became a rigid supporting organ (Figure 16–1). The legs now outgrew the arms in length. The hand retained its primitive simplicity and prehensile power but, freed from its locomotive functions, became progressively more skilled as a manipulative organ.

II. MAN AS THE TOOL-MAKING PRIMATE

Differentiation between anthropoid apes on the one hand and fully evolved men on the other is readily made on the basis of comparative anatomy, but the question of how to distinguish ''men'' from their immediate forerunners, which would have been smaller-brained and rather ape-like, is still open to discussion. There was an evolutionary tendency among most primates to increase in body-size, and for their brains to increase at least in proportion. In the later stages of the evolution of man there was enlargement of the brain unrelated to any increase in body-size. Yet, even so, brain-size is an unreliable criterion of humanity, and it is now recognized that a functional criterion, as, for example, ability to make tools, is at least equally valid. We may consider some of the chief factors which led to man's becoming a tool-maker.

It has been said that ''Man's place in nature is largely writ upon the hand.'' Any evidence bearing on the evolution of the human hand would be extremely interesting. Unfortunately the fossil evidence on this point is very meager, but it is not probable that the origin of tool-making was related to any advancement in the functional anatomy of the hand. Regarded anatomically, the prehensile hands of the less specialized monkeys would be capable of making tools if directed by an adequate brain. In many ways our own hands are more primitive than those of the anthropoid apes, our closest living relatives. The reason is plain: the hands of the apes are specialized for brachiation, but our forerunners, while developing specialized feet, retained the pliant generalized hands characteristic of the small tree-dwelling creatures, the distant ancestors of apes and men. In fact, the pentadactyl or five-fingered hand of man is so generalized that one would have to seek among the first mammals, or even go back to the reptiles from which they were derived, to find such primitive simplicity.

In its musculature, the hand of man is in fact closer to that of an Old World monkey than to that of any of the great apes. No ape can extend all its fingers flat on the ground and at the same time extend its wrist, for if the wrist is extended flexion on the fingers is inevitable. Consequently, when apes walk on all fours they support themselves on their knuckles, but men and monkeys can walk on their palms. There is no sign in the hand of man of any of the muscular specializations connected with brachiation, but there is evidence that our ancestors were climbers.

It is a common fallacy to suppose that monkeys cannot oppose the thumb to the other digits. Most Old World monkeys do this in catching insects. It is true that apes and men have developed a greater power of rotating the thumb, which facilitates its opposition to the other digits. In man, the thumb is relatively longer and more powerful than in apes and monkeys. Even so, Wood Jones writes: "We shall look in vain if we seek for movements that a man can do and a monkey cannot, but we shall find much if we look for purposive actions that a man does do and a monkey does not." In other words, manual skill reflects a fine central nervous mechanism rather than a specially delicate distal muscular apparatus. Men with coarse hands are sometimes capable of much finer craftsmanship than those with refined hands; moreover the remarkable skills developed by those whose hands have been maimed, or even lost, is testimony for our conclusion that so-called manual dexterity is mainly of cerebral origin. One must, however, bear in mind that any anatomical structure can evolve only in relation to the whole organism.

Man owes much of his skill to his visual powers, and yet apes and many monkeys have eyes capable of refined stereoscopic and color vision. Man is, however, psychologically distinguished by his capacity for close visual attention, and for prolonged co-ordination of eye and hand. These are reflections of cerebral rather than ocular functions. Convergence of the eyes upon hand-work is largely dependent on conscious concentration— in other words, it is under the control of the cortical motor areas, which act in response to co-ordinated impulses from the eyes. It has been reported that chimpanzees can learn to use their hands under the direction of their eyes for long enough to thread a needle, but in general the attention that an ape can give to manipulating an object is very fleeting. Furthermore, the erect posture of man, and the fact that his skill is poised above the top of the spine instead of being slung in a forwardly projecting manner as in apes, make it easier for him to pay close attention to any point over a wide field of vision.

There is evidence suggesting that some early *Hominidae,* beginning to walk upright on open ground but possessing brains no larger than typical apes, may have been anatomically well enough equipped to use tools. What is in doubt is when and why in their evolutionary career the *Hominidae* became tool-makers. It is probable that at first they were, like many of the lower creatures that we have discussed, occasional users of ready-to-hand tools and weapons.

Tools (including weapons) may be regarded as detachable additions to the body, supplementing mainly the functions of hands and teeth. So long as our early Tertiary ancestors led an arboreal life, their prehensile hands were fully occupied in climbing and feeding. They had neither need nor opportunity to use external objects as functional extensions of the limbs. But when they began to walk or sit on open ground, their hands were free to handle objects, first perhaps out of idle curiosity, later to some purpose. Baboons, which are ground-dwellers, sometimes use pebbles to kill scorpions—a favorite food—and if followed they will sometimes scamper up a hillside and dislodge stones or roll boulders down the slope to deter their pursuers. Observations on captive anthropoid apes have shown that emancipation from arboreal life offers wider scope for their latent intelligence. Chimpanzees make use of sticks for various purposes when captivity forces them to spend most of their time on the ground.

Though they have less concentration in solving problems, some monkeys are as quick-witted as apes. From the results of one intelligence test, a capuchin monkey was rated as high as a chimpanzee. This is probably exceptional, but it is worth bearing in mind as we attempt to trace the origins of human behavior, because the evidence of fossils and of a study of comparative anatomy both suggest that the *Hominidae* arose from monkey-like ancestors. If they were like monkeys of today, they would have been intensely active in body and mind, restlessly inquisitive, and quick in perception and plan. Judging by the experimental tendencies in the behavior of monkeys, the early *Hominidae* may well have begun to leave the forests out of sheer restless activity and curiosity. Recent behavior tests showed that even in rats the instinct to explore exists as a measurable urge.

The earliest *Hominidae* are believed to have existed in Miocene times. In so far as they were adapted to life on the ground, they would have been capable of using improvised tools and weapons, as do baboons and chimpanzees when circumstances demand. Such a need would arise more often in the open, where life was more precarious than in the forest. All this would have reacted favorably on the evolution of the brain, for those individuals with a well co-ordinated cortex were obviously most likely to survive. The *Hominidae* may have remained for millions of years at the stage of occasional tool-using. . . .

. . . Because there is a tendency to be . . . impressed by the occasional manufacture of tools by apes . . . the difference in level of mentality implied between these and the earliest efforts of man may be overlooked. Even the crudest Paleolithic artifacts indicate considerable forethought. The range of types of tool in the earliest Stone Age industries shows that almost at the dawn of culture tools were being made to make other tools. Using a hammerstone to make a hand-axe, and striking a stone flake to use in shaping a wooden spear, are activities which epitomize the mental characteristics of man—as most logically defined.

The capacity for foresight in man arises from efficient utilization of the records of the individual's past experience; that is, it reflects an improvement in cortical function. This is worth considering further. The nerve-cells in the cerebral cortex have been compared to the [tubes] of an electronic computer. They are organized to receive information from the sense-organs and, by a process compared to the calculating mechanisms of a computer, to solve problems and direct suitable bodily activity through the motor cells and nerves controlling muscles. The calculations made by the cortical cells are based not only on information received in the present, but on the patterns of activity left by past experience, that is to say on memory. The co-ordination of past and present information, leading to reasoning and voluntary action, is largely the function of the so-called ''association areas'' of the cortex.

The difference in size between the brains of ape and man is mainly due to the expansion in the human brain of those cortical parts concerned with the integration through which conceptual thought becomes possible. The most distinctive anatomical feature in the human brain is the large size of the frontal and temporal lobes. There is reason to suppose that these are particularly connected with the higher mental faculties. The human brain is also distinguished by an increase in the importance of the area containing motor cells. These are concentrated in a band extending from the top or crown to half-way down the side of each cerebral hemisphere, thus including the hind part of the frontal lobe, adjacent to the front margin of the parietal lobe which receives sensations of touch. . . .

However skilled behavior in man be viewed, the conclusion that it is dependent on a large and efficiently organized cerebrum is unavoidable. Even those movements which have been so deeply impressed by training or practice as to be habitual, such as walking or knitting, are impaired or lost if one side of the motor area becomes damaged, as by cerebral hemorrhage. Acts based on reflexes in the lower part of the brain or spinal cord, like the movements of flight in birds, or the discharge of urine in man, are unaffected by such damage.

It is evident that the powers of conceptual thought on the one hand, and of skilled behavior on the other, are closely related. Owing to the interconnections between the motor area and the higher association areas, the movements initiated in the human brain are those which the individual can see and feel himself doing. In the association areas some patterns of past activity are stored and, on being revived as memory, serve as the origin of ideas, and therefore of consciously planned conduct.

Since the skills of man depend so much on education, it is evident that language has greatly facilitated such activities as systematic tool-making. Oral tradition, in effect a new kind of inheritance, is sometimes regarded as more distinctive of man than tool-making. Apes have a language of the emotions, but the trick of giving names to things as well as to feelings implies conceptual thought. Moreover, it is extraordinarily difficult, if not impossible, to think effectively, to plan, or to invent, without the use of words or equivalent symbols. Most of our constructive thinking is done in unsounded words. The mental processes of our ancestors, before the invention of language, must have been similar to those of the uneducated born-deaf, who think in terms of events as a whole, not in terms of one thing at a time which has a name or comparable symbol. Helen Keller, deaf, dumb, and blind since infancy, has described how at seven she suddenly realized that "everything had a name." This discovery had a tremendous effect on her mind, for it opened the way to communication with other human beings. Verbal language is a technical aid, a tool which had to be invented. Through its introduction man acquired the power of logical thought.

When things have been given names—or symbols of some sort, for language does not necessarily demand speech—the mind can isolate and regroup them instead of thinking of them only as parts of a continuous sequence of events, as in a dream or silent film. The ability to tap memories, and at the same time to isolate and rearrange the ideas they present, is the prerequisite of invention and planning.

It is reasonable to infer that the brains of such *Hominidae* as were capable of making tools involving foresight would have been functionally advanced enough for speech, but that does not mean that the earliest tool-makers did in fact speak. Speech had to be invented. No one could deny that the brain of Helen Keller was advanced enough for verbal language long before she was seven. There are indications that speech, as we know it, though not necessarily language, was invented only at a comparatively late stage in cultural development. The invention was not delayed by any imperfection of the vocal apparatus; the larynges and tongue and lip muscles of apes are capable of articulating words. Chimpanzees have been taught to articulate such words as *papa, cup*. There is much in favor of the view that man's earliest means of communicating ideas was by gestures with the hands, and there is some evidence that these generate, in sympathy, unconscious movements of the mouth. Sympathetic action of hand and mouth has been observed in chimpanzees and children. It has been suggested that an increasing preoccupation of the hands with the making and use of tools could have led to the change from manual to oral gesturing as a means of communicating. The earliest words to be invented probably represented actions; the naming of objects would have come later.

It is no longer thought that speech is connected with the development in man of a special center in the cerebral cortex. Speech depends on the functioning of various cortical mechanisms which were already established in lower primates. Speech and its associated activities are disturbed by any injury within a broad zone extending along the side of the dominant (usually the left) cerebral hemisphere from just in front of the visual area, by the auditory area, to just below the motor area. If the injury is near the visual cortex, the patient will see printed words without realizing what they mean; if near the auditory area, he will hear words without understanding them; and if below the motor area the patient will suffer from aphasia or inability to articulate words. Injury at corresponding points in the opposite hemisphere rarely causes any disturbance of speech.

Owing to the fact that the nerve-fibers cross over in their way from the cortex to the stem of the brain, the left side of the brain controls movements on the right side of the body, and vice versa. The fact that, in most individuals, language-associations are built up in the part of the cortex which controls the right hand is probably connected with their being right-handed—another indication of the close connection between manual activity and speech. Both may be considered as forms of tool-making.

III. ORIGINS OF TOOL-MAKING

We may now return to the origins of regular tool-making. Perhaps within the Pliocene, certainly by the dawn of the Pleistocene, that is about a million years ago, the typically human level of cerebral development had been reached. Stone artifacts of standardized types have been found in Lower Pleistocene deposits in various parts of Africa, and in deposits only slightly more recent in Asia and western Europe. They show that tool-making was no longer merely occasional, but served permanent needs of these earliest men.

The apes of today are forest creatures subsisting on fruits, leaves, shoots, and insects, but all races of man include a substantial proportion of flesh in their diet. Early Paleolithic men were hunters. Meat-eating appears to be as old as man. In so far as the early *Hominidae* were adapted to a mixed environment, partly wooded, partly open, their diet would inevitably have been more varied than that of forest-bound primates.

It seems probable on the analogy of baboons that any hominids living in open country like the African savanna, as some of them did, would take to flesh-eating when the struggle for existence was intensified by excessive drought. Baboons, almost the only monkeys completely adapted to life away from woodlands, prey on poultry and occasionally on lambs and other animals of similar size, using their powerful canine teeth as offensive weapons. This habit becomes more prevalent when conditions of existence are hard. A recent report on the habits of baboons in Zululand states that they often join in organized hunts. Usually, led by a veteran of the troop, they surround a small antelope or other victim and, at a given signal, close in on it and tear it to pieces. After the affair is over only the skull and limb-bones are left.

In men, the canine teeth are much smaller than in baboons or in the apes, and are level with the other teeth (Figure 16–2). It has been sug-

FIGURE 16–2—Dentition of gorilla (left) and modern man (right). Canine teeth shaded. (Adapted by Jacquelyn Hetrick.)

gested that reduction of these teeth in the evolution of man occurred as and when their functions were taken over by the hands, and by weapons and tools. In the fossil *Australopithecinae* of South Africa, probably slightly modified descendants of our Pliocene ancestors, the canines are small and level with the other teeth, even in the earliest stages of wear, and even in males. These hominids may have been tool-users, but there is no evidence that they were tool-makers. Thus it appears that the canine teeth were already reduced in the *Hominidae* at an evolutionary stage below that of tool-making. The Australopithecines lived in open country, probably hiding in caves and rock-crannies for protection. Whether the smallness of their canines was related to the use of hand weapons or not, the Australopithecines and the proto-men of Pliocene times would have needed means to defend themselves when foraging in the open. Walking on two legs with hands free, they may well have used stones as missiles, and sticks or animal long-bones as clubs.

In times of drought, then, our precursors would readily have taken to eating flesh. Although they lacked teeth suited to carnivorous habits, they were no doubt at least as ingenious as baboons in killing small animals. Life in the open set a premium not only on cunning but on co-operation. In view of the mentality and social life of other primates it is likely that the proto-men hunted in hordes, and killed medium-sized mammals by cornering them and using improvised hand-weapons.

Direct evidence of the Pliocene *Hominidae* and their habits is still lacking, but there is reason to suppose that they were not very different from the Australopithecines, now regarded as a side-branch of the family which survived locally into Early Pleistocene times. There are indications that some at least were carnivorous. The scattered fragments of animal bones, egg shells, and crab shells found with *Australopithecus* in the cave deposits at Taungs, Bechuanaland, had all the appearance of food refuse. In the *Australopithecus* level in one of the Makapan caves, Transvaal, quantities of antelope limb-bones were found, some apparently smashed as if to extract the marrow, but there were no undoubted tools.

By the time that the *Hominidae* had evolved into tool-makers they were evidently largely carnivorous; quantities of meat-bones were associated with the remains of Pekin man (*Pithecanthropus pekinensis*). It is easy to see how tool-making might arise out of the adoption of carnivorous habits. Though they may have killed game easily enough, the proto-men must often have had difficulty in removing skin and fur, and in dividing the flesh. Without strong canines, sharp pieces of stone would provide the solution. Here surely was the origin of the tradition of tool-making. Where no naturally sharp pieces of stone lay ready to hand, more intelligent individuals saw that the solution was to break pebbles and produce fresh sharp edges. Perhaps accidental breakages in using pebbles as missiles had been observed. Once this tradition had begun, the manifold uses of chipped stones became obvious.

Dentally, and from the alimentary point of view, we should be vegetarians. We lack the teeth of true carnivores, and we have the long gut associated with herbivorous diet. Furthermore, our nearest living relations, the anthropoid apes, are herbivores, and consume only small quantities of animal protein. Man's change of habit from herbivore to semi-carnivore gave a new potential. To store a given amount of energy, a carnivore needs a smaller quantity of food than a herbivore. Its way of life is accordingly very different, from the point of view of the economy of energy. Instead of eating almost continuously, like their fruit-and-plant-eating ancestors, the earliest men must have spent most of their daytime in hunting. This activity increased interdependence and encouraged social grouping. New skills and aptitudes were thus developed, through which man was able not only to survive climatic changes, but even to create his own environment. The evolution of new bodily equipment in response to environmental change normally requires hundreds of thousands, if not millions, of years; but by inventing extra-bodily equipment—such as tools, weapons, shelter, clothing—which could be discarded or changed as circumstances dictated, man became the most adaptable of all creatures.

With fire, weather-proof shelters, and skins or, other clothing at his command, man became free to spread into every climatic zone. These cultural activities depended on tool-making, but were made possible through man's power, not only of conceptual thought, but of communicating inventive ideas and thus of building traditions. Where tradition is limited, culture ceases to evolve and may degenerate. Of this there are many examples.

IV. EVOLUTION OF HUMAN SKILL

Having inquired into the factors of the origin and development of human skills, we find three questions to be considered: (i) Can stages in the evolution of human skill be recognized? (ii) If so, is there evidence that they are correlated with stages of physical evolution? (iii) Does skill vary with species or racial type?

It is possible to distinguish six main levels of culture on the basis of the use and making of tools, and to correlate them broadly with known types of *Hominidae*:

(a) Occasional use of improvised tools and weapons. "Eolithic." *Australopithecus* and Pliocene hominids?

(b) Occasional tool-making. Dawn of Early or Lower Paleolithic. Earliest species of *Pithecanthropus?* and of *Homo?*

(c) Regular tool-making, but little or no standardization. Lower Paleolithic. *Pithecanthropus* (e.g. of Pekin), and some early precursors of *Homo sapiens* (e.g. of Fontéchevade in the Charente).

(d) Regular tool-making, with marked standardization, but little specialization. Lower Paleolithic. Early precursors of *Homo sapiens* (e.g. of Kanam in Kenya, and Swanscombe, Kent).

(e) Manufacture of specialized tools and weapons:
   (1) Elementary. Middle Paleolithic. *Homo neanderthalensis* and some early *Homo sapiens.*
   (2) Composite. Upper or Late Paleolithic and Mesolithic. *Homo sapiens* (e.g. Cro-Magnons).

(*f*) Use of mechanical principles (machine tools). Modern *Homo sapiens*. Characteristic of Neolithic and Metal Ages, but foreshadowed in some Upper Paleolithic and Mesolithic practices.

Though man's Pliocene ancestors were not tool-makers, they were tool-users. Direct proof is difficult to obtain, but it is supported by evidence from the Australopithecine sites in South Africa. None has yielded any undoubted tools or weapons, but at Taungs there were baboon skulls which seemed to have been artificially pierced. It is also suggested that occasional river pebbles in the dolomite fissure deposit at Sterkfontein, containing remains of an Australopithecine, had been carried to the site by that creature.

Even when tool-making became widespread among the first men, it was probably for long only an occasional practice, since improvised implements and weapons often served well enough. Improvisation has played an important part in human culture at all periods. Some modern Australian aborigines carve wooden implements with naturally sharp pieces of stone. Thus a man of the Pitjendadjara tribe will take an unflaked piece of stone to chop a slab of wood from a tree-trunk, and with another unflaked stone deftly work the wood into a highly finished spear-thrower. This example of primitive craftsmanship may remind us that we cannot estimate exactly the skill of the earliest men from the crude stone tools which are almost the only evidence of their culture, for much of their equipment may have been of wood and other perishable materials. Identification of the first stone tools is almost impossible, for not only were they usually pieces of naturally fractured stone, but man's first attempts to improve their shape would have been indistinguishable from the accidental chippings produced by natural agencies. For this reason, none of the so-called eoliths can be accepted unreservedly as human work. Except for their occurrence in a cave deposit with hearths and human remains, few of the stone artifacts of Pekin man would have been recognized as human work.

There were no recognizable tools with the remains of the oldest known fossil man, the species *Pithecanthropus robustus* found in lake-clays at Sangiran in Java; or with the later *P. erectus* from river gravel at Trinil, Java; or with the species of *Homo* in river sands at Mauer near Heidelberg. This is not surprising when one considers that their dwelling-sites are unknown, and that in any case some human groups may have long remained at the stage of occasional tool-making.

Though not the oldest industry, that in the cave deposits at Choukoutien in China, with remains of *Pithecanthropus pekinensis*, is among the most primitive known. Thousands of artificially broken pieces of stone, of kinds foreign to the site, were found in all the occupation layers. Few are recognizable implements. It appears that Pekin man collected stones from a nearby river-bed and from neighboring cliffs, and brought them to the cave in order to work them into implements when required. He broke up the lumps by using a stone slab or large bone as an anvil and striking them with a hammerstone. Usually he found it most convenient to use the resulting flakes, though sometimes the residual cores proved more useful (Figure 16–3A,B). Occasionally, flakes were crudely trimmed into

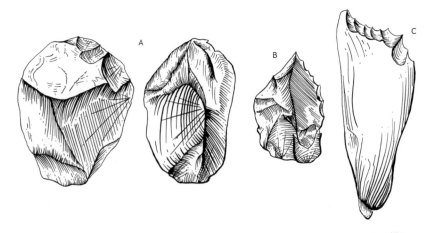

FIGURE 16–3—Tools of Pekin man. (A) Quartz chopper tool. (B) Pointed flake of quartz. (C) Broken animal bone chipped for use as tool. (Adapted by Jacquelyn Hetrick.)

points or scrapers. Rough choppers were made by removing a few flakes from the surfaces of oval boulders. The rarity of definable tools in the Choukoutien deposits indicates that though Pekin man was a regular and systematic tool-maker, he made little attempt at standardization; in fact many of his implements were evidently of the occasional type.

For some purposes he used broken bones as implements (Figure 16–3C). The crudity of his industry is partly accounted for by the poor quality of veinquartz, the only raw material easily available to him, but this is not the whole explanation, for the precursors of *Homo sapiens* in Africa made shapely hand-axes from equally intractable stone. In the higher occupation layers at Choukoutien there was a noticeable increase in the percentage of tools chipped in more readily flaked stone (chert). Therefore the later stages of the industry appear more highly evolved, not through any advance in manual dexterity, but because of greater care in securing suitable raw material. Chert was already known to Pekin man at the time of his first occupation of the caves, but was presumably less accessible. Its more frequent use in the upper layers seem to indicate the development of a tradition leading to increased persistence and fore-thought.

All we know of the hand of Pekin man is a wrist-bone. It shows no feature which distinguishes it from that of modern man. An analysis of the better-defined tools from Choukoutien has shown that the majority were chipped by right-handed persons. Monkeys and some other animals show individual preference for the use of one hand or paw, but the acquisition of greater skill in the one hand is a human trait linked with the dominance of one side of the brain, and doubtless connected with the habitual use of tools. Ninety-five per cent of modern adult human beings are right-handed, but left-handedness was commoner in early times, as it still is among untrained infants. Our word dexterity is from the Latin root *dexter* (Greek *dexios*), which means "on the right (hand)."

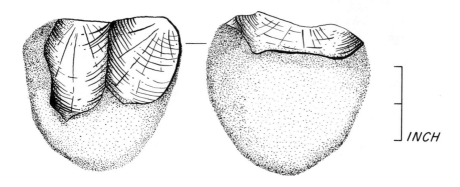

FIGURE 16–4—Quartzite pebble-tool from southern Rhodesia. Lower Paleolithic. (Adapted by Jacquelyn Hetrick.)

Pekin man had considerable skill as a hunter, for his own remains are associated with quantities of bones of butchered animals, chiefly deer, but also bison, horse, rhinoceros, elephant, bear, hyena, and tiger. The killing of some of these must have involved the use of pits or traps. Throughout the long period of their occupation of the caves—probably seasonal—the Choukoutien hunters regularly used fire. The discovery of how to make fire was man's greatest step forward in gaining freedom from the dominance of environment.

The earliest known Stone Age industries in Africa are probably older than those of Choukoutien. They are represented chiefly by pebbles flaked to produce a cutting or chopping edge. These pebble-tools approach a standard form (Figure 16–4), and are usually accompanied by rough flakes which may themselves have been occasionally used as tools . . . .

At Olduvai, in Tanganyika, it has been shown that pebble-tool culture evolved into the Chelleo-Acheulian culture, which was distinguished by the hand-axes widespread throughout Africa and parts of west Europe and south Asia during much of the Pleistocene. Hand-axes (Figure 16–5, left) were made by flaking a pebble or stone slab round the edges from both sides, so as to produce a pointed tongue-shaped tool with a sharp margin. These were the first standardized implements; they served a great variety of purposes. They were not hafted, nor (apart from the forms known as cleavers—see Figure 16–5, right) were they axes in the true

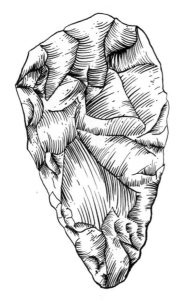
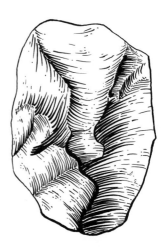

FIGURE 16–5—Acheulian flint hand-axe from Wolvercote, Oxfordshire (left). Acheulian cleaver in quartzite from Madras, India (right). (Adapted by Jacquelyn Hetrick.)

sense. They were probably used mainly as hunters' knives, but may have served also for cutting wood or for digging up grubs and roots. Acheulian peoples used flake-tools to some extent, but the hand-axe was the predominant tool of a cultural tradition which not only spread over nearly one-fifth of the land-area of the globe, but persisted for more than a hundred thousand years. The hand-axe peoples lived mainly in open country, ranging from the hot African deserts to the cool grasslands and open wooded valleys of northwest Europe.

Chellean and Acheulian implements collected from successively younger deposits in any one region show on the whole a gradual refinement of workmanship, but the comparative uniformity of industries of this group over so vast an area is most remarkable. Many Acheulian hand-axes from the Cape, Kenya, Madras, and London are indistinguishable from each other as regards form, whether made of flint, sandstone, quartz, or lava.

Men who made tools of standard type must have formed in their minds images of the ends to which they labored. Human culture (and by culture we mean here all that a society practices and produces) is the outcome of this capacity for conceptual thought. The leading factors in its development are tradition coupled with invention. The primitive hunter made an implement in a particular fashion largely because as a child he had watched another at work. The standard hand-axe was not conceived by any one individual *ab initio,* but was the end-product of exceptional individuals in successive generations, not only copying but occasionally improving on the products of their predecessors. As a result of co-operative hunting, migrations, and trade, the traditions of different groups of Paleolithic hunters sometimes became blended.

The development of speech must have greatly facilitated these processes. The extreme slowness of cultural evolution during the Lower Paleolithic may have been related to the rudimentary form of language. It has been suggested that the hand-axe people were still communicating by gesture and gabble, and had not yet achieved true word-making.

We have no reason to infer that all Early Paleolithic men had brains qualitatively inferior to those of the average man of today. The simplicity of their culture can be accounted for by the extreme sparseness of the population and their lack of accumulated knowledge. A supposed hallmark of the mind of *Homo sapiens* is the artistic impulse—but archeological evidence suggests that this trait manifested itself almost at the dawn of tool-making. Crystals of quartz were collected by Pekin man many miles from his home, and one may presume that, partly at least, this was because their shape and appearance appealed to him. Some of the finer Acheulian hand-axes are masterpieces of artistic craftsmanship, displaying perfection which exceeds bare technical necessity (Figure 16–11).

The only undoubted skull of an Acheulian hand-axe maker is that found in gravel at Swanscombe, near Dartford in Kent, England, in 1935–6. In so far as it is preserved, it is barely distinguishable from some skulls of modern *Homo sapiens,* though it is probably more than 100,000 years old. Human skulls of modern type were also found with Acheulian hand-axes at Kanjera in Kenya, though their contemporaneity is more open to doubt.

Like their more brutish contemporaries in China, the hand-axe people were well advanced in hunting skill. Lake-side dwelling sites of Acheulian man, in both Kenya and Spain, revealed quantities of broken bones of fast-moving animals such as gazelle and zebra, as well as of elephant and other big game. There is evidence of the use of fire by Acheulian hunters at only a few localities, in the Transvaal (Makapan), Spain, and Palestine.

Early stone industries are sometimes classified according to whether most of the tools were made by trimming a block of stone to the required shape (core-tool), or by detaching a flake from the pebble or block and using that (flake-tool). Acheulian hand-axes are classed as core-tools. Probably, however, in the basic stone-working tradition both cores and flakes were used with little discrimination. The Choukoutien industry was not far removed from that stage, and in parts of Africa and Europe there were groups of people who for long retained or reverted to it. The Clactonian of Europe (Figure 16–6), and the industries of the type of that of

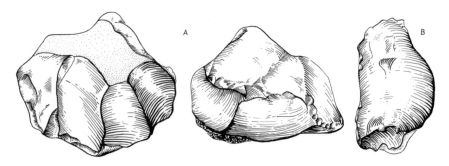

FIGURE 16–6—Clactonian flint artifacts. (A) Core. (B) Flake-tool. Swanscombe, Kent. (Adapted by Jacquelyn Hetrick.)

Hope Fountain in southern Africa, are examples of such primitive Paleolithic cultures, which existed alongside the more advanced Chelleo-Acheulian. Skulls of Late Clactonian man recently found at Fontéchevade, in the Charente, appear to be similar to the Swanscombe type (primitive *Homo sapiens*).

The evidence indicates that man originated in Africa but spread fairly rapidly into Asia and Europe, carrying a basic stone-working tradition out of which various specialized cultures evolved. In Africa the core hand-axe culture developed; in eastern Asia another core-culture, distinguished by standardized chopping tools (Figure 16–7); and in western Asia and Europe, flake-cultures. There was considerable overlapping of these traditions, with consequent hybridization of cultures in some regions.

It would be wrong to give the impression that there was no specialization of tools in Lower Paleolithic times. The hammerstone or anvil for flaking, the flake for cutting skins, the crude chopping-tool for splitting bones or wood, were primary specializations in the most primitive known

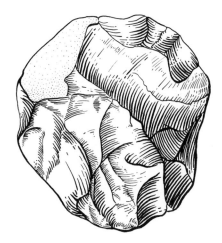

FIGURE 16–7—East Asiatic chopper-tool in silicified tuff. Java. Lower Paleolithic. (Adapted by Jacquelyn Hetrick.)

industries. But the use of a single standardized tool-type for a variety of different purposes was a leading feature of Lower Paleolithic culture. The pointed hand-axe is an extreme example of an all-purpose tool, for it served equally well for piercing, cutting, and scraping. With the advent of what is generally known as the Middle Paleolithic stage of culture, specialized types of tool were devised to perform each of these functions, and specialization then became a conspicuous feature of culture. For example, it became the fashion among some later hand-axe people, and also among some of the flake-tool people, to prepare blocks of stone in such a way that a flake of accurately determined form could be struck. The preparatory flaking aimed at so shaping the block that the flake eventually detached was immediately serviceable as an implement, without further trimming. This was the specialized tortoise-core technique used by many different groups of hunters in Africa, Asia, and Europe, including the Neanderthalers. Cultures in which this technique was extensively employed are generally termed Levalloisian.

The typical Levallois tool struck from a tortoise-core combines the plano-convex form of some hand-axes with the straight cutting-edge of the ordinary flake, and was thus very well suited for use as a skinning-knife. The tortoise-core technique is interesting for the evolution of skill, because its manufacture implies much more forethought than that of any of the tools characteristic of Lower Paleolithic culture. An unstruck tortoise-core so closely resembles a high domed plano-convex hand-axe that one way in which the technique was discovered might have been through the accidental breaking of such a tool. The Levalloisian or tortoise-core technique long continued in use with various modifications, particularly in Africa.

It has been convenient to use the term "tool" to include weapons. During Lower Paleolithic times these were simple missiles such as pebbles or all-wood spears, and presumably also pits and traps. The frontal bone of a hyena skull at Choukoutien had been smashed by a missile boulder. The oldest known actual weapon (and, incidentally, the oldest surviving piece of woodwork) is the pointed end of a yew-wood spear associated with the typical Clactonian industry in the water-logged Elephant Bed at Clacton-on-Sea in Essex, England. It has been shaped by the use of flint flakes. Judging from the practice of modern Australian aborigines, many of the so-called scrapers from Lower Paleolithic sites were probably used for working wood rather than for dressing skins as was formerly supposed. A complete spear of yew-wood, with fire-hardened tip, within the skeleton of an elephant and associated with a Levalloisian flint industry, was found at Lehringen, about 30 kilometers southeast of Bremen, Germany.

The typical Neanderthalers, or *Homo neanderthalensis,* formed a specialized offshoot of mankind, the earliest members of which (for instance at Ehringsdorf, Germany) were barely distinguishable from the precursors of *Homo sapiens.* They were essentially a European and west Asian group. Their culture, known as Mousterian, had Clactonian roots and followed a flake-tool tradition, but was locally influenced by the Acheulian. The early Neanderthalers lived under the warm conditions that prevailed in Europe during the third interglacial period, and their mode of life was similar to that of the Acheulians. The later or typical Mousterian culture developed under the wet or tundra conditions associated with the fourth glaciation. The Neanderthalers adapted themselves to the severe climate by using caves as dwellings wherever possible, and probably by wearing animal pelts as rough cloaks in severe weather, as do the modern inhabitants of Tierra del Fuego.

In material equipment the Neanderthalers showed little more inventiveness than the Lower Paleolithic peoples. They do not appear to have mastered the craft of working bone, but like Pekin man they sometimes used broken long bones of animals as tools. They selected dense bones for chopping-blocks and pressure-flakers (Figure 16–8C), and broke fibulae of bear for use as skin-sleekers. Mousterian industries consist principally of stone flake-tools, struck either in the simple Clactonian fashion, or by the Levalloisian technique, but with edges finely retouched by pressure-flaking to make them more durable. They include three main standard types, (*a*) triangular points with both edges retouched (Figure 16–8A); (*b*) D-shaped side-scrapers (Figure 16–8B); (*c*) small heart-shaped hand-axes. The flake-tools were predominant. The Neanderthalers used spears of wood. A Neanderthal skeleton at Mount Carmel had a clean-cut

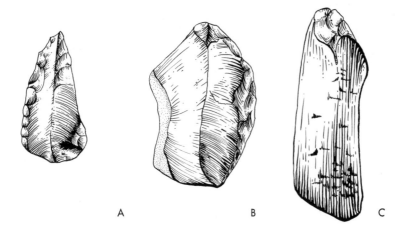

FIGURE 16–8—Mousterian artifacts. (A) Flake point and (B) side-scraper in flint, from Le Moustier, Dordogne. (C) Bone compressor from La Quina, Charente. (Adapted by Jacquelyn Hetrick.)

hole, extending through the head of one thigh bone into the pelvis, which was the work of a wooden spear point. Some of the more advanced Neanderthalers appear to have used hafted narrow flint points as detachable spearheads. Occasionally they applied the principle of hafting to scrapers. Thus their equipment was more specialized than that of their predecessors, though still very elementary. They were fearless and proficient hunters, for they slew mammoth, rhinoceros, and bear. Their weapons included missile stones, but it is doubtful if they were slung or used in the form of a bolas. The abundance of limb-bones of game animals, and the rarity of ribs and vertebrae, in the Neanderthal cave-dwellings show that they did not drag whole carcasses to the cave, but cut them up and carried away portions. They made extensive use of fire, and cooked their meat.

Judging from the few arm and hand bones known, Neanderthal men were usually right-handed. Their fingers were relatively shorter and thicker than those of modern man, but the joints allowed easy movement. Their implements, although simple, were often exquisitely finished, particularly in the Upper Mousterian, indicating considerable dexterity, and pride in exercise of skill. At Sergeac, in the Dordogne, they made a few tools in rock-crystal of gem-stone quality, indicating some artistic sense.

In most parts of Europe, Middle Paleolithic culture gave place with almost dramatic suddenness to the Upper Paleolithic, distinguished by a wide range of new specialized tools and weapons, and by various new techniques. These rapid cultural advances were associated with the emergence of highly successful types of *Homo sapiens*, notably the Cro-

Magnons. They spread from southwest Asia during the second half of the last glacial period, and entirely supplanted the Neanderthalers, whose disappearance may be likened to the reduction in the number of aborigines in contact with European culture. The Cro-Magnons and related groups were not only much more inventive than their predecessors, but exhibited remarkable aesthetic sense and displayed artistic skills scarcely excelled in any later period. This rapid evolution of culture may have been due to the invention of a system of verbal symbolism.

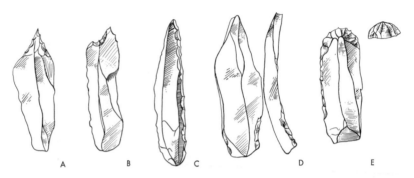

FIGURE 16–9—Upper Paleolithic blade tools in flint. (A) Solutrean piercer or "hand drill," Dordogne. (B) Magdalenian concave end-scraper or "spoke shave," Dordogne. (C) Gravettian knife-point, Dordogne. (D) Magdalenian burin, Dordogne. (E) End-scraper, Vale of Clwyd, Wales. (Adapted by Jacquelyn Hetrick.)

Upper Paleolithic industries show an increased mastery over materials. New techniques had been evolved for working flint and similar stone, such as the production of narrow blades with parallel sides by means of punch and hammer, and the surfacing as well as the edge-trimming of flakes by indirect percussion or pressure (e.g. Solutrean spearheads). Artifacts of complicated form were wrought in bone, antler, and ivory by a combination of sawing, splitting, grinding, and polishing. By now, tools were not only used to make implements in the sense of end-products, such as meat knives or spears, but many tools were made which were tool-making tools. This is good evidence that the hunter-craftsman was showing considerably greater foresight, and no longer worked merely to satisfy immediate ends. Thus, numerous specialized types of flint chiseling-tools (burins) were devised mainly for working bone, antler, ivory, and probably wood into other tools (Figure 16–9A–E).

It may be noted that many of the tools and weapons of the Upper Paleolithic peoples were composite (Figure 16–10). Missile and thrusting spears were regularly provided with hafted heads of bone, antler, or flint, and some of the flint blade-tools were set in bone or wooden handles. One

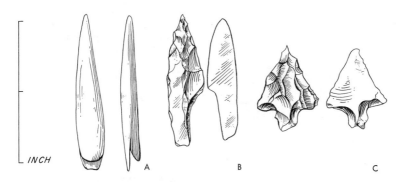

FIGURE 16–10—Upper Paleolithic hafted weapon-tips. (A) Aurignacian split-base bone point, Dordogne. (B) Solutrean shouldered "willow-leaf" point showing pressure-flaking, Dordogne. (C) Aterian arrowhead, Morocco. (Adapted by Jacquelyn Hetrick.)

important factor in the efficiency of a tool or weapon is the means of giving its working edge or point the desired motion through the material to be worked or penetrated. Originally all tools were grasped in the hand; the first step towards a mechanical device was hafting. In Upper Paleolithic times, men were beginning to apply mechanical principles to the movement of tools and weapons. Spears were launched with throwers which, working on the lever principle, increase the effective propelling power of a man's arm. The bow was invented late in this period, probably in north Africa. It was the first means of concentrating muscular energy for the propulsion of an arrow, but it was soon discovered that it also provided a means of twirling a stick, and this led to the invention of the rotary drill.

Bone and ivory bodkins, bone needles with eyes, belt-fasteners, and, rarely, even buttons have been found in Upper Paleolithic sites. Carved representations of clothed figures show that these hunters wore sewn skin garments with fitting sleeves and trousers. These greatly increased their efficiency in the very cold winters that they had to endure.

Thus men were making their own environments in various ways. In the limestone hills of western Europe, the Upper Paleolithic tribes made their winter homes in shallow caves or rock-shelters. They were principally hunters of reindeer and horse. In the summer, they followed the migrating herds and used tents or huts as dwellings. In eastern Europe, they specialized in hunting mammoth, and adapted themselves to life on the open steppe by constructing permanent communal huts deeply sunk in the ground. The cave-art of the western tribes shows that some of these hunters had remarkable powers of observation and visual memory. Most of the drawings and paintings were done in the dark innermost recesses of caverns, usually by the light of open stone lamps. The acuity of vision

FIGURE 16–11 (Photographs courtesy of the Robert H. Lowie Museum of Anthropology, University of California, Berkeley.)

(Above) Percussion-flaking with small hammer stone.

(Right) Anvil technique in which artifact is struck against fixed anvil to remove flake from upper surface.

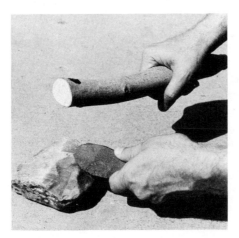

(Left) Indirect percussion on anvil. Artifact edge is placed on a fixed point of anvil and held by its other end. Baton strikes center of artifact causing flake to detach from upper surface above point of contact with anvil.

(Right) Pressure-flaking chert with deer antler. Point of antler is placed near edge of artifact and pressed downward and away from worker to remove a small flake from the desired place on undersurface of artifact. Pad of leather or cloth is necessary to prevent cutting hands.

(Left) Pecking groove in granite stone with a smaller fine-grained stone. Repeated blows crush bits of the surface to produce the groove shown. The groove will be used to lash hammer to a wood handle.

(Right) Boring a hole with a drill. Both surfaces are first pecked as deeply as possible, and then the stick is rotated in one hole using wet sand as an abrasive.

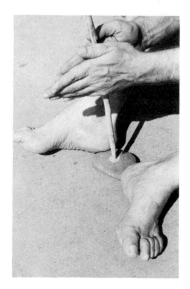

and co-ordination of hand and eye which late Paleolithic tribal artists possessed is illustrated by the fineness of some of their tools and engravings.

In spite of their artistic and other skilled achievements, the Upper Paleolithic people of Europe and Asia were economically no more than

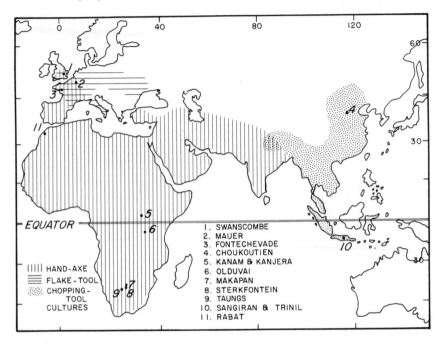

1. SWANSCOMBE
2. MAUER
3. FONTECHEVADE
4. CHOUKOUTIEN
5. KANAM & KANJERA
6. OLDUVAI
7. MAKAPAN
8. STERKFONTEIN
9. TAUNGS
10. SANGIRAN & TRINIL
11. RABAT

||||| HAND-AXE
≡≡≡ FLAKE-TOOL
CHOPPING-
TOOL
CULTURES

FIGURE 16–12—Distribution of Lower Paleolithic industries and sites of early hominids. (Adapted by Jacquelyn Hetrick.)

food-collecting savages. Their varied culture, probably reflecting an increase in population and a certain amount of leisure within each group, was possible only because game was abundant.

By various inventions, men now came to adapt their mode of life to the new environments consequent on the climatic changes which brought the last glaciation to an end. In this Mesolithic phase, life remained at the level of bare subsistence until certain groups in the Middle East began the revolutionary practice of cultivating plants and domesticating animals as sources of food and raw materials. With food-production, man passed from the hunting stage and was on the way to civilization. He ceased to be a rare species. Larger, settled communities could be supported, and it was no longer necessary for all their members to be occupied in gathering or producing food, with the consequence that a great variety of new skilled crafts could develop. . . .

17

THE ORIGINS
AND ADAPTIVE RADIATION
OF THE AUSTRALOPITHECINES

J. T. Robinson

*In the interpretation of the early hominid fossil record,
one of the major areas of disagreement focuses on the significance
of the differences separating the representatives of early hominid populations known as the australopithecines. Some
paleoanthropologists have been inclined to minimize the
differences among the early tool-using bipedal ape men; others,
such as J. T. Robinson, find the differences sufficiently great
as to justify a separation into two groups of australopithecines, one
leading to the later hominids.*

*In this article, Robinson describes the australopithecine fossils
in detail and provides a taxonomy of the australopithecines
that makes some of these early populations "human" and
others, not. Robinson worked closely with Broom and Dart in the
pioneer research on the South African man-apes of the early
Pleistocene.*

Understanding the australopithecines has advanced enormously since
the first paper concerning them was published in 1925. At first material
of this group was known from South Africa only and scientific opinion
was strongly inclined to discount the views of the local workers. This
situation has changed greatly: it is now generally agreed that the australopithecines are hominids, not pongids. While by far the greater proportion of the considerable number of specimens now known are South
African, there are very encouraging signs that other areas will contribute

(From *Evolution und Hominization*, Gottfried Kurth, editor. Gustav Fischer
Verlag, Stuttgart, West Germany, 1962, pages 120–140. By permission of
the author and the publisher.)

significantly to our knowledge. It is greatly to be hoped that these promises are to be fulfilled since, in my opinion at least, australopithecines were spread across the Old World from South Africa to the Far East and it would be very valuable to have specimens from widely separate localities.

The chief purpose of the present paper is to speculate about the nature of the forces which operated to bring the australopithecine group into existence and which controlled its evolution.

AUSTRALOPITHECINE
TAXONOMY

Any consideration of the evolution of the australopithecines must first take notice of the taxonomy of this group. This has been dealt with in a number of publications but will briefly be referred to here again. The reason for this is that without recognition of taxonomic differentiation within the group, it is futile to consider adaptive radiation within it. Furthermore, it would appear that many authors tend to think of the group as being essentially taxonomically uniform and make statements purporting to refer to all the known australopithecines when this is not the case. As an example may be quoted the statement ". . . the whole canine-premolar complex is reduced in the australopithecines. . . ." This hardly does justice to the fact that the whole complex, as listed . . . differs very considerably in *Australopithecus* and *Paranthropus*. Furthermore, these differences have far-reaching implications. Or again . . . in referring to the australopithecine discovery at site FLK in the Olduvai Gorge, [it was stated:] It affords clear-cut evidence that these primitive hominids (i.e., the australopithecines) were to some extent carnivorous and predaceous. . . ." Now quite apart from the fact that the interpretation here given is one of several which may be drawn from the actual evidence and is therefore not clear-cut proof, the evidence concerned refers to one type of australopithecine only. In view of the fact that the dental specializations of the two main types of australopithecine differ appreciably, it surely is unsafe to generalize from a small amount of information at one site which at the time had yielded only one type of australopithecine. Similarly, discussions about a possible osteodonto-keratic culture of australopithecines proceed as though the evidence being debated concerns australopithecines in general. In actual fact most of the evidence so far employed comes from a single site, with some additional information from two others—but all are *Australopithecus* sites. *Paranthropus* may or may not have had such a culture, but whether it did or not cannot be determined from sites which have yielded only *Australopithecus*.

The above point has been dealt with at some length, not in order to attempt to refute the views of [others] but to stress the need to remember when discussing the australopithecines that at least two types are known which differ considerably in their morphology and apparently also in their ecology and behavior. If this fact is ignored, discussions are as likely to lead to obfuscation as to clarification of the issues involved.

SOUTH AFRICAN
AUSTRALOPITHECINES

The two types of South African australopithecine are *Australopithecus africanus* DART and *Paranthropus robustus* BROOM. Previous to the latter analysis the only taxonomic analysis was that of Broom who placed the known forms in 5 species of 3 genera—but who thought that a fourth genus should be erected for the Makapan form. Several other schemes have been suggested without being legitimate taxonomic analyses lending legality to the suggested classifications. One may note here in passing that paleoanthropologists in general seem to pay very scant, or no, attention to the international rules governing nomenclature. Mayr suggested placing the australopithecines and all true men together in the genus *Homo* so that the family Hominidae would contain the one genus alone. Washburn and Patterson suggested putting all the hominids in two genera, *Australopithecus* and *Homo*. Howell seems to agree with the latter view except that he would split the genus *Australopithecus* into two subgenera: *A. (Australopithecus)* and *A. (Paranthropus)*.

The practicing taxonomist is in the first place primarily concerned with identification and therefore looks for what are generally referred to as good diagnostic characters which enable him to distinguish as easily as possible between closely related forms. The characters adopted are arrived at empirically: that is to say, if observation shows that a particular feature, *taking its range of variation into account,* characterizes the group concerned and no others, then it is a good taxonomic character. In some cases it will be found that a single character is so clearly diagnostic that it is not necessary to use others in order to identify accurately the form concerned. Usually however it is necessary to use a group of characters in order to achieve certainty of identification. Where a new form is being dealt with it is always necessary to use a constellation of characters in order to determine its relationships. The level at which a character is useful is again determined by observation. For example, in arthropods the number of bristles on a particular segment of a limb may vary from one species to another but remain constant within any one species. Such a character would be useful only at the species level. But the number of limbs or of wings, for example, are constant over far larger groups than the species and are therefore useless for distinguishing species but are invaluable as characters defining much larger taxonomic groups. Limb number, for instance, is a diagnostic arthropod character at the class level.

In this practical, workaday taxonomic sense, the characters which distinguish *Australopithecus* and *Paranthropus* are legion since the two can be distinguished by means of almost any bits of skeleton now known in both forms. This in itself is an instructive fact since at low levels of taxonomic distinction general similarity is so great that good diagnostic characters are not common. In general it may be said that taxonomic experience in mammalogy shows that if two forms are readily distinguishable by means of almost any part of the skeleton, then it is highly unlikely that the taxonomic difference between them will be of less than generic magnitude. It does not follow, however, that generically distinct forms will necessarily differ markedly in all skeletal characters. It should be emphasized that this statement is not a theoretical one suggested as a standard for taxonomists, but is a generalization based on what is found by experience to be the case in mammalian systematics.

There are a number of very good taxonomic characters which distinguish *Australopithecus* and *Paranthropus* according to the known material. For example the first lower deciduous molar not only allows instantaneous recognition (even when very considerably worn) of which group is being dealt with, but serves to distinguish *Paranthropus* from all other hominids in which the tooth is known. Furthermore, this tooth is of the same type in *Australopithecus* as it is in all fossil and living hominines in which its nature is known. Fortunately the deciduous first lower molar is known in Pekin man and also Neanderthal man. Consequently the morphology of dm_1 serves not only to emphasize the distinction between *Paranthropus* and *Australopithecus*, but at the same time underlines the similarity between the latter and hominines. The permanent lower canine is another good diagnostic feature. The two australopithecines can be separated at a glance by means of this tooth, which is relatively large and highly asymmetric in crown structure in *Australopithecus* while in *Paranthropus* the crown is small and more symmetrical with little relief on the lingual surface though the root is substantial. The large difference in size between the postcanine teeth and the anterior teeth is also a good diagnostic feature. In *Australopithecus* the canines and incisors are fairly large for a hominid and the postcanine teeth are of proportionate size. In *Paranthropus*, on the other hand, the canines and incisors are appreciably smaller while the postcanine teeth are larger than those of *Australopithecus*. The *Australopithecus* condition fits very well with that found in the hominines, whereas that of *Paranthropus* is quite aberrant and unlike that seen in any other known hominid.

These are some of the most striking diagnostic features distinguishing the two forms, and there are many others: the nasal cavity floor and its relation to the subnasal maxillary surface, the nature and shape of the palate, the shape and structure of the face and of the braincase, etc. However lack of space prohibits detailed discussion of them here.

In contrast to this view, which I have described as the practical, workaday taxonomic approach, there is a larger and more satisfying view which sees the animal not as a series of taxonomic characters, but as an individual which is part of a population in its natural environment. In such a view the isolated characters of the other approach or aspect of systematics are seen as part of an integrated pattern. According to this viewpoint the difference between the two types of australopithecine is even more obvious.

In *Paranthropus* it seems clear that the architecture of the skull and head in general is strongly related to specializations of the dentition. The small anterior teeth, in the maxilla set in relatively lightly-constructed bone and in the mandible in a more or less vertical symphysial region with no trace of chin, results in a relatively orthognathous face. The massive postcanine teeth with strongly developed root systems are set in massive bone. The areas of support and the channels of dissipation of the forces generated by chewing are well developed. Examples of these are the thickened columns up either side of the nasal aperture, the enormously thickened palate anteriorly (over a centimeter thick in one adolescent where it can be measured opposite M_1), the pterygo-palatine complex and the zygomatic process of the maxilla. The strongly developed musculature required to operate this massive postcanine dental battery has also affected the architecture of the skull in an obvious manner. The temporalis and masseter muscles were manifestly very large. The former was so large as to cover a large portion of the calvaria and more than reach the midline, since all known adults of both sexes with this portion of the skull preserved have a sagittal crest. The origin of the masseter, especially the superficial portion, is very clearly marked and extensive. Similarly the insertion is extensive on the broad and high ramus. The masseter must thus have been large and powerful. The pterygoid muscles were evidently large also as evidenced, for example, by the relatively great development of the lateral pterygoid plate.

The relatively poor development of the anterior teeth reduces maxillary prognathism. The support needed for the relatively massive postcanine dentition has resulted in a strongly stressed, hence completely flat, nasal area. The massive chewing muscles go with a strongly developed zygomatic region—among other things. These factors result in the typically wide, massive, but either flat or actually dished face of *Paranthropus*. The total lack of a true forehead and the relatively great postorbital constriction make the brow ridges seem massive and projecting; though in actual fact they are not especially strongly developed. The well developed postorbital constriction—which is in part at least associated with the great development of the temporalis muscle, the sagittal crest—which is directly due to the relatively great size of the temporalis as compared to the size of the braincase—and the absence of a true forehead result in a braincase shape quite distinct from that seen in all other known hominids. The robust jugal arch and the attachment requirements of massive nuchal muscles result in a mastoid region which projects laterally significantly more than does the braincase above this region.

It is therefore apparent that the effect of the dental specializations on skull architecture has been far-reaching in *Paranthropus;* more so even than here indicated since only the more obvious features have been mentioned. The result is a skull which bears a considerable superficial resemblance to that of some pongids. However, another important factor has affected skull architecture in the former: erect posture. This has resulted in a very significant lowering of the relative height of the occiput which is quite differently oriented in the erectly bipedal hominids compared to the condition in the quadrupedal pongids or all other terrestrial vertebrates. This clearly distinguishes the skulls of both types of australopithecine from those of pongids, though not from each other, as has been shown by the use of Le Gros Clark's nuchal-area height index.

In *Australopithecus* the dental picture is quite different from that in *Paranthropus.* The anterior teeth are relatively larger and the posterior teeth relatively smaller than in the latter—a condition which very closely resembles that found in early hominines. Because of the large anterior teeth, the face is more prognathous. Owing to the smaller postcanine dentition the chewing forces were weaker and the musculature less strongly developed. This is shown by such things as the much weaker root systems of the postcanine dentition, less robust bone in which the teeth are set, more slender zygomatic bone and zygomatic processes of maxilla and temporal, as well as lateral pterygoid plate. Furthermore the attachments for muscles are far less obvious than in *Paranthropus.* Besides these points there is normally no trace of sagittal crest since the temporalis muscles do not normally approach the dorsal midline of the calvaria at all closely. However, while the evidence listed above indicates clearly that the temporal muscle was smaller in *Australopithecus* than in *Paranthropus,* the lack of sagittal crest is not entirely due to this fact since another factor is also operative in this case: the braincase is relatively higher. The index devised by Le Gros Clark and called by him the supraorbital height index, shows clearly that calvaria height above the superior margin of the orbits is very near the hominine condition in *Australopithecus* but of approximately average pongid condition in *Paranthropus.* The usual absence of a sagittal crest in the former is thus due both to reduced temporalis muscle size and increase in relative height of the braincase.

Both types of australopithecine are hominids, hence the basic similarity of their skulls inherited from a common ancestor. Since both were also erectly bipedal, the modifications of the occiput resulting from this locomotor specialization are also found in both. Beyond this the two skull types differ sharply. The differences, as I have tried to show, appear to belong in each case to a pattern controlled chiefly by the specializations of the dentition. Within the context of hominid affinity and morphology, it is very difficult to see how these differences of dental specialization can be due to anything other than dietary specialization. The dental specializations thus at once reflect also ecological and behavioral features of the creatures. As has been argued elsewhere, it seems clear that *Paranthropus* was a plant eater. The evidence for the presence of grit in the diet suggests that the plant food included roots and bulbs. On the other hand the very great similarity in the dental and skull morphology of *Australopithecus* and early hominines leads one to suppose that their dietary habits were similar and included a substantial carnivorous element. Circumstantial support for this view comes from the climate data which indicates that the vegetarian was present in the Sterkfontein valley in the wetter climatic periods, not the drier ones. One may note that the term 'vegetarian' is used here in the spirit of the Oxford Dictionary definition which is not concerned with what type of plant tissue is eaten but rather with the fact that flesh does not feature in the diet.

If these conclusions are correct—and the morphological differences do not make sense to me if they are not—then they concern a matter of considerable importance since an anatomically specialized vegetarian is far from typical of hominids as we know them. As has already been demonstrated, the morphology of *Australopithecus* links it very closely with hominines; the differences between the latter and it being just the sort of differences normally found between more and less advanced members of a single phyletic sequence. But the morphology of *Paranthropus* is aberrant, no matter with what part of the known *Australopithecus*-hominine sequence one compares it. Furthermore, it is aberrant not only in such major adaptive features as the modified size and proportion along the tooth row—reflecting dietary adaptation—but also in such relatively minor features as the modified crown pattern of dm_1. It is difficult to conceive of the latter as being a feature of real adaptive significance. Consequently both the ecological and behavioral evidence, on the one hand, and the morphological on the other, agree precisely in demonstrating an adaptive difference of considerable magnitude between the *Paranthropus* phyletic line and the *Australopithecus*-hominine one. In effect *Paranthropus* is a pongid-like hominid. Again circumstantial evidence is available which supports this conclusion. At Swartkrans remains of *Paranthropus* and a hominine were found at the same level scattered amongst each other. It must be accepted, therefore, that both forms occurred in the Sterkfontein valley at the same time. In Java the Sangiran site has yielded both "Pithecanthropus" and "Meganthropus" remains. According to von Koenigswald "Pithecanthropus" IV and the type mandible of "Meganthropus" came from the black clay (Putjangan beds) and not far from each other. The 1952 mandible of "Meganthropus" came from the later Kabuh conglomerate of the Sangiran dome, as did "Pithecanthropus" II and III. Evidently, therefore, these two creatures were not merely contemporaneous in this region, but remained so over a substantial period of time. As indicated elsewhere and later in this paper, "Meganthropus" is fairly clearly a *Paranthropus*. The evidence therefore indicates that an early hominine and *Paranthropus* co-existed in two different places separated by many thousands of miles. This is hardly likely to have occurred if the ecological requirements of the two were virtually identical, but is readily understood if the requirements and behavior of the two lines were as different as the present analysis indicates. A final point of significance is that all of the australopithecine material so far discovered falls readily into one or other of the two groups—whether found in the Far East, East Africa or the Sterkfontein valley—and are as different when both occur in the same valley as when occurring far apart. This suggests that the two groups are clear-cut and stable, rather than being merely minor modifications of the same thing.

NON-SOUTH AFRICAN AUSTRALOPITHECINES

Australopithecines are at present known from two areas outside of South Africa: Java and East Africa. The Javanese form was first designated *Meganthropus palaeojavanicus,* but detailed analysis of the available information resulted in this form being placed in the genus *Paranthropus.* The reason for this is that, with only trivial exceptions, the features of the known specimens fall within the observed range of the known *Paranthropus* material. Among these features are the massive mandible and the combination of small canines and incisors with enormously robust postcanine teeth. Although no incisor crowns are known, roots of both are present in the 1952 mandible and, along, with the roots of the canine and other teeth, reflect the characteristic *Paranthropus* condition.

The conclusion that "Meganthropus" is a *Paranthropus* has been contested by von Koenigswald who has, however, produced no cogent evidence to refute it. A few points from the evidence which has been advanced will here be considered briefly to show that in almost every case the disagreement stems from not taking into account the observed variation in the known material.

It is stated that the anterior fovea of P_3 in "Meganthropus" is "broad" while that in australopithecines is "pit like." The observed range of variation in both sorts of australopithecine actually includes a range from pit-like to broader than that of the Javanese form. The latter form is stated to differ from australopithecines in that the lower permanent molars and dm_2 have uninterrupted connection between protoconid and metaconid, while in the australopithecines this is absent. However, both types of australopithecine have both conditions; i.e., both presence in various degrees, or absence of a trigonid crest connecting protoconid and metaconid. Such a crest appears to be normal on dm_2 and common on M_1 in *Paranthropus*. Great stress is placed on the observation that the Javanese form has P_3 larger than P_4 (crown) and that the reverse is true of australopithecines. This is a matter of proportion, not absolute size, and can thus be checked on a good cast since shrinkage will not have been strongly differential between two adjacent crowns of similar shape and size on the same cast. Employing the same measuring technique as that used in the monographic study of the australopithecine dentition, it appears that in the 1941 mandible the two teeth are virtually identical in size with P_4 actually slightly the larger. The roots of these teeth in the 1952 mandible suggest that P_4 may have been relatively even larger in that specimen. In which case it would be fair to say that on available evidence the Javan form has P_3 either subequal to P_4 or larger. The proportion between these two teeth actually varies apparently in the australopithecines, ranging from virtual identity in size to P_4 being considerably larger than P_3. The Javan form is said to differ from the australopithecines in that P_4 is single-rooted in the former and double-rooted in the latter. The 1941 specimen from Java certainly has the buccal face of the root of P_4 single, but the lingual aspect is so much broader that it seems probable that a lingual cleft is present. That is, like the root of P_3 of that specimen, the root is partially divided. On the other hand the 1952 specimen manifestly had double-rooted P_4 on the left side. The crown of this tooth is gone and two roots with two pulp cavities are clearly visible on the cast kindly made available to me by Dr. Marks. Here again the australopithecines exhibit both of these conditions and both can be demonstrated in *Paranthropus* alone.

From these remarks it will be evident that in each case the characters of the Javanese "Meganthropus" fall within the observed range of the corresponding features in the far more extensive collections of australopithecine material. Not only is there no valid evidence differentiating

"Meganthropus" from the australopithecines, but the former exhibits some features which are diagnostic [of] *Paranthropus*. It is therefore reasonable to regard "Meganthropus" as a member of the genus *Paranthropus*.

Leakey has reported the discovery of a good skull of a late adolescent australopithecine from Olduvai. He regards this form as being new and has named it *Zinjanthropus boisei*. It has, however, been shown that the skull and dental characters, and their pattern of specialization, are typically those of *Paranthropus*. As in the case of "Meganthropus," the morphological differences which are held to validate generic distinction from *Paranthropus* either disappear or become very slight if the *observed* range of variation of these features is taken into account. Hence the proposal that this form be placed in the genus *Paranthropus*.

In 1939 Kohl-Larsen discovered in the Laetolil beds near Lake Eyassi in East Africa, a fragment or maxilla containing P_3 and P_4 as well as an isolated upper molar. These were named *Präanthropus* (*a nomen nudum* since no species name was given) by Hennig and *Meganthropus africanus* by Weinert—a conclusion supported by Remane. This matter has been considered at some length and the conclusion drawn that (1) since one form is known only by mandibular and the other only by maxillary material, no evidence exists for placing them in the same genus; (2) since the East African specimen exhibits characters which all fall within the observed range of the corresponding features of *Australopithecus*, the logical course is to refer the material to the latter genus. This is also the opinion of von Koenigswald.

Very recently Leakey has announced the discovery of further material at Olduvai, including a juvenile mandible from the bottom of Bed I. The mandible appears to have the characteristics of *Australopithecus*, though perhaps not the parietals.

We may conclude, therefore, that:—

(1) *Paranthropus* is a very well defined genus which includes a somewhat aberrant type of hominid whose morphological, ecological and behavioral adaptions are quite distinct from those of all other known hominids;

(2) *Paranthropus* is known from South Africa, East Africa and Java;

(3) *Paranthropus* occurs synchronously at the same site, both in Java and South Africa, with an early hominine;

(4) *Australopithecus* differs clearly in morphological, ecological and behavioral adaptions from *Paranthropus*, but exhibits very considerable similarity in these respects with hominines;

(5) *Australopithecus*, like *Paranthropus*, is known from both South Africa and East Africa, but not from the Far East—on currently available evidence.

CULTURAL STATUS OF THE
AUSTRALOPITHECINES

The cultural status achieved by the australopithecines is also related to the subject of this paper. Since the relationship between the australopithecines and the stone industries found with them in the Sterkfontein valley and at Olduvai has been discussed elsewhere recently, the argument will not be repeated here. The conclusion was reached that, despite commonly held opinion to the contrary, there is as yet no proof that either form of australopithecine possessed a settled stone culture.

The evidence in fact favors the conclusion that the australopithecines were primarily no more than tool-users, employing whatever came conveniently to hand in the form of sticks, stones, bones, etc. This aspect of Australopithecus behavior has been dealt with at considerable length by Dart. In my opinion the evidence provided is enough to establish that this form was a tool user, though this is disputed by some other authors. For example Mason holds that since a bone culture (due presumably to *Homo sapiens*) has been found in a Middle Stone Age (end-Pleistocene) deposit and since early hominines were already in existence in australopithecine times, therefore the Makapan Limeworks bone culture should be attributed to a hominine who preyed on *Australopithecus* there. Washburn has argued against *Australopithecus* having had a bone culture. His argument turns on whether the bones associated with this form represent bone accumulation by the latter or by carnivorous animals such as hyaenids. Washburn and Howell accept the bone associated with the Olduvai *Paranthropus* as food remains of this vegetarian form and therefore as proof of predatory activity. However, in the same paragraph they state: "It is very unlikely that the earlier and small-bodied australopithecines (i.e., *Australopithecus*) did much killing, . . ." without explaining why associated faunal remains are accepted as food remains of an australopithecine in the one case but not in the other. The logic of this is not clear, especially as the form for which predation is accepted is a specialized vegetarian while the other is not, and both of these authors believe both forms of australopithecine to have had a stone culture.

Tool-using is by no means confined to primates, as is very well known. It must be deemed highly probable that primates of the degree of development of the australopithecines and which were erectly bipedal, hence having emancipated front limbs, used tools sometimes. Since later hominines are known to have used bone tools—indeed some still do—the australopithecine cannot be held to be too advanced to use bone. But since many authors believe the australopithecines to have *made* stone tools, these authors at least cannot hold them to have been too primitive to have *used* tools. As much bone is associated with *Australopithecus* as a rule, and as some of it appears to have been altered in a manner suggesting use, it seems entirely reasonable to conclude that *Australopithecus* was a tool-user. This is supported, but not proved, by the fact that the two main accumulations of *Australopithecus* remains are older than the first definite evidence of the presence of a more advanced hominid in that general geographic region. However, it would seem that the osteodontokeratic prowess of *Australopithecus* has been over-rated. On general grounds it seems probable that *Paranthropus* also used tools, though such activity may have been much more poorly developed in this vegetarian.

THE ORIGIN OF THE AUSTRALOPITHECINAE

The subfamily Homininae includes forms broadly distinguished morphologically by having erect bipedal posture and a large brain, and behaviorally by relatively complex cultural activity. The latter feature is largely dependent on the large brain since it appears that intelligence of the hominine caliber is not associated with brains smaller than an ill-defined lower limit in volume of the general order of about 800 cc.

The subfamily Australopithecinae includes forms which have the erect posture, but not the large brain, of the hominines. Erect posture is more than adequately proven by the morphology of one virtually complete pelvis with most of the spinal column and a proximal portion of femur; three other adult innominate bones and two juvenile specimens; two proximal ends of femora and two distal ends, as well as a number of skulls showing the structure and orientation of the occiput. The pelvic morphology is very closely similar to that of hominines. There is a short broad innominate with expanded posterior part of the ilium, consequently a well developed, deep, greater sciatic notch, and an iliac crest in the form of a sinusoidal curve when seen from the top; a broad sacrum; distinct lumbar lordosis and femur with a strong lateral lean of the shaft from the vertical when the distal articular surfaces are placed on a flat horizontal surface with the shaft as nearly vertical as possible. The occiput has the near-horizontal disposition found in erect bipeds. Functionally the locomotor mechanism appears to be that of an erect biped. For example the arrangement of the origin and insertion of *gluteus maximus* are such that this muscle must have acted as an extensor of the thigh. *Gluteus medius* must have been an abductor. A well developed anterior inferior iliac spine suggests a powerful *rectus femoris* —and therefore probably *quadriceps* as a whole. This is a very important muscle in erect bipedal locomotion and unsupported standing. A well defined attachment area just below that for the direct head of *rectus femoris,* and a pronounced femoral tubercle, indicate a powerful ilio-femoral ligament strengthened and functioning in the manner of that in hominines and there is even evidence for locking of the knee joint with the leg straight. In function and morphology the locomotor mechanism of australopithecines differed in relatively minor points only from that of hominines.

The subfamily Australopithecinae must have originated from some more primitive primate group. It is not our aim here to inquire closely into what that group might be. The ancestral form may have been a member of the same early hominoid stock to which Proconsul belongs, as is commonly believed, or it may have been part of an independent line already quite distinct at the time the early Miocene East African pongids lived. *Amphipithecus* and *Oreopithecus* suggest that the hominids may have resulted from a line, slow-rate during most of its history, which has been independent since the prosimian stage.

The Australopithecinae would appear to differ from pongids primarily in having erect bipedal posture, a primitive culture and in the nature of the dentition. The main differences between pongid and australopith-ecine dentitions occur in the anterior teeth, especially in the canines, the incisors and P_3. The reduction in canine size, as was suggested already by Charles Darwin, probably resulted from the use of tools. Effective tool-using could only have become possible after erect posture had been acquired. The altered character of the incisors and canines in early hominids may therefore have been a consequence chiefly of changed posture and locomotion. The differences between the pongid and hominid types of P_3 cannot primarily have been due to these changes, however, as is clearly shown by the evidence.

The key feature, then, in the origin of the australopithecines is the change to erect bipedal posture and locomotion. This represents a major adaptive shift which opened up entirely new evolutionary possibilities in this primate line as compared to all known previous ones.

The manner of origin of erect posture is, however, not clear. A critical part of the change centers around the shift in function of *gluteus maximus* from being primarily an abductor of the thigh to an extensor. The power provided by this muscle, especially in the second half of a stride, is largely responsible for the efficacy of upright locomotion; without it the inefficient, shuffling gait seen in pongids walking upright is the best that is possible. Naturally this statement is an oversimplification; but whereas the rest of the pelvic and thigh musculature of pongids and hominids is very similar in function, *gluteus maximus* functions very differently in the two groups and this difference is of great importance in locomotion. It is readily apparent that a short, broad innominate—

with most of the breadth increase being in the posterior part of the ilium
—is a major cause of the change in function of *gluteus maximus,* since
these changes place the origin of the muscle well behind the acetabulum.
This, and the fact that the thigh is normally in at least a fairly extended
position in erect bipeds, places the main line of action of the muscle
behind the hip joint; hence contraction causes extension of the thigh,
not abduction.

Higher primates are much given to rearing up on their hind limbs
under various circumstances normal to their way of life. This probably
occurs mainly for purposes of getting food, improving visibility or play
—though the gibbon often does this in the trees as part of locomotion.
It seems reasonable to suppose that members of a population in which
the point has been reached wherein the erect position *gluteus maximus*
functions chiefly as an extensor, would find it easier to use this posture
or mode of locomotion and would therefore use it more frequently. This
is especially the case if, as seems likely, the population was ground-
dwelling and living in broken forest and grass country, and avoidance
of becoming food for other animals depended chiefly on vision and alert-
ness, rather than on speed, large canine teeth, horns, etc.

If erect posture and locomotion came to be used frequently under such
circumstances, the nature of selection on the locomotor apparatus would
alter considerably. Relatively minor changes only would at that stage
be required to adapt fully to erect posture as the normal habit. Rapid
adaptation to erect posture could thus be expected. The other important
part of this same change, which would make selection favor the new
adaptive shift and increase its rate is, of course, the advantage conferred
by having freed hands. It is now well recognized that even a small advantage is sufficient to allow selection to operate effectively and in this
case the advantage would certainly not be small. Consequently it is very
easy to see how natural selection would bring about a rapid re-adaptation
of the group in respect of posture and locomotion once the innominate
became sufficiently broad and short for the change of function of *gluteus
maximus* to occur.

The difficulty—at least for me—is explaining the process which led
to the changes in the innominate. Starting from the general sort of pelvis
found in the prosimians and arboreal monkeys, it is difficult to see what
manner of locomotory specialization could have brought about the required pelvic changes. Forms specializing in the direction of brachiating
seem to acquire a pelvis which is long and narrow. This is the case in
the pongids as well as in *Ateles,* which is a New World monkey which
brachiates to an appreciable extent. The innominate of the gorilla has
a broadened ilium and it could thus be argued that since the gorilla has
reached a size too large for it to be a successful brachiator and has be-

come largely a ground-dweller, this could be the answer. That is to say, a brachiator which came down out of the trees would have a broadened innominate, which could have been the starting point for the changes culminating in the hominid pelvis. However, this is clearly not the case since the increase in ilium breadth is entirely in the anterior portion of the bone and related to the stoutness of trunk in this animal. There is no shortening of the pelvis and no expansion of the posterior portion of the ilium. Brachiators, whether modified for ground-dwelling or not, do not appear to offer any suggestion of tendencies in the required direction. Postulating that an arboreal form without brachiating specializations descended to the ground does not appear to help either. The chacma baboon can be taken as an example. Here again there is no evidence of a tendency for the pelvis to become short and broad in the required manner. The known non-hominid primate locomotory specializations therefore do not appear to afford any help in explaining how an arboreal primate pelvis could have become modified to the point where changed muscular function could provide a basis for altered selection pressures causing adaptation to erect posture.

Probably the pelvic modifications were associated with changes which were not primarily concerned with locomotion but which rendered the pelvis preadaptive for erect posture, though it is not clear what these could have been.

Whatever the reason for the pelvic changes, it is a fact that they did occur and once they had, a new adaptive trend came into being. It would seem that the process occurred in two phases: the first during which it is difficult to see how selection for erect posture as such could have been operating, can in retrospect be regarded as the preadaptive phase; followed by the adaptive phase during which selection pressures were directly concerned with erect posture. This is, of course, typical of instances where a sharp adaptive shift occurs. In this instance the threshold involves the changed function of *gluteus maximus*. Before this, changes in the pelvis represent a prospective adaptation; after the threshold was crossed, adaptation to the new adaptive zone was rapid under the direct control of selection.

In this connection it is of great significance that, according to Schultz, *Oreopithecus* had a somewhat shortened innominate with a relatively broad ilium. Not only this, but the increased breadth is primarily posteriad in the region of the sacro-iliac articulation, judging from an illustration published by Schultz. No other modern fossil pelvis of which I am aware exhibits a clear tendency toward modification in the direction of that of hominids; but that of *Oreopithecus* unmistakably does, judging by Schultz's paper. Since *Oreopithecus* apparently dates from the very early Pliocene, it would appear to have occurred at an appropriate time to have been an early, pre-bipedal, australopithecine ancestor or a member of a group which provided such an ancestor. This evidence would appear to be very strong support for the opinion of Hürzeler that *Oreopithecus* is related to the known hominids more closely than to pongids or cercopithecoids. What is known of the skull and dental morphology appears to be entirely consistent with such a view. The short face, relatively small canines (still substantial in males), compact tooth row with little or no diastemata, occlusal pattern of the upper molars and vertical chin region, all fit in with the suggested early hominid affinity but do not appear to constitute powerful evidence of such a view. Also the occlusal pattern of the lower molars is not clearly of the dryopithecus pattern type found in hominoids, but this feature is not a serious difficulty with regard to hominid affinity. The strongly bicuspid P_3 does not in any way fit with what is known of either cercopithecoid or pongid dentitions but does suggest hominid affinity.

Apart from *Oreopithecus*, hominids are the only known higher primates which are characterized by having a fully bicuspid P_3. This feature, along with the innominate which shows a tendency to shorten and for the ilium to expand posteriorly, appears to me to suggest a very real possibility that *Oreopithecus* is part of the hominid stream of evolution, though not necessarily a hominid.

In any event, by whatever route and for whatever reason it may have occurred, the adaptive shift in the locomotor apparatus *did* occur and so gave rise to an erectly bipedal primate. This was the first hominid and the ancestor of the known australopithecines. Since vegetarianism in its broadest sense is characteristic of non-hominid higher primates, it is probable that the stock in which this change occurred was also primarily vegetarian. There is no reason to suppose that diet could have been an important factor in the locomotory changes. Furthermore, if hominine carnivorousness had had a very long history, then one could expect to find some clear evidence of dental specialization for herbivorousness in the later forms. This is not the case. We may assume, therefore, that the first product of the adaptive shift centering around emerging erect posture—that is to say, the first australopithecine—was a predominantly bipedal vegetarian.

Since the conclusion has already been reached that *Paranthropus* is a vegetarian, it is worth inquiring into the possibility that this form could be a little-modified descendant of the early type of australopithecine. As has been seen, erect posture is likely to have led to tool-using and this probably in turn, would lead to reduction of canine teeth. One might expect, however, that reduction of canines would proceed more rapidly in a vegetarian tool-user. Until the use of tools had been appreciably refined, substantial canines would be advantageous to a meat eater. *Paran-*

thropus has much reduced canines and incisors, but large postcanine teeth and thus agrees with expectation. But the skull in some respects is primitive for a hominid. There is no true forehead, the brow ridges are rendered prominent by a well-developed postorbital constriction and the vertex rises very little above the level of the supraorbital ridges. This latter point is well demonstrated by the supraorbital height index of Le Gros Clark. The value of this index for *Australopithecus* (Sts. 5) is 61 (68 according to Le Gros Clark, 74 according to Ashton and Zuckerman). This approaches the figure for *modern* hominines which, according to Ashton and Zuckerman averages about 70 and ranges from about 63 to about 77. The value for several specimens of Pekin man, determined from illustrations, appears to range from about 63 to 67. On the other hand the three great apes have mean values for this index which range from 49 for the orang to 54 for the gorilla according to Ashton and Zuckerman. The figure obtained for *Paranthropus* from Swartkrans is 50 and that for *Paranthropus* from Olduvai, determined from photographs, appears to be just over 50. It will therefore be seen that this feature (which reflects some aspects of cranial, and presumably also brain, morphology) presents a typically pongid appearance in *Paranthropus* but closely approximates the early—and even modern—hominine condition in *Australopithecus*. If the conclusion that *Australopithecus* was carnivorous to a significant degree is sound, then this is yet a further feature in which this genus is more advanced in the hominine direction than was *Paranthropus*.

The fact that a characteristic feature of the hominine skull—relatively high-domed calvaria—had not yet started to appear in *Paranthropus* but was already well advanced in *Australopithecus,* and the vegetarian specialization of the former, indicate that it is the more primitive of the two australopithecine types. It would therefore seem probable that *Paranthropus* is a descendant of the earliest australopithecines which retains the same basic adaptational features of that early stock.

If *Paranthropus* represents basically the original australopithecine stock and *Australopithecus* represents an adaptively different line evolving in a different direction, how did the latter line arise?

It seems unlikely that the earliest australopithecines can have been as recent in age as the Pleistocene since the two forms were already well differentiated early in that period. On the other hand it seems logical to suppose that tool-using, tool-making and increased brain size are virtually inevitable consequences of erect posture and that they will have followed the origin of the latter fairly rapidly in terms of the geological time scale. It is therefore likely that australopithecines will have originated in the latter half of the Tertiary; probably in the Pliocene, possibly in the Miocene.

There is reason to believe that most of the Miocene was a period of expanding forests in Africa, but that the late Miocene and Pliocene was a time of desiccation and shrinking forests. The Kalahari sands of central and southern Africa throw some light on this matter. The original Kalahari sands overlie unconformably the Kalahari Limestone plain which resulted from the African erosion cycle of early to mid-Tertiary times. However they pre-date the cutting of the Kalahari rivers into the Limestone in the Lower Pleistocene. It would therefore seem that between the wetter period of the earlier Miocene and that of the early Pleistocene, considerable desiccation occurred, during which the extensive deposits of Kalahari sand were formed. These extend from fairly far south in South Africa right up into the Congo basin. The studies of botanists and of entomologists studying humicolous faunas support these conclusions in demonstrating marked forest expansion in the Miocene with equally marked recession in the Pliocene, leaving residual forests in a ring round the central Congo basin and in East Africa, and with a certain amount of expansion again in the Pleistocene.

One may conclude from this that suitable habitats for the vegetarian, original australopithecine (*Paranthropus*) line will have become increasingly scarce through the late Tertiary. This will have been as true for other forms requiring forest or broken forest habitat and reasonably moist conditions, hence it could be expected that competition for such environments may have been more severe than usual. On the other hand grass savannah and other more arid environments will have expanded at this time and so provided increased opportunity for animals adapted to, or capable of adapting to, such conditions.

The climatic changes will not have been sudden. Australopithecines living in areas which subsequently became semiarid or arid, will have found that the dry season of the year gradually became longer and drier. Finding food will thus have become more difficult in these times and it is reasonable to suppose that insects, reptiles, small mammals, birds' eggs and nestlings, etc., will have been eaten to supplement their diet. It is known that purely vegetarian primates will eat meat readily in captivity and that baboons, for example, will upon occasion do so in the wild. Taking to a semi-carnivorous diet under environmental pressure could therefore occur fairly easily. As desiccation proceeded such a deme will have found that it had to rely on the seasonal supplement to its normal diet more frequently and to a greater degree. Under these circumstances it could be expected that the population density will have dropped—to vanishing point in some areas. But it is not inconceivable that in at least some areas the creatures will have adapted reasonably well to altering circumstances and adopted a certain amount of carnivorousness as a normal part of their way of life.

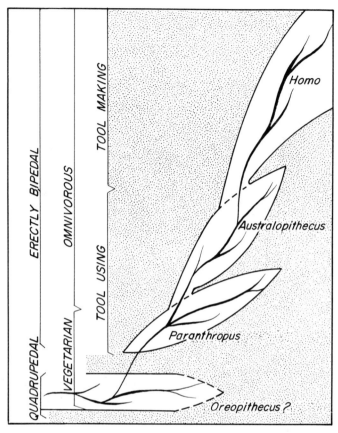

FIGURE 17–1—Diagrammatic representation of the more important adaptive zones occupied by the hominid evolutionary stream. The threshold between the quadrupedal and bipedal stages is a major one between essentially discontinuous zones. The second and third thresholds—change to omnivorous diet and tool manufacture—are of great importance but did not involve clearly discontinuous zones. It should be emphasized that this is not a family tree but an adaptive grid. (Adapted by Jacquelyn Hetrick.)

However, with such modifications in their environment, selection pressures will have altered. What may have been at that stage no more than a fairly elementary level of tool-using will have had obvious advantages in the changing food situation. Improved tool-using will have been favored by selection and any improvements will have made the creatures better adapted to carnivorousness. Similarly, improved intelligence will have had obvious benefits under the circumstances and will therefore certainly have been favored by selection. Since there appears to be some relationship between intelligence and brain volume with regard to that

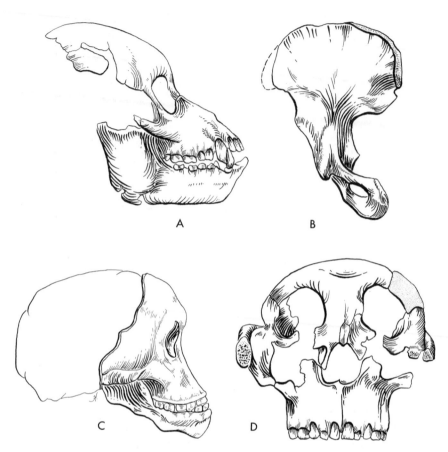

FIGURE 17–2—(A) Although the skull of *Proconsul* has been crushed and distorted by the pressure of overlying material, it nevertheless provides evidence of *Proconsul africanus,* a small ape of the Lower Miocene, which was not completely adapted to a brachiating mode of tree life. Also unspecialized were its relatively smooth frontal bone and front teeth. (B) The broken pelvic fragment of Makapanskat man, an early Pleistocene australopithecine, was broader than that of today's pongids and closer in structure to that of man, providing evidence of its bipedal stance. (C) The Taung infant was the first of the australopithecine fossils to be unearthed. Although its small brain barred it at first from membership among the Hominidae, this fossil, as well as the other australopithecines, are now accepted as hominid. (D) The discovery of *Zinjanthropus* at Olduvai gorge by Louis S. B. Leakey in 1959 provided evidence of the tool-using character of the australopithecines. (Drawings not to scale. Adapted by Jacquelyn Hetrick.)

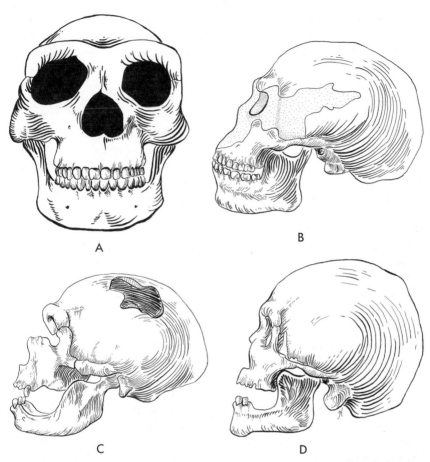

FIGURE 17–3—(A) By the time of Peking man, about four hundred thousand years ago, human brain size had doubled over that of the australopithecines, and *Homo erectus,* mid-Pleistocene man, had spread widely over the unglaciated areas of the Old World. (B) The early part of the fourth glaciation saw humans much like ourselves in Europe, Africa, and western Asia. Skhul, found in Israel, is typical of the Upper Pleistocene populations before the evolution of *sapiens* men. (C) In western Europe, specialized populations of "Neanderthal" humans evolved during the fourth glaciation, presumably in response to the narrow set of climatic conditions that prevailed. Shown here is the fossil from La Chapelle-aux-Saints. (D) Early fossils of man are scarce in the New World. Tepexpan, somewhat more than ten thousand years old, is believed to be one the earliest representatives of human populations in North America. (Drawings not to scale. Adapted by Jacquelyn Hetrick.)

portion of the range of primate brains between the brain size of the larger pongids and that of the early hominines, it is probable that this part of the process of selection for improved intelligence will have been accompanied by increase in brain volume. Improved intelligence will have led, in turn, to improved tool-using ability and this to even better adaptation to partially carnivorous diet and general adaptation to a more arid environment.

The changed environmental circumstances resulting from the known desiccation of a substantial part of Africa during the later Tertiary could therefore very easily have led to a second adaptive shift and the establishment of a second phyletic line in the australopithecines in which carnivorousness and an enhanced level of cultural activity were important features. *Australopithecus* is evidently just such a line and it is of interest that this form is present in the Sterkfontein valley in the more arid periods, while *Paranthropus* is present only in the wetter periods. The canines of *Australopithecus* are appreciably less reduced than those of *Paranthropus;* suggesting that the former genus arose from the *Paranthropus* line well before the reduction of the anterior teeth in the latter had reached the stage found in the known forms. The increase in adaptation to arid or semi-arid conditions and carnivorousness will have kept the canines as large as they originally were or even increased their size slightly.

Naturally, once the line adapting to drier conditions had become established, producing *Australopithecus* as we know it, its evolution would not stop there. The selection pressures operating—and entirely different from those controlling the direction of the *Paranthropus* line—would not cease to operate and therefore it is virtually inevitable that adaptation would be carried well past the *Australopithecus* stage. By this stage it would appear that the cultural situation would be the vital factor. The need for tool-using in successfully adapting to the different way of life would, as indicated, place a high premium on intelligence. As this improved, presumably by an increase in size of the cerebral cortex so as to provide increased correlation and association areas, cultural facility also improved. When the modification of the brain had proceeded to the point where hominine levels of intellectual ability began to appear—apparently when the brain volume reached the order of 750–1000 cc.—facility with tools reached a point where a characteristically hominine phenomenon appeared: the deliberate manufacture of tools for particular purposes. This provided still further scope for development and it appears that increase in brain size now occurred rapidly to approximately the modern volume. At this point it seems that correlation between brain size and intelligence is not especially close. Cultural activity did not improve as rapidly at first, but subsequently the improved use of the cultural capacity occurred with rapidly increasing momentum. "Telanthropus," from Swartkrans, was apparently an early member of this hominine stage. It has now been included in the genus *Homo*. From the Sterkfontein valley have come, therefore, members of both the major lines of australopithecine evolution as well as members of both stages of the *Australopithecus-Homo* stream.

It seems to me that the adaptive shift occasioned by increasing aridity and the necessity to use meat as a normal part of the diet was a second critical point in the evolution of hominines. The first was the adaptive shift to erect posture; this provided the possibility of becoming an efficient tool-user. The second point was that of being forced by changing environmental conditions to take to meat-eating, thus placing a heavy premium on tool-using and improved intelligence. The development of the hominine grade of organization was a natural consequence. The third point or threshold was that where simple cultural activity and increasing intelligence reached a stage where tool-using gave way to tool-making and the typical cultural activity and approach to environmental challenges of man appeared. The potentialities which then came into existence are still being explored and developed.

APPENDIX

The genera *Australopithecus* and *Paranthropus* were defined [in 1954] in terms of the information then available. At present only three genera are recognized by me in the family Hominidae; the above two and *Homo*. These three are defined below. It is recognized that not all of the characters mentioned are independent: in such definitions it is not easy to indicate overall patterns.

Genus Paranthropus

This genus includes vegetarian hominids with an endocranial volume of the order of 450–550 cc. Forehead completely absent; supraorbital height index about 50 (about the average for pongids). Bony face either quite flat or actually dished. Distinction between floor of nasal cavity and subnasal maxillary surface totally absent. Zygomatic arch strongly developed; temporal fossa large. Palate appreciably deeper posteriorly than anteriorly. Lateral pterygoid plate strongly developed and large. Sagittal crest normally present in both sexes. Internal mandibular arch contour V-shaped. Ascending ramus vertical and high. Tooth row compact, without diastemata. Anterior teeth very small compared to postcanine teeth. Canine small and wears down from tip. Virtually completely molarised dm_1 with anterior fovea centrally situated and with complete margin. Maxillary canine and incisor sockets in almost straight line across front of palate. Cultural development relatively poor.

GENUS AUSTRALOPITHECUS

This genus includes omnivorous hominids with an endocranial volume of the order of 450–550 cc. Distinct forehead, but never markedly developed; supraorbital height index about 60. Bony face moderately—not completely—flat. Distinction between floor of nasal cavity and subnasal maxillary surface present but poor. Zygomatic arch moderately developed; temporal fossa of medium size. Palate of more or less even depth. Lateral pterygoid plate relatively small. Sagittal crest normally absent— may occur in extreme cases. Internal mandibular arch contour V-shaped. Ascending ramus usually sloping backward and of moderate height. Tooth row compact, no diastemata. Anterior and postcanine teeth harmoniously proportioned. Canine wears down from tip, moderately large in all known cases. Incompletely molarised dm_1, anterior fovea displaced lingualward and open to that side. Maxillary incisor and canine sockets in parabolic curve. Cultural development relatively poor.

GENUS HOMO

This genus includes omnivorous hominids with an endocranial volume in excess of 750 cc. and with considerable variability. Distinct forehead always present—may be markedly developed; supraorbital height index above 60. Bony face aquiline to moderately flat. Distinction between floor of nasal cavity and subnasal maxillary surface always sharp. Zygomatic arch moderately to poorly developed; temporal fossa medium to small. Palate of more or less even depth. Lateral pterygoid plate relatively small. Sagittal crest never present. Internal mandibular arch contour U-shaped. Ascending ramus usually sloping and of moderate height but rather variable. Tooth row normally compact and without diastemata— latter present in some early individuals. Anterior and postcanine teeth harmoniously proportioned. Canines wear down from tip; moderately large in early members to small in later forms. Incompletely molarized dm_1, anterior fovea displaced lingualward and usually open to that side. Maxillary incisor and canine sockets in parabolic curve. Cultural development moderate to very strong.

18

BONES OF CONTENTION

Wilfrid E. Le Gros Clark

*There may be some risks in washing the dirty linen of
paleoanthropologists in public in a book of readings directed
to nonprofessionals. On the other hand, it may come as no
surprise to students to learn that the history of tracing the course
of fossil man has had its blind alleys, its errors, and its
disagreements. In this article the eminent British anatomist,
Sir Wilfrid E. Le Gros Clark, administers a series of gentle but
firm rebukes to some of his colleagues who have persisted in the
misapplication of learning in unraveling the human evolutionary
story. This article may almost have the form of an historical
reminiscence, but many of the ideas Le Gros Clark criticizes
are found today in the work of reputable anthropologists.*

When Darwin published *The Descent of Man* in 1871, he affirmed his
conviction that "Man is descended from some lower form, notwithstanding that connecting links have not hitherto been discovered," and as may
be supposed, the opponents of the idea of evolution were very quick to
make play with the absence of such links. It is true that the archaic
fossil skull and associated limb bones of Neanderthal, discovered in 1856,
had been described by Professor D. Schaaffhausen of Bonn University
as exceeding all modern types "in those peculiarities of conformation
which lead to the conclusion of their belonging to a barbarous and
savage race," and, in fact, Darwin did make a passing reference to the
skull in his book, but only to note that in this ancient type of man the
size of the brain was evidently quite considerable. Huxley made a special
study of the Neanderthal skull, of which the results were published as
one of his essays in *Man's Place in Nature* in 1863. He was very cautious
in expressing his opinions on the significance of this fossil material, for,
in spite of the fact that he refers to its "most extraordinary characters"

(From *Journal of the Royal Anthropological Institute*, Vol. 88, 1959, pages
131–145. By permission of the author and the publisher.)

and believed it to be "the most pithecoid of human crania yet discovered," he doubted whether it differed to such a degree from the skull of primitive modern races such as the Australian aboriginal to merit a taxonomic distinction. Referring to the Neanderthal remains as a whole, he concluded that "at most, they demonstrate the existence of a man whose skull may be said to revert somewhat towards the pithecoid type." This particular remark is an excellent example of Huxley's insight, for the accumulation of remains of fossil man since his day has now made it probable that the extreme, or specialized, Neanderthal type of later Mousterian date was indeed the result of a retrogression from an earlier and more generalized type which was more closely akin to *Homo sapiens.* But, in spite of his careful and judicious appraisal of the evidence, Huxley very quickly found himself involved in the controversies which ensued and which gave expression to a diversity of opinions advanced by other anthropologists. Quite extreme views were expressed by some of these authorities—for example, that the man of Neanderthal was a microcephalic idiot or suffered from some pathological deformity, or even (according to Professor Mayer of Bonn) that he was only "a rickety Mongolian Cossack belonging to the hordes driven by Russia, through Germany, into France in 1814." With the evidence now available of numerous remains of the Neanderthal type of man (found at different sites in Europe, the Near East, and North Africa), it may seem perplexing that eminent authorities offered such contrary interpretations of the original specimens found in 1856, and also that they expressed their opinions with such vehemence. In fact, however, it is the case that discoveries of fossil hominids which appear (at any rate in some respects) to fulfill Darwin's predictions of connecting links always have aroused controversies of a polemical nature, and the controversy in which Huxley found himself involved was merely the first of a long series of contentious disputes of a similar type. We may recall that the remains of *Pithecanthropus,* discovered by Dubois in 1891, were at one time claimed by some critics to be not human at all, but those of an extinct and hitherto unknown type of giant ape. And in more recent days, the early discoveries of *Australopithecus* in South Africa were almost immediately followed by conflicting claims of an extreme kind, too hastily put forward on insufficient or mistaken evidence. Thus, on the one hand it was claimed that these primitive hominids were so advanced as to be acquainted with the use of fire, while the disputants of the opposing camp claimed with equal vehemence on the basis of inadequate, and in some cases faulty, statistical data that they were not to be differentiated from the apes.

Undoubtedly, one of the main factors responsible for the frequency with which polemics enter into controversies on matters of paleo-anthropology is a purely emotional one. It is a fact (which it were well to recognize) that it is extraordinarily difficult to view with complete objectivity the evidence for our own evolutionary origin, no doubt because the problem is such a very personal problem. Even scientists of today may not find it easy to clear their minds entirely of an emotional element when they come to consider the evidence in detail, and this emotional element is only too frequently betrayed by the phraseology with which disputants claim with equal insistence to be assessing the same evidence dispassionately. It is partly for this reason (as I shall mention later) that it is an advantage, in discussing the earlier stages of hominid evolution, to avoid altogether the colloquial and unscientific terms "man" and "human" (which have a wide and not easily definable connotation), and to use only those terms (such as *Hominidae, Homo,* and *Homo sapiens*) proper to the zoological nomenclature of taxonomy. Naturally, the problem of human origin is of quite compelling importance, so much so that each fossil discovery which appears to throw light on it immediately arouses interest to the extent that interpretations of its possible significance tend always to be advanced before detailed and systematic comparative studies (which may take a long time) have been completed. This tendency for premature appraisals has the further unfortunate effect that, should the author's first interpretation of a fossil specimen prove by subsequent and more extended analysis to be mistaken, he may well find it difficult to retract unconditionally his original opinion. And so the controversies are apt to be prolonged far beyond their limits of usefulness.

Apart from these general considerations (which have reference to defects of human nature rather than defects of scientific methodology), it has become apparent in recent years that much of the controversial character of discussions on fossil man is commonly based on misconceptions of well-recognized principles of paleontology, or even on quite simple terminological confusions. I should like to take the opportunity . . . to draw attention to some of these sources of misunderstanding, with particular reference to certain relevant remarks of Huxley's which we should do well to remember. It is my hope that, by so doing, some of the confusion of ideas which still complicate discussions on the evolutionary origin of Man may be avoided.

TYPE SPECIMENS AND TYPICAL SPECIMENS

Probably the one single factor which above all others has unduly, and quite unnecessarily, complicated the whole picture of human phylogeny is the tendency for the taxonomic individualization of each fossil skull or fragment of a skull by assuming it to be a new type which is specifically, or even generically, distinct from all others. As a result, the species and genera of fossil hominids have been multiplied far beyond the limits which would be regarded as justifiable in any other equivalent group of Primates, and this has introduced a complexity into problems of human evolution which is quite illusory. Possibly one of the reasons for this tendency is the misunderstanding of the term "type specimen" by those not fully conversant with the principles of taxonomy. When a fossil specimen in found which is adjudged on morphological evidence to represent a new species or a new genus, it is given an appropriate specific or generic name, and the specimen is taken to be the "type" on which the new name is based. But, as Simpson has emphasized, "Types are almost never really average specimens within a species, or fully central species in a genus. Types were formerly, and still are by many students, supposed to be not only name-bearers but also the bases on which group concepts are erected and the standards of comparison for those concepts." Anthropologists and others have undoubtedly tended to fall into this error of assuming a type specimen to be a typical specimen, so that any newly discovered fossil which deviates even to a slight degree from the "type" has commonly been assigned to a supposedly new species or genus. Thus, for example, within the limits of what is evidently a common taxonomic group comprising the genus *Pithecanthropus* there have been arbitrarily created a variety of "types" such as *Pithecanthropus, Sinanthropus, Meganthropus, Homo modjokertensis*, and so forth. Again, the remains of Early Mousterian man have by several authorities been split up into an astonishing diversity of "types" such as *Homo krapinensis, Homo steinheimensis*, and *Palaeoanthropus palestinus*. Apart from the fact that there is no sound morphological evidence for making such taxonomic distinctions, the common practice of doing so has had the unfortunate result of obscuring the all-important principle that populations, and not individuals, are the units of evolution, and that it is fundamentally the variation within a population which provides the raw material available for evolution. Thus, there has been an inevitable tendency, in attempting to construe the course of human phylogeny, to focus attention on the arbitrary individual "type" and not on the broad range of populations of which they are merely individual representatives (and in some cases, perhaps, rather extreme variants). The general outline of human evolution becomes at once simplified, and more intelligible, if the fossil record is considered in its proper perspective, bearing in mind that the evidence now available makes it increasingly apparent that at each phase of evolution the hominid population then existing included a sufficiently wide range of variants to provide the opportunity for selective processes to lead on to the next phase. For example, the *Pithecanthropus* group, as we now know from their remains in Java and China, showed a high variability in features such as the relative development of the frontal region of the skull and the size of the jaws and teeth, and their cranial capacity actually ranged from 775 cc. to as much as 1,200 cc. So high a variability may be correlated with the fact that in the Early and Middle Pleistocene the rate of hominid evolution was proceeding rather rapidly with the deployment of relatively small (and often contiguous) populations into widely dispersed areas with contrasting and changing environments. A population displaying the wide variability of *Pithecanthropus* would clearly have provided a particularly favorable opportunity for selective processes to modify its genetic constitution, and thus to produce a systematic shift in the total range of variation to the point where the transition to the more advanced genus *Homo* would be effected. The unfortunate splitting of the australopithecine fossils into numerous genera and species has also had the effect of introducing quite a spurious complexity into what may be termed the "*Australopithecus* phase" of hominid evolution, for, again, there is no valid morphological basis for recognizing in their variety more than one genus. Like *Pithecanthropus*, they show a considerable range of variation in skull form and cranial capacity and, while broadly contemporaneous in the geological sense, they probably represent a sequence of regional varieties of a local nature (the equivalent, perhaps of the racial varieties of modern *Homo sapiens*) which may actually have occupied the Transvaal region over a period of a hundred thousand years or more. As a matter of fact, it is now generally agreed that the initial multiplication of australopithecine genera and species made on the basis of the earlier discoveries was unwarranted, but there still remains some disagreement regarding the validity of the genus *Telanthropus*. It was on the basis of small jaw fragments found at one of the australopithecine sites, which in their size and dental morphology appear to approach more closely to more advanced hominids, that the separate genus *Telanthropus* was created, and on anatomical grounds Robinson has suggested that it is "an australopithecine which had reached euhominid status." It seems doubtful, however, whether a generic distinction is justified even in this case (at any rate by reference to such fragmentary material), for it is not clear that the morphological differences between "*Telanthropus*" and *Australopithecus* exceed those known to exist in other hominid genera. One of the main points of interest of the australopithecines, surely, is just the very fact that as a generic group they do display such a high degree of variability, for this obviously could account for a relatively rapid transition to a more advanced phase of hominid evolution by selective processes.

In the case of the Early Mousterian populations of Europe, if it is recognized that such differences as their individual remains may show in skull structure and so forth are merely the expression of the variability of a single taxonomic group (and not indicative of so many different genera and species), it again becomes clear at once that they could have provided the genetic material for a subsequent diversification on the one hand into the extreme (or "classical") Neanderthal type of later Mousterian date, and on the other into modern races of *Homo sapiens*. It seems now almost certain that this actually did occur, particularly on the evidence of the high variability of the sample of the Upper Pleistocene population found at Mount Carmel. The suggestion that this population consisted of different taxonomic groups living in close association, or that it represents the results of cross-breeding between two different species, *Homo neanderthalensis* and *Homo sapiens*, seems much less plausible and less probable. At any rate, such an interpretation is perhaps hardly justified on the basis of such limited material.

The multiplication of species on the basis of other fossil skulls which it now seems clear are not morphologically distinguishable from *Homo sapiens* has been due simply to the failure to recognize the range of variation to be found in modern races of mankind, and it has had the unfortunate effect of distorting considerably the perspective of Upper Pleistocene man. For example, the designation of the Combe-Capelle skull, found in Aurignacian deposits in the Dordogne, as a separate species *Homo aurignaciensis,* as well as other instances of similar specific distinctions, has tended to obscure the important point that our own species *Homo sapiens* is in fact very ancient, and that Aurignacian man and his immediate predecessors, who lived about 30,000 years ago, were not different anatomically from ourselves. Such specific designations, similarly based on no valid evidence, have also tended to obscure the fact that *Homo sapiens* was very widely spread over the Old World in those early times.

Apart from other considerations, it is an interesting but not generally recognized fact that practically none of the genera and species of fossil hominids which have from time to time been created have any validity at all in zoological nomenclature. A newly named genus or species only becomes valid if it is accompanied by a formal diagnosis which clearly states in what respects the new type differs from other known genera or species, and it is perhaps rather surprising that paleo-anthropologists have not been in the habit of conforming to this important principle of taxonomy. There is little doubt that the fossil record of the Hominidae would be immediately and immensely clarified if all those taxonomic terms which have not been validated by a formal diagnosis should once and for all be discarded (unless, indeed, it should be found possible by detailed comparative studies to validate them in this way).

In order to avoid the confusions of thought which result from the unwarranted multiplication of new species and genera, it should be accepted that, in future, no new genus is to be created on the basis of a fossil specimen unless it can be demonstrated with reasonable assurance *that the morphological characters of the specimen deviate from those already known to an extent at least equivalent to the differences between recognized and already well-established species or genera in allied groups.* Further, in presenting the formal diagnosis which is necessary for the validation of a new species or genus, the diagnosis should be so framed as to cover a range of variation at least equivalent to that found in allied groups. In this connection, it is well to bear in mind the remarkable range of variation common to all the higher Primates, that is to say, in both the Hominidae and the anthropoid ape family, a characteristic of these groups which has been sufficiently emphasized in the numerous publications which have been recorded in the systematic studies of Professor A. H. Schultz. Indeed, these studies raise serious doubts whether even the range of variation observed in the extinct genera *Australopithecus* and *Pithecanthropus* is really as exceptional as some have supposed.

Only by careful attention to these desiderata will it be possible to give expression to the hope implied in a recent statement by Dr. Ernst Mayr that "the time has now come . . . for bold hypotheses aiming to make sense of the diversity of remains of fossil man. Such hypotheses can be made only through analogy with the variation, in space and time, of other species of mammals." As I have tried to make clear, the "diversity" to which Dr. Mayr refers is to a large extent quite illusory as far as their generic and specific labels are concerned.

EVOLUTIONARY TRENDS AND LINEAR SEQUENCES

When Huxley first studied the fossil evidence for the evolution of the horse family, he suggested that the European fossil genera *Paleotherium—Anchitherium—Hipparion—Equus* represent a temporal series making the gradual evolution of the modern horse. He was actually very careful in giving expression to this interpretation, however, for he regarded it as "highly probable that many forms of *Anchitherium*-like and *Hipparion*-like animals existed . . . and it is highly improbable that the particular species of *Anchitherium* or *Hipparion* which happen to have been discovered should be precisely those which have formed part of the direct line of the horse's pedigree." The fact that the direct line of the evolution of the modern horse was later found to be represented by American fossil genera such as *Miohippus, Merychippus,* and *Pliohippus,* and that Huxley's genera were collateral offshoots of the main line, was not really of very great importance from the point of view of the objective demonstration of equid evolution, for the latter demonstrated clearly enough the main trend of evolutionary development which had characterized the group. It may be put this way. Trends of evolution can be inferred from a consideration of the end-results. Fossil evidence may confirm the fact of these trends and, if sufficiently complete, may demonstrate an actual evolutionary sequence in terms of successive types. It is useful to recognize this difference between an evolutionary trend and an actual linear, or ancestor-descendant, sequence, for it is only rarely that the fossil record of any taxonomic group is sufficiently abundant to permit the establishment of a true linear sequence. In the case of hominid evolution, the fossil record is still not adequate to allow firm conclusions regarding the entire linear sequence of the Hominidae which culminated in the emergence of *Homo sapiens,* but it is sufficiently adequate to demonstrate some of the main evolutionary trends which have occurred in human phylogenesis.

The importance of recognizing the distinction between the fossil evidence of trends and the evidence of sequences has reference to those controversies aroused by the discovery of fossil hominid remains which seem to be based on a confusion of the two conceptions. Huxley himself put the matter very clearly when he wrote "it is convenient to distinguish those intermediate forms between two groups, which do not represent the actual passage from the one group to the other, as *intercalary* types, from those *linear* types which, more or less approximately, indicate the nature of the steps by which the transition from one group to the other was effected." So far as the later stages of hominid evolution are concerned, the series *Australopithecus—Pithecanthropus—Homo* may well represent a linear sequence, for, in fact, the gradations from the one type to the other are quite close, and also, as it now appears, they comprise a temporal succession; such a proposition therefore, is a perfectly reasonable interpretation of the evidence *at present available.* Even so, however, it must be regarded as no more than a provisional interpretation until a more complete fossil record of these genera has accrued. On the other hand, there can be no question but that this series represents an evolutionary *trend.*

BRAIN SIZE AND INTELLIGENCE

Following the publication of Darwin's *Origin of Species,* much of the ensuing anatomical controversies on the question of man's relationship to lower animals naturally concerned the differences in the size and proportions of the brain. The large brain of modern *Homo sapiens* is such an obvious and distinctive human trait, and is in such strong contrast with the smaller brain of the large apes, that some authorities were tempted to regard it as sufficient justification for the widest separation of man in any scheme of classification. But apart from the size factor, attempts were made to prove that in certain structural details the human brain was also quite distinct from the ape's brain and, as is well known, one of these features (the hippocampus minor) provided the central theme for a celebrated debate in which Huxley took part. In the second edition of Darwin's *Descent of Man* there is included an appendix by Huxley on the comparative anatomy of the human and ape brain in which he demonstrated that they are constructed on the same basic pattern, and that the differences between the two are not greater than those which occur between the large apes and the Catarrhine monkeys. He went even further, and in considering the gradations in cerebral development which are shown in the whole series of modern Primates he notes that "it is a remarkable circumstance that though, so far as our present knowledge extends, there *is* one true structural break in the series of forms of Simian brains, this hiatus does not lie between Man and the man-like apes, but between the lower and lowest Simians; or, in other words, between the Old and New World apes and monkeys, and the Lemurs."

With our present knowledge, it has become evident that even in modern man the size of the brain shows an extraordinary variability; for example, the cranial capacity (which is closely correlated with brain volume) ranges in individuals of "normal" intelligence from less than 900 cc. to about 2,300 cc. And yet, so far as it has been possible to apply appropriate tests, there is within such limits no marked correlation between the brain size and intelligence. To the paleoanthropologist this lack of correlation is particularly disconcerting, for it means that he has no sure method of assessing the mental capacity of extinct types of hominid simply by reference to cranial capacity. Incidentally, Darwin himself remarked that "no one supposes that the intellect . . . of any two men can be accurately gauged by the cubic content of their skulls." In the extinct genus *Pithecanthropus* the cranial capacity (as already noted) was also highly variable, but the mean volume was about 1,000 cc. which is considerably lower than that of modern *Homo sapiens* (1,350 cc.), and the capacity of the smallest skull of *Pithecanthropus* so far found has been estimated to be not more than about 775 cc. Since the largest cranial capacity recorded for a gorilla is 685 cc., the actual volume difference between apes and *Pithecanthropus* seems to bear no relation to the difference in mental powers, for it is known from archeological evidence that those representatives of *Pithecanthropus* which inhabited China could fashion stone implements, and they even knew the use of fire for culinary purposes. From what has been said, it seems evident that actual brain mass by itself (at any rate up to certain limits) can hardly be used as a direct index of intelligence in the study of fossil hominids. This question became one of great importance when skulls of *Australopithecus* were excavated at various sites in South Africa. One of the outstanding features of this Early Pleistocene hominid (which was recognized from the first) is the remarkably small size of the brain; indeed, it was this very apelike feature which led Dart to propose the generic name *Australopithecus* (i.e. Southern "Ape"). We still have no accurate data indicating the range of variation in its cranial capacity; on the available evidence it probably ranged from about 450 cc. to about 700 cc.—that is to say, at its upper limits the cranial capacity was closely comparable with the largest figure for the gorilla. Unfortunately, however, while the cranial capacity can provide an indication of the brain size, it can tell us nothing of the intrinsic neural organization which may be supposed to be much more closely related to intellectual functions than mere mass of nervous tissue. The importance of recognizing this point is relevant to the evidence, lately accumulated, suggesting the possibility that the australopithecines may have been capable of fashioning stone implements of a very primitive kind. Such implements have been found *in situ* in consolidated breccia deposits also containing the remains of *Australopithecus* (but containing no remains, so far discovered, of a more advanced type of hominid). The association of skeletal relics of hominids with stone artifacts would in most cases lead to a reasonable supposition that the former were responsible for making the latter. But there has quite naturally been an element of doubt in the case of *Australopithecus,* partly because of preconceived (but as yet unsubstantiated) assumptions regarding the minimum size of the brain requisite for the ability to fabricate tools, and it will be necessary to await further evidence before it can be definitely decided whether this primitive hominid was a toolmaker. However, apart from this question, in discussions on the taxonomic status of *Australopithecus* there has been a curious misunderstanding based on the *non sequitur* that a large brain is an essential feature of "true man," therefore *Australopithecus* is a "true ape." This type of argument at once makes clear the essential need either to define these colloquial terms in scientific phraseology or, preferably, to replace them by scientific terms proper to zoological nomenclature. Of course, a large brain is a distinctive feature of modern man, and indeed of the genus *Homo* as a whole. But, as we have already seen, it was not so characteristic of *Pithecanthropus,* for even the totally inadequate sample of this extinct type includes one specimen with a cranial capacity of less than 800 cc. Further, it may be assumed on *a priori* reasoning that in the immediate evolutionary precursors of *Pithecanthropus* the cranial capacity would have been still less expanded and, indeed, could hardly have exceeded that of the modern large apes. The fact is, then, that while a voluminous brain is characteristic of the genus *Homo*, it is not characteristic of the family Hominidae as a whole, and it has become clear from recent discussions on hominid phylogeny that a good deal of misunderstanding has arisen simply because these taxonomic terms have been confused with the colloquial (and unscientific) terms, "man," "human," "humanity," and so forth.

We may perhaps clarify the matter in the following way. Probably most students of human evolution agree that the evolutionary line which led to the emergence of *Homo* separated from that which led to the modern large apes somewhere about the Early Pliocene or the Miocene period (or perhaps even earlier). Translated into taxonomic terminology, this is equivalent to saying that the Hominidae (comprising the hominid sequence of evolution) became segregated as an independent lineage from the Pongidae (comprising the anthropoid ape sequence of evolution) as far back as the Early Pliocene or the Miocene. Since there is no evidence that in the hominid sequence of evolution the brain began to expand to the dimensions characteristic of *Homo* before the Lower or Middle Pleistocene, it seems clear that there was a prolonged period during which the earlier Hominidae were not to be distinguished from the anthropoid apes on the basis of brain size. Once it is recognized that a large brain has only been characteristic of the *later* phases of hominid evolution, some of the misunderstandings regarding the phylogenetic status of *Australopithecus* immediately become clarified.

The discussions on the comparative anatomy of the brain of man and apes, in which Huxley played such an important part, were complicated by the tacit assumption that human intelligence must be based on quite outstanding structural differences in the brain, and that these assumed differences by themselves would imply a very remote relationship to the anthropoid apes. It is interesting to note Huxley's commentary on this type of argument: "The argument, that because there is an immense difference between a man's intelligence and an ape's, therefore, there must be an equally immense difference between their brains, appears to me to be about as well based as the reasoning by which one should endeavor to prove that, because there is a 'great gulf' between a watch that keeps accurate time and another that will not go at all, there is therefore a great structural hiatus between the two watches. A hair in the balance-wheel, a little rust on the pinion, a bend in a tooth of the escapement, a something so slight that only the practiced eye of the watchmaker can discover it, may be the source of all the difference." In making these comments Huxley was of course speaking as a comparative anatomist, and he took the view that the assessment of phylogenetic relationships is primarily a morphological problem, the data for which are to be acquired from the study of the anatomy of living and fossil types. But it is interesting to note his suggestion that the efficiency of the brain as an organ of intelligence may be related not to any major structural feature demonstrable by anatomical studies, but perhaps to some other factor of quite a different order.

THE PITHECOMETRA THESIS

Huxley made the statement that "the structural differences between Man and the highest Ape are of less value than those between the highest and the lower Apes." Stated in such general terms this proposition has not only stood the test of time—it has been considerably reinforced by the accumulation of comparative anatomical studies since Huxley's days. But it was given the somewhat spurious title of the "pithecometra thesis" by Haeckel, who thus implied that degrees of affinity could readily be quantified simply by the direct metrical comparison of structural resemblances and differences. Now it is one thing to compare selected measurements, for example of the skull, teeth, or limb bones, and quite another to evaluate the taxonomic significance of such measurements. Clearly, the comparison of dimensions which have little or no taxonomic significance for deciding degrees of affinity is likely to give rise only to negative (and sometimes very misleading) results. I have elsewhere indicated the numerous pitfalls which may entrap the unwary biometrician who attempts, without adequate knowledge of the biological fundamentals of his material, to apply statistical methods to the assessment of phylogenetic relationships, and I will not repeat these warnings in detail here. But I would like to draw particular attention to a paper by Bronowski and Long demonstrating the importance of employing statistical methods which treat a set of variates as a single coherent matrix; such a method is the technique of multivariate analysis which permits the comparison of morphological *patterns* rather than the comparison of individual measurements as though they were independent and isolated abstractions. Another important paper demonstrating the application of the technique has more recently been contributed by Ashton, Healy & Lipton, in which they were able finally to resolve certain conflicts of opinion which had unhappily arisen over the very obvious hominid features of the australopithecine dentition (incidentally confirming the results of my own earlier statistical studies and also those of Bronowski and Long).

In general, the statistical comparisons of a few selected measurements or indices may be of considerable value in assessing degrees of affinity in forms already known to be closely related, e.g. geographical varieties, subspecies, or even species, but they become of less and less practical value as the relationship becomes more remote and the types to be compared become more disparate. This is because factors of parallelism and convergence greatly complicate the situation, and also because the more fundamental contrasts which differentiate the more distantly related types make it difficult or impossible to adhere to the important "principle of morphological equivalence" in making metrical comparisons.

So far as I am aware, zoologists have not found it practicable to apply statistical data for the assessment of evolutionary affinities except for the differentiation of local varieties. But anthropologists have attempted to do so. That great pioneer of biometrical inquiry, Karl Pearson, made a brilliant attempt to find out how far metrical analysis would provide evidence of relationship in the phylogenetic sense, and subsequent attempts to apply this method of approach have led to a realization of its inherent difficulties. For example, Seltzer, applying Pearson's "Coefficient of Racial Likeness" to several series of skulls, found that it showed the greatest racial differences among three English series, and the least racial difference between a group of Tibetans and a group of Central African negroes! In their comparative study of the femur, also, Pearson & Bell were led to make the statement that their statistical evidence "indicates the great divergence of the Galley Hill femur from that of Recent Man." We now know (from the evidence of fluorine analysis) that the Galley Hill skeleton was of comparatively recent date, and certainly not distinguishable from *Homo sapiens*. It must not, of course, be inferred from these examples that biometrical methods are not at all applicable to the study of phylogenetic relationships, but they do serve to emphasize the difficulties involved in their application, even in the most expert hands. The well-known aphorism "Science is measurement" is strictly true, but it by no means follows that all measurements are scientific. In this connection, it is worth while drawing attention to the caveat in a recent review that "Statistics can enter the picture only after biologically valid measurements have been obtained."

In any assessment of the phylogenetic status of fossil types, and particularly in attempts to determine whether those which show an unusual combination of characters belong to one or other evolutionary sequence of two major taxonomic groups, it is essential to recognize that while species (and to some extent genera) can be defined morphologically in static terms, the larger categories such as families are only to be defined in dynamic terms of evolutionary trends. For example, the family Equidae is not to be defined simply by reference to the terminal products of its evolutionary history—this history is itself fundamental to its definition. The general principles of classification are intended to reflect evolutionary sequences of this kind; herein lies the difference between the so-called "vertical classifications" based on phylogeny, and "horizontal classifications" which, so to speak, merely serve to compare and catalogue in arbitrary fashion the end-products of evolution without direct reference to their phylogeny. The contrast between these two lines of approach is emphasized by Simpson's remark that "the linking of *Hyracotherium* [i.e. *Eohippus*] with *Equus* in the Equidae is solely on the basis of temporal variation and is flatly contradicted by any horizontal criteria."

Let us now briefly consider the sort of problem which arises when the phylogenetic status of a fossil hominoid is in question—whether it is the product of an early phase in the evolutionary sequence of the Hominidae or in that of the Pongidae. We may assume with confidence that the grouping together of these two families in the common superfamily Hominoidea accurately reflects the facts that they had their origin in a common ancestral stock (though authorities differ in their estimates of the geological date at which they became segregated from this stock). In the accompanying diagram are represented schematically the two diverging lines of evolution, and the morphological characters of the common ancestral stock are indicated by black circles. Now, some of these ancestral characters are of course inherited and retained in common by both families—such characters may be termed *characters of common inheritance*. But when the lines of evolution segregate and branch out to form the two separate groups, each of the latter gradually acquires its own special and peculiar pattern of morphological characters by which it comes to be distinguished from the other. Characters of this sort may be called *characters of independent acquisition*. In the diagram those which are distinctive of the Hominidae are indicated by [asterisks], and those of the Pongidae by white circles. Since the pongid sequence of evolution has been much more conservative than the progressive hominid sequence, its terminal products (the modern anthropoid apes) have preserved more of the original characters of the ancestral stock. As divergent evolution proceeds, characters of common inheritance will become progressively supplemented or replaced by characters of independent acquisition in each line. Conversely, if the lines are traced backwards in retrospect they will be found to approximate more and more closely to each other in the characters of common inheritance which they share. Thus, for example, in representatives of an early stage in the hominid sequence (H^1 in the diagram) it may well be found that characters of common inheritance predominate over characters of independent acquisition, the latter being as yet relatively few in number or only showing an incipient development. If, now, the remains of an individual corresponding to the stage H^1 are examined and the morphological characters compared quite indiscriminately—if, that is to say, the characters are simply enumerated without giving to each one an appropriate weighting according to its

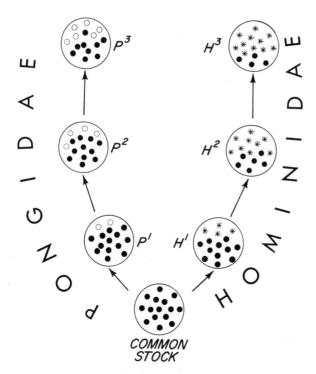

FIGURE 18-1—A diagram representing the divergence of two evolutionary sequences, the Pongidae (anthropoid ape family) and the Hominidae (the family which includes recent and extinct types of man). The two sequences inherit from a common ancestry *characters of common inheritance* (black circles). As the lines diverge each one acquires its own distinctive features, or *characters of independent acquisition;* those distinctive of the hominid sequence of evolution are represented by asterisks and those of the pongid sequence by white circles. (Adapted by Jacquelyn Hetrick.)

evolutionary significance, the erroneous conclusion may be reached that because in the *sum* of its characters it shows a closer resemblance to apes than to modern *Homo sapiens,* therefore it is taxonomically a pongid. But this would be to ignore the highly important principle of taxonomic relevance in comparing morphological characters. Haldane has succinctly stated the position in his remark that, in constructing a natural system of classification, "paleontologists rightly lay more stress on differences which at a later date become the basis of familial or ordinal distinctions," that is, on differences which by their progressive development later become important diagnostic characters of major taxonomic groups. The decision as to the taxonomic status of a previously unknown fossil— whether it is a primitive representative of one or other of two divergent lines of evolution corresponding to two related families—must therefore depend on a recognition of the fundamentally different trends which have distinguished the evolution of the two families and which are thus diagnostic of each of them as a natural taxonomic group. In the particular case which we are considering, the taxonomically relevant characters on which the diagnosis of "pongid" or "hominid" depends are the characters of independent acquisition which serve to distinguish the divergent trends in the two sequences, the nature and direction of the trends of each sequence being at once made evident by a consideration of the objectives actually reached by its terminal products. The stage H^1 of hominid evolution might be exemplified by the fossil genus *Australopithecus,* which is a particularly apt illustration for our present purpose. In the early discussions following the discovery of this primitive hominid, some anatomists, basing their judgment exclusively on the characters of common inheritance (such as the relatively small brain-case and large jaws), were led to suppose that it really was an ape in the taxonomic sense. But more careful studies soon made it clear that many of the characters of independent acquisition distinctive of the Hominidae (particularly in the dentition and pelvis), but none of those distinctive of the Recent Pongidae, had already been developed in *Australopithecus* and superimposed on the characters of common inheritance. In other words, in those characters in which this fossil type has undergone modification away from the ancestral stock of the Hominoidea, the direction of change has been in that of the hominid sequence and divergent from that of the pongid sequence.

Another serious difficulty which complicates any attempt at a quantitative assessment of the taxonomic position of fossil types is related to what has been termed "mosaic evolution." This principle has recently been emphasized by de Beer with particular reference to his new studies of the famous fossil *Archaeopteryx.* As he pointed out, there has been a common assumption that the evolutionary process ordinarily involves a gradual and general transformation of the whole animal. But this is by no means the case, for different morphological characters may evolve with apparent independence at different rates, so that the representative of one particular phase of evolution may be compounded of a mosaic of characters, some of which still preserve almost entirely archaic characters while others have achieved almost entirely the terminal stage of their development. In the paleontological study of hominid evolution it is hardly possible to overstress the importance of this principle. Following Darwin's reference to connecting links, and the invention of the popular and much abused phrase "the missing link," the conception seems to have been widely held that such an intermediate phase must be represented by a creature almost exactly half-way in every major character between modern man and modern apes. Thus arose what may be termed the "half-way illusion," which even today appears to color the judgment of some anthropologists. But almost a hundred years ago Huxley drew attention to this type of fallacy when he said "the stock whence two or more species have sprung, need in no respect be intermediate between those species." It follows from the concept of mosaic evolution that a fossil type representing a connecting link in an evolutionary series may not be recognizable as such by the statistical comparison of isolated morphological characters. This is made very clear by reference to the discussions which followed the discovery of the skull cap and femur of *Pithecanthropus* in Java. A metrical study confined to the frontal region of the skull might appear overwhelmingly to favor the suggestion that this extinct genus was an ape in the taxonomic sense, and a similar study of the femur would find no essential difference from *Homo sapiens.* Indeed, the contrast between the skull and thigh bone led some authorities to suppose they belonged to different creatures altogether. Mosaic evolution in the Hominidae is equally well shown in *Australopithecus,* in which the dentition and pelvis are fundamentally of the hominid type, while the brain and brain-case still retain archaic proportions closely approaching those of the large apes. Clearly, the relevant features for the phylogenetic assessment of *Australopithecus* are those in which this type had already advanced some considerable way in the direction of terminal characters distinctive of, and diagnostic of, the hominid sequence of evolution.

I mentioned above that statistical comparisons of morphological features for establishing taxonomic affinities involve the most serious difficulties except in rather closely related groups. But there is another means of quantitative comparison which does not involve similar complications —the technique reported in the classic work of Nuttall on Blood Immunity and Blood Relationship. The precipitin reaction which formed the basis of Nuttall's work (and which has been considerably developed since by Dr. A. A. Boyden) has the advantage of being able to provide an objective and quantitative assessment of affinities and has thus proved of the utmost value for testing the validity of conclusions based on comparative anatomy. It is also a test which may help in some degree to overcome one of the main difficulties which the morphological taxonomist has to meet—the difficulty of determining whether a similarity in structure really betokens a correspondingly close relationship, or whether it is the result of convergent evolution, for according to Boyden so far as serological convergence is concerned there is "as yet no proven case for protein antigens. As further work is undertaken, they may appear, but it is unlikely that they will be frequent." We may note, incidentally, that the serological test shows a close relationship between man and the anthropoid apes, a less close relationship with the quadrupedal Old World Monkeys, and no more than a distant relationship with the lower Primates. Perhaps one of the most interesting aspects of this test is that it provides the final justification for grouping the Pongidae and Hominidae in a common superfamily, Hominoidea.

CHRONOLOGY AND HOMINID EVOLUTION

There is one other source of misunderstanding in discussions on hominid evolution to which I should like to draw attention; it has reference to the importance of the time factor in the interpretation of fossil remains. In the past it sometimes happened that a great antiquity was assigned to the skeletal remains of *Homo sapiens* on the basis of what we now know to have been quite inadequate geological data. Today the situation is very different, partly because of the development of technical methods for arriving at a relative or absolute dating, and partly because of progressive refinements in the methods of analyzing stratigraphical evidence. Consequently, it is now possible to state with much more assurance the temporal sequence of the various types of fossil hominids at present known, and it is only by reference to this time factor that conclusions can safely be drawn regarding their evolutionary position. It was during the Pleistocene period that the later stages of hominid evolution occurred, leading finally to the emergence of the genus *Homo,* and in this connection it is important to recognize that as the result of the redefinition of the term Pleistocene in recent years this period has been quite considerably extended into what was previously regarded as late Pliocene. The Pleistocene, as it is now understood, includes the so-called Villafranchian period, the greater part of which preceded the first major (Günz) glaciation of the Ice Age. This means, in effect, that the duration of the preglacial Pleistocene may have been almost as long as the whole of the rest of the period. With the redefinition of the Pliocene-Pleistocene boundary, there has been a significant revision of the subdivisions of the Pleistocene, a revision which has perhaps not yet been fully recognized by anthropologists. For example, much of what was generally termed the Lower Pleistocene is now included in the Middle Pleistocene. For a brief summary of the relation of these now accepted subdivisions to fossil hominids, reference may be made to a . . . lecture by Dr. K. P. Oakley. According to this authority the genus *Homo* is known to have extended back into the upper part of the Middle Pleistocene, the remains of the genus *Pithecanthropus* so far discovered are probably not older than the lower part of the Middle Pleistocene, while the earlier group of australopithecine fossils found in South Africa are definitely of Villa-franchian, or Lower Pleistocene, antiquity. In other words, so far as we know from the scanty records at present available (and it needs to be recognized that they still are scanty), there is no evidence that any more advanced type of hominid was in existence at the time when the earliest known representatives of *Australopithecus* existed, or that there was any more advanced type of hominid in existence at the time when the earliest known representatives of *Pithecanthropus* existed. The genera *Australopithecus—Pithecanthropus—Homo* thus appear to fit into a temporal sequence, even though they almost certainly overlapped in time in different parts of the world. But the fact that some later representatives of *Pithecanthropus* (for example) may have been contemporaneous with early representatives of *Homo* in other parts of the world does not, of course, exclude the possibility (which seems likely enough on purely morphological grounds) that the one genus was ancestral to the other. It is well known from the vertebrate paleontological record that a genus may survive in one region long after the same or a closely related genus has given rise by progressive evolution to a more advanced type in another. It is well to bear this in mind, for it has sometimes been argued, on the basis of the few fossils so far discovered, that *Pithecanthropus* was too late in time to have been ancestral to *Homo*. But a genus (as distinct from a local population) commonly has a wide distribution in time, and very often in space as well. In the evolutionary history of the Equidae there was a sequence of probably not more than nine genera from the Eocene *Hyracotherium* to the modern *Equus*, covering a span of fifty million years or so. It may be, of course, that hominid genera, at any rate in the later stages of evolution, succeeded each other more rapidly. It is not to be supposed, however, that their temporal range was limited to the geological time during which their local representatives so far known happened to have lived. The genus *Australopithecus* was already in existence in South Africa during the Lower Pleistocene, and (apart from extreme ideas of "explosive exolution") it may be presumed, as a genus, to have extended back at least into the immediately antecedent period of the Upper Pliocene.

SUBSCRIPT

Lest it might seem that the title of my lecture is itself of a contentious nature, let me insist that it is not meant to be so. Every discovery of a fossil relic which appears to throw light on connecting links in man's ancestry always has, and always will, arouse controversy, and it is right that this should be so, for it is very true that the sparks of controversy often illuminate the way to truth. After all, Huxley himself was a noted controversialist in many fields of thought, and in every one of them he brought to bear a penetrating insight which did much to clear away confusion of thought. My own modest intentions have been simply to draw attention to certain recurring patterns of disputation in the field of paleo-anthropology which, because of the evident misunderstandings they involve, still tend to becloud, rather than to clarify, the atmosphere of controversy. By so doing, it may be that I can to some degree help to ensure that the illumination from controversial sparks is less diffused over irrelevancies and more firmly focused on fundamentals.

19

THE HUMAN BRAIN IN THE LIGHT OF ITS PHYLOGENETIC DEVELOPMENT

Franz Weidenreich

What can paleontologists learn about the brains of fossil men? What do fossil skull fragments tell us about the mental capacities of prehistoric man? What is the relation between brain size and shape, and intellectual endowment? Answers to these questions are offered in the following article in which the distinguished paleoanthropologist, Franz Weidenreich, reviews the relevant evidence in a consideration of the intelligence of prehistoric man. Although this discussion was first published twenty years ago, it is still valid and, moreover, still timely in view of the continuing controversy over the possibility of mental abilities being differentially distributed among modern human populations.

(Reprinted from *Scientific Monthly*, Vol. 67, August 1948, pages 103–109, by permission.)

The discovery of the remains of Peking man in the cave of Choukoutien, and evidences of a relatively advanced culture at the same site, confronted the paleoanthropologist with a new, unexpected, and vital problem. The find of ash layers and burnt stones and bones revealed that the man who lived there had knowledge of fire; and the find of stone implements, some of them skillfully chipped, proved that this man was already an able artisan.

On the other hand, the anatomical record of the skulls show that the cave dwellers represented a very primitive type, morphologically inferior to any fossil human type unearthed up to that time. The cranial capacity of the first skull to be found is not much over 900 cc. Davidson Black, who described the first finds, had no scruples about identifying the human individuals whose bones were dug out together with the cultural objects as the bearers of the Choukoutian culture. However, Marcellin Boule, the French paleontologist, thought otherwise. He argued that a human individual whose brain was not larger than a little over 900 cc could not be credited with the degree of intelligence that would be necessary to produce such a highly developed culture. From this premise, Boule deduced that a man with the physical appearance of modern man must have lived contemporaneously with Peking men, and that this advanced human type, not Peking man, must have been the bearer of the culture of Choukoutien. Boule regarded Peking man with his small brain as a savage brute who was hunted and killed like any other game by an unknown, more advanced human type. The irony of the implication that the mental and cultural superiority of this man would be evidenced by his chasing, killing, and probably also eating his physically and culturally less advanced fellowman, did not embarrass Boule. In all the years during which the cave of Choukoutien has been explored, no trace of a second human type has ever come to light; therefore, there is no reason to doubt the identity of Peking man and the culture of Choukoutien. But Boule's objection brings up a general biological problem that has broader implications than may at first be seen.

Is it possible to infer from the size of the brain the degree of intelligence and cultural efficiency of its bearer, regardless of whether this bearer lived several hundred thousand years ago or lives today? Almost everyone, layman as well as scientist, seems to be convinced that such a correlation is a well-established fact. Some time ago I came across a pamphlet, published in 1934, which was written by an English physician. In the author's opinion the only factors that determined man's evolution since his beginnings as a primitive primate are environment and natural selection. But his starting point is the premise "Cranial capacity is a fairly accurate measure of the mental status from the most primitive primates to *Homo sapiens*." The self-confidence with which this statement is made is typical.

Of course, there is no doubt that the size of the primate skulls from the lemurs of the Eocene up to modern man has greatly increased. Compared with the great apes, the average cranial capacity of modern man is three times greater—ca. 1,350 cc against ca. 450 cc. Skull II of Java man (*Pithecanthropus erectus*), the smallest skull of an adult fossil hominid thus far found, has a capacity of only 775 cc. This is 43 percent smaller than the average skull of mankind today, or a little more than half the size of the brain of an average American male adult. The cranial capacity of that Java man corresponds to that of a child of today of eleven to twelve months of age. The average capacity of the skull of Peking man is a little over 1,000 cc. This is still one quarter less than the average capacity of modern man. The apelike ancestors of man are unknown. The fossil Australopithecinae of South Africa, which are regarded by Broom as forms lying directly in the human line, have a cranial capacity of not more than ca. 450 cc. This is about the average capacity of living anthropoids. If Broom is right in his phylogenetic ranging of the Australopithecinae, then the human brain would have increased considerably since the evolution of man from the South African ape-men.

However, we do not know of any fact which proves that the mere increase of the size of the brain is tantamount to an advance in mental ability. Is modern man really more intelligent than Peking or Java man or any great ape only because his brain is larger? This is what Boule's argument implies. More than sixty years ago Marsh claimed that the mass of the brain, particularly that of the hemispheres, has increased considerably in some mammalian orders since early Tertiary times. Tilly Edinger, who quite recently studied the evolution of the brain of the horse from Eohippus, its earliest recognizable ancestor in the Eocene, to the modern equine form, found that its brain, especially the neopallium, has been enlarged, although the horse did not change its basic organization. This suggests the question: What about the progress of the "mental" qualities of the horse? Is there any indication that the enlargement of the brain implies a greater advantage in the struggle for survival and that the horse only survived because its higher intelligence, bound to the enlargement of the neopallium, conducted it safely for millions of years through the perils lurking about it? Since the horse has survived, it must have been equipped from the beginning and at all times with a certain quantity of brain sufficing to let it find its food and evade its enemies. Were the living conditions of earlier horses much easier? Did they therefore require less attention and precaution than in later times so that the horse could survive in earlier times with a minimum of neopallium, whereas later on it could do so only because the brain enlarged in the meantime and gave it a greater chance? The extinction of the horse in

North America was already an accomplished fact by the late Pleistocene, although the animal had already acquired a well-developed neopallium.

On the other hand, increase of body size is always accompanied by an increase of brain size. The elephant, for example, has a brain that weighs almost 5,000 gr and the brain of one of the big whales weighs around 10,000 gr. But the increase of the body alone cannot be made responsible for the growth of the brain; for, in proportion to the weight of the body, the whale has a much smaller brain than man. The whale has 1 gr of brain substance for 8,500 gr of body substance whereas man has 1 gr of brain substance for 44 gr of body substance. Nevertheless, man is far surpassed in this respect by the dwarf monkeys of South America, the marmosets, which have 1 gr of brain per 27 gr of body substance; and man is surpassed even more in these proportions by the capuchin monkey with 1 gr of brain substance for 17.5 gr of body substance.

Therefore, neither the absolute nor the relative size of the brain can be used to measure the degree of mental ability in animal or in man. So far as man is concerned, the weights of the brains or the volumes of the cranial cavities of a hundred celebrities of all branches of knowledge all over the world have been listed. At the bottom of those lists are Gall, the famous phrenologist, Anatole France, the French novelist, and Gambetta, the French statesman, each with about 1,100 cc brain mass. The lists are topped by Dean Jonathan Swift, the English writer, Lord Byron, the English poet, and Turgeniev, the Russian novelist, all with about 2,000 cc. The latter group has nearly double the amount of brain substance of the first group, although the size of their respective bodies does not justify such great differences. Now our mental test! Had Turgeniev really twice the mental ability of Anatole France? If not, and if Turgeniev's body was not of elephantine proportions, which structure of the brain was increased in Turgeniev and the others to such an extent that it answers for the surplus weight, obviously dispensable even for uncommon psychical functions? Gall, Anatole France, and Gambetta, together with innumerable modern human individuals of all races, could perform mental deeds by means of a brain mass which does not surpass the brain mass of Peking man. In addition, the enlargement of the brain does not seem to have reached its climax with modern man. Provided the paucity of the material available warrants such far-reaching conclusions, the climax may already have been reached in the Neanderthal stage, the evolutionary stage that precedes that of modern man. In any case, the average cranial capacity of the Neanderthal skulls available is greater than the average capacity of modern human skulls. On the other hand, it can be stated that, at least for the majority of modern mankind, there is no increase of brain mass when compared with that of Neanderthal man.

Thus far only the enlargement of the brain, as such, has been dealt with. There is in addition, however, another kind of enlargement of the brain that goes hand in hand with it but obviously depends—at least in part—upon the space of the cranial cavity in which the brain has to be accommodated. This enlargement concerns the surface of the hemispheres. Their outer layer, the cortex, is the most vital part of the brain, since it is the main seat of the nervous cells. Together with their connecting fiber system, it represents the switchboard at which all the stimuli arrive from the periphery of the body and from which reactions and impulses emanate. The expansion of the cortex is brought about by a series of foldings which transform the originally smooth surface into a confusing maze of wrinkles (convolutions and fissures). The greater the number of wrinkles, the larger will be the surface area and the more cortex elements—cells and fibers—could be accommodated. Among the primates, the more primitively organized the forms, the smoother the surface, and the more advanced the forms, the more complicated are the convolutions; the climax is reached in man.

Fossil brains, of course, have not been preserved, but the wrinkles of the surfaces of their hemispheres have left their imprints on the cerebral side of the brain case, where they now appear as ridges. These negatives tell the same story as the wrinkles of the brain surface of living creatures. In primitive fossil forms, the pattern of the wrinkle system appears simpler than in more advanced primitive forms. This can only be ascertained provided the wrinkles have left their marks on the walls which, however, does not occur in all cases. In any event, the hominid pattern differs from the simian pattern. Each of the living anthropoids has its characteristics, although they have some features in common that make possible their distinction from man.

Again we have to state that when discussing the pattern of the surface of the hemispheres, primates and man do not differ from other mammalian orders with regard to presence and abundance of the wrinkle system. In the evolution of the horse, the surface of the hemispheres is smooth in the beginning, and their folding becomes more complex the more the neopallium increases in size. Indeed, this process is an almost general phenomenon, and any explanation confronts us with the same difficulties encountered in the attempt to interpret the increase of the brain size itself. We are lost again if we suppose that the number or the complexity of the wrinkles is correlated with progress or perfection of the mental faculties. The capuchin monkey, which many experimental psychologists and physiologists regard as equal in docility to any highly gifted chimpanzee, possesses an almost smooth brain surface, whereas the chimpanzee has a wrinkled one that comes close to that of man. The whale and its relatives, however, again steal the show. They have the greatest number and finest wrinkles all over the hemispheres, and the most intricate arrangement, in the whole animal kingdom. Many human and comparative anatomists have spent years classifying and identifying all the individual convolutions and fissures occurring in the different orders of mammals. It may be possible to distinguish the brains of gorilla, orang-utan, chimpanzee, and man from one another by this method, but only main fissures which represent the first folds both in ontogenetic and phylogenetic evolution are recognizable and comparable. Their location obviously depends on the manner and rate of growth of the hemispheres in relation to that of the brain case. Except for this basic pattern, the variability is enormous; it differs greatly with regard to the number, length, breadth, depth, and arrangement of the wrinkles, not only between two individuals of the same zoological group or race, but also between right and left hemispheres of one and the same individual. It is therefore hopeless to expect any result or even indication with regard to certain mental faculties—degree or differences—by such a comparison.

In the face of all these facts it is hard to understand why people cannot get rid of the idea that mere size or configuration of a special convolution or fissure must give a clue to the mental qualities in general and to those of certain individuals in particular. The desire to gaze into the crystal ball seems to exist not only among the clients of fortunetellers but also among scientists.

One hundred and fifty years ago phrenologists indulged in palpating the head and the skull to look for bulges on its outside; from their presence or absence they deduced the presence or absence of psychical qualities which they regarded as strictly localized. The basic conception of the phrenologists which underlay this reasoning has not changed in the course of time in spite of the great progress made in our knowledge of the structure of the central nervous system. The search has only shifted to a different type of indicator of hidden ability; now it is supposed to be manifested by bulges on the surface of the hemispheres themselves, which allegedly tell of right- or left-handedness, the faculty of speech, musical or mathematical talents. One wants to find out whether certain human races differ from others in their wrinkle patterns and whether those differences are indicative of spiritual inferiority or superiority, etc. Of course, there may be more justification today for such a search than in former times. Owing to pathological incidents and experiments, it is known that certain areas of the cortex are the centers of certain perceptions and impulses. They can be localized fairly accurately, and their nature can be defined. It is furthermore known that those centers are marked by characteristic microscopic structures which permit identification wherever they may be found. It is also known that those differentiations in the structure are not at all bound to the convolutions as such but only to certain areas of the hemispheres, regardless of whether this area is smooth or wrinkled and, if wrinkled, to what degree or extent. As a matter of fact, surgeons are able to remove large portions of the hemispheres, which may result in a temporary or permanent loss of sensibility or power of movement if certain areas are affected. But the defect, as such, does not necessarily interfere with psychical functions or endanger purely mental ones. Modern ''psycho-surgeons'' deliberately destroy fiber systems of the frontal lobe, widely considered the main seat of the intelligence, affecting a return to almost normal reasoning power of some persons formerly considered incurably mentally deranged.

Therefore, the claims of paleoanthropologists, for instance, to the effect that Neanderthal or Peking man was right- or left-handed, was able to speak or write or could only stammer, all deduced from shallower and narrower or deeper and broader impressions on the inside of the brain case, have no scientific basis even if the interpretation of the imprints could be accepted as correct.

If the variation of a normal human brain from average to almost double its usual size and the multiplying of the individual wrinkles of the hemispheres have no bearing on mental functions, how can a strictly localized bulge produce such an effect? On the other hand, thorough studies have revealed a surprisingly perfect equality in weight and surface area between the two hemispheres of the same individual, irrespective of all eventual inequalities in details of their forms. Unilateral bulges are the result of changes of the whole skull form. Artificially deformed heads or skulls enclose brains with abnormal bulges, depressions, or asymmetries on the surface of one or both hemispheres, according to the character of the applied deformation. But it has never been reported that the people so deformed behave conspicuously differently from others of the same population with normal skulls; nor do they show any change in their mental faculties.

The faculty of the brain to adjust its form and that of its main parts to any form enforced on the enclosing brain case by altering body conditions is extraordinary. One of the most characteristic features of all known earlier hominids, including Neanderthal man, is the flatness of the brain and brain case in proportion to the length, irrespective of the size of the brain and the capacity of the brain case. In all modern human races—whatever the brain size or skull capacity—the vertex region is distinctly elevated and the length of the skull base is shortened. These differences are the effect of a sharp bend of the base of the brain case which runs in a straight line in quadrupedal animals, even in the great apes. Early hominids (Solo man) are in an intermediate position in this regard. The transformation of the modern human skull is the final result of a change in the static and dynamic conditions entailed by a more perfect adaptation to man's upright position. That this alone is responsible for the alteration of the form of brain and brain case can be deduced from the fact that in whales and related forms—regardless of the size of their brains—almost exactly the same change takes place, with one re-markable difference—that is, the bend is reversed. The base of the brain case is curved upward in accordance with a perfect adaptation of the skeleton of these animals to fast and powerful swimming and diving.

All recorded facts indicate that neither the size nor the form of the brain or the surface of the hemispheres or their wrinkle pattern in gen-eral or in detail furnishes a reliable clue to the amount and degree of general or special mental qualities. Nevertheless, there seems to be a parallel between the expansion of the hemispheres, the advance of the bodily evolution of man, and the increase of mental qualities. But no one can tell what the nature of those correlations may be. In any case, this is a problem that principally concern neurologists and psychologists. Fossil human material can, if at all, furnish only circumstantial evi-dence. There have been suggestions that blood supply may play a de-cisive role in the differences between the psychical functions of notable brains and ordinary ones. If this is so, it may also be true for the dif-ference between the brains of early hominids and those of modern man. Indeed, the holes and gaps of the bony case which lodges the brain and through which both arteries and veins pass are distinctly wider in modern man than in early hominids. There is a definite tendency for these ways of communication between the cranial cavity and the outside to widen in the course of evolution as part of a general trend to reduce the thick-ness of all cranial bones, which are suprisingly massive in early hominids. In general, the passages through the brain case are distinctly narrower in skulls of races morphologically more primitive than others. But no data with regard to differences in their width are available for small- and large-brained individuals.

Another point may be of some interest. It is known that in lower verte-brates the mass of the spinal cord is greater in proportion to that of the brain than in mammals. Even compared with the great apes (goril-las), the mass of the spinal cord of modern man seems to be much smal-ler. This suggests that the brain tends to "swallow" the spinal cord and thereby to bring more reflex centers under control of consciousness. This certainly broadens the basis of psychic reaction.

As to the size of the brain, its white substance (medullated nerve fibers) profits most by the enlargement. But the great accumulation of myeline in these fibers used as insulation material may not be its only purpose. Hollow spaces within the bones are used in all mammals as stor-age rooms for fat and for the lodging of organs of blood formation. It may be that the central nervous system not only has a nervous function but also serves as storage for some stuff which is an essential in the metabolism of the organism.

To return to our starting point: the course of man's bodily evolution can be clarified by the study of fossil human remains if it is done by people trained in comparative human anatomy. But studies made on skeletons alone will never enable us to make statements about either the mentality of the individuals concerned or about mental change or progress over a period of time. Cultural objects are the only guide so far as spiritual life is concerned. They may be fallacious guides, too, but we are completely lost if those objects are missing. And the closer we come to more primitive stages, the less likely we are to discover cultural objects.

SELECTED READINGS

Aberle, David F., et al., 1963, "The Incest Taboo and the Mating Patterns of Animals," American Anthropologist, 65:253–265.

Bartholomew, George A. and Joseph B. Birdsell, 1953, "Ecology and the Protohominids," American Anthropologist, 55:481–498.

Birdsell, J. B., 1957, "Some Population Problems Involving Pleistocene Man," Cold Spring Harbor Symposia on Quantitative Biology, 22:47–69.

Brace, C. Loring, 1964, "The Fate of the 'Classic' Neanderthals: A Consideration of Hominid Catastrophism," Current Anthropology, 5:3–43.

———— and M. F. Ashley Montagu, 1965, Man's Evolution; An Introduction to Physical Anthropology. New York: Macmillan.

Brues, Alice, 1959, "The Spearman and the Archer—An Essay on Selection in Body Build," American Anthropologist, 61:457–469.

Clark, Wilfrid E. Le Gros, 1964, The Fossil Evidence for Human Evolution; An Introduction to the Study of Paleoanthropology, 2d ed. Chicago: University of Chicago Press.

Coon, C. S., 1962, The Origin of Races. New York: Knopf.

DeVore, Irven, and the editors of Life, 1965, Early Man, from Life Nature Library, New York: Time Inc.

Dumond, D. E., 1965, "Population Growth and Cultural Change," Southwestern Journal of Anthropology, 21:302–324.

Garn, Stanley, A. B. Lewis, and R. S. Kerensky, 1964, "Relative Molar Size and Fossil Taxonomy," American Anthropologist, 66:587–592.

Heberer, G., 1959, "The Descent of Man and the Present Fossil Record," Cold Spring Harbor Symposia on Quantitative Biology, 24:235–244.

Howell, F. Clark, 1957, "The Evolutionary Significance of Variation and Varieties of 'Neanderthal' Man," Quarterly Review of Biology, 32:330–347.

———, 1959, "The Villafranchian and Human Origins," *Science,* 130: 831–844.

———, 1960, "European and Northwest African Middle Pleistocene Hominids," *Current Anthropology,* 1:195–232.

Leakey, L. S. B., 1959, "A New Fossil Skull from Olduvai," *Nature,* 184:491–493.

Meighan, C. W., D. M. Pendergast, B. K. Swartz, Jr., and M. D. Wissler, 1958, "Ecological Interpretation in Archeology, Part I," *American Antiquity,* 24:1–23.

Simons, E. L., 1960, "New Fossil Primates: A Review of the Past Decade," *American Scientist,* 48(2):179-192.

Slater, M. K., 1959, "Ecological Factors in the Origin of Incest," *American Anthropologist,* 61:1042–1059.

Tobias, Phillip V., 1965, "Early Man in East Africa," *Science,* 149:22–33.

Washburn, S. L., ed., 1963, *Classification and Human Evolution.* Chicago: Aldine Publishing Company.

PART SIX

RACE
AND
RACIATION

It is regrettable that, with the vital need for reliable information about the biological bases of differences among human populations, there is no substantive agreement among anthropologists as to even an elementary definition of the word *race*. No concept in physical anthropology has been the focus of more heated controversy than that of race. The record of the use of the term itself would almost constitute an intellectual history of anthropology.

Although the traditional approach that retains the concept of racial "types" is maintained by few American or western European anthropologists, there are several respectable positions on race.

The most widely accepted concept of race is illustrated by the population approach of Dobzhansky who, as a population geneticist, is interested in problems of human evolution. He sees race as an array of populations with similar distributions of hereditary characteristics, differing from other similar arrays of populations within the species. This definition is based on the acceptance of the Mendelian population as the basic unit of evolutionary change. Hence a race is viewed as a collection of populations characterized not by the absolute presence or absence of some hereditary characteristic but by the relative incidences of certain hereditary traits.

The definition is a flexible one in that it incorporates a certain permissiveness as to where the lines that separate the races are to be drawn. One could easily distinguish the extremes—populations with profoundly different distributions of traits like blond hair or very dark skin or heavy brow ridges—but the boundaries *between* races are much more tenuous. From this genetic point of view, they are not "real" boundaries, since populations are distributed continuously in all geographic areas, and a certain amount of gene flow between neighboring populations is assumed to occur. Stanley Garn, who has written extensively on race and has proposed several racial taxonomies, shares this point of view.

Another, perhaps more limited, opinion as to what constitutes race is that held by the serologist, William Boyd. Using a similar definition, he has restricted his classification of races to a blood-group frequency basis. Using the distribution of the frequencies for the genes that determine the A-B-O-AB blood groups, Rh-factor compatibility, and M-N-MN blood groups, he has proposed a classification of large clusters of human populations that is in accord with the traditional Caucasoid-Negroid-Mongoloid-Australoid-American Indian classification most nonanthropologists assume to be adequate. However the layman's roughhewn taxonomy is based on "ideal" phenotype differences whereas Boyd's taxonomy rests exclusively, if narrowly, on those few characteristics for which the genetic basis is known and for which population distributions are well documented.

Julian Huxley, the eminent British biologist, has proposed no classification nor constructed any list of races as such. Yet he does defend the reality of human races; he believes that at the close of the Pleistocene there were three sharply demarcated stocks (corresponding to Caucasoid, Negroid, and Mongoloid) and that, although population expansion and migration have meanwhile attenuated the differences through hybridization, these three stocks are still discernible in modern populations.

The race concept is not taken for granted by all authorities, however. Ashley Montagu has suggested that, in view of the kind of thinking the term "race" has engendered, that is, "racism"—attitudes about how people should be treated based on their "racial" characteristics—the term should be dropped entirely, and the term "ethnic group" be substituted. For Montagu, ethnic group means a group distinguishable by the possession of biological *and* cultural characteristics.

Frank Livingstone has gone even further in questioning the validity of the concept of race. Beginning with a view quite different than that of

Montagu, he argues that each of the traits that make up the traditional racial "type" are distributed differently, and that the race concept is worthless as a tool in organizing or classifying what we have learned about the differences among human populations, and how these differences have arisen. Livingstone's article, "On the Nonexistence of Human Races," forcibly presents this point of view.

There is no disputing that there are biological differences among human populations, and there is general agreement that genetic differences among populations are, for the most part, differences in frequency of genes, or, phenotypically, differences in the incidence of observable characteristics. The epicanthic fold of the eye, which in former days was said to be "typical" of the Mongoloid race, can be observed in low incidence among European populations, and in much higher incidence among southwest African Khoisan-speaking populations, the Bushmen and the Hottentot peoples. Its highest incidence is, of course, among east Asian populations. But what distinguishes Asian populations from other arrays of population is not the *absolute* presence or absence of the epicanthic fold, but rather its observed *high frequency* among them.

For the most part, the hereditary differences that anthropologists study probably fall into the category of relative frequency of traits that are generally present in most populations, for example, hemoglobins, haptoglobins, blood groups, and peppercorn hair form. Nevertheless, occasionally characteristics are encountered by which populations are capable of being described on an all-or-nothing basis—extremely dark pigmentation, blue eyes and blond hair, presence of lip seam, and others.

Investigation of the differences among human populations follows the lines laid down by commitment to the theory of evolution: the degree to which human populations differ from one another is the degree to which the evolutionary agencies of mutation and recombination, natural selection, gene flow, and the random fluctuation of gene frequencies in small isolated populations operate and interact to differentiate one population from another and to maintain such differences.

Since hereditary differences are the result of feedback to the gene pool of a population from forces and factors outside itself, that is, the environment within which the population must carry on life, considerable inquiry has been directed to such environmental factors as climate, intensity of solar radiation, humidity, mineral concentrations in soil, disease vectors, and the like. Accordingly, several of the articles that follow discuss attempts to account for population differences in terms of natural selection for traits that are adaptive to climatic and other environmental factors.

Admittedly, we seem to be very far from definitive answers to questions about the sorts of differences that we have been taught to regard as significant in our culture. The adaptive value of human skin pigment, for instance, is still very much an open arena for disagreement. Carleton Coon may be said to represent one extreme in this regard, and H. F. Blum, another. An example of active research to illuminate the question is provided by Paul T. Baker.

For all populations, however, the major "environmental" factor in the "ecological niche" is culture itself—the sum total of patterns of social life, symbolic transaction, and technology, all of which, transmitted from generation to generation, distinguish the human species from all others. The greater part of human evolution, as we have seen, has been evolution toward greater adaptive flexibility and adaptiveness for cultural life.

In the past there has been considerable question (mostly by writers who had the answer in mind even as they asked) as to whether human populations are equally endowed with the hereditary basis for culture-building and cultural life. Some authorities such as Ashley Montagu and Dobzhansky believe that the phyletic evolution of man extends to the evolution of the capacity for culture and that no population has ever been separated from other populations long enough for significant differences in this potential to arise and to be maintained. Other authorities, such as Carleton Coon, have tried to build theories about human evolution that provide for the appearances at the *sapiens* threshold for different human populations at different times, so that differences in such abilities follow logically from the theories.

The cultural component of human behavior needs no emphasis here, nor do physical anthropologists of any persuasion deny it. There is agreement that many of the differences in performance and ability among different population samples are obviously maintained in different cultural contexts. The major point of disagreement is the degree to which cultural differences and hereditary differences are responsible for population differences in behavior.

This question has long been dormant in anthropological circles. Cultural anthropologists have occupied themselves with exploring the variety of human cultures and salvaging the more exotic ones in monograph form. On the other hand, physical anthropologists have pursued their love affair with population genetics and gene counts among populations everywhere.

The current political atmosphere, coupled with the resurgence of American Negro political and social activity in behalf of integration into twentieth-century society, has had effects on the nature of statements concerning race.

The political controversy is perhaps more responsible than anthropologists are willing to concede for the fact that spirited defenses have been made of the concept that human populations do not differ significantly in their distribution of genes for ability, or at least, that such differences are not scientifically demonstrable.

This section on "Race and Raciation" begins with a definition of human race by the eminent geneticist, L. C. Dunn. Paul T. Baker next presents research in human resistance to heat stress and its implications for understanding racial differences. Harold F. Blum challenges the widely held view that human skin color differences can be explained by natural selection to climate differences, and Frederick S. Hulse discusses race in terms of evolutionary dynamics. The concluding article by Frank Livingstone questions whether the race concept as applied to human differences can have any validity at all.

Several approaches to the study of raciation are represented here: their common thread is the evolutionary base on which each is built as well as the acceptance in each case of the fact of human differences and the tentativeness of the theories that are advanced to explain these differences.

20

RACE AND BIOLOGY

L. C. Dunn

If the race concept is to have any substantive meaning for
biologists, it must be couched in terms that are evolutionary,
populational, and, of course, genetic. In the following extract,
L. C. Dunn, a noted geneticist, examines the race concept and
delimits it in biological terms, offering a definition of human race
that is congruent with what has been learned about the nature
of hereditary differences among populations, and how these
differences arise.

HOW RACES FORM

If all men living today are descended from common ancestors, and
there is good evidence that this is the case, how has mankind become
divided up into different races? History alone cannot answer this question, since the great groups of man had already become different before
written history began. We must find out about it as we find out about
other scientific questions, by studying the processes responsible for it.

We can ask ourselves: why should not all men have remained biologically alike? We . . . found that the elements of heredity, the genes,
sometimes change by a process called mutation, and this gives rise to a
great variety of genes. These, by coming into new combinations during
reproduction (the baby has father's nose, mother's hair, and Uncle
John's bad eye-sight) produce an almost endless array of kinds of people,
so that literally no two persons are the same.

Now the process of heredity is such that we should expect this great
variety to continue within any population in which genes have assumed
different allelic forms by mutation. This is implicit in Mendel's original
theory that genes enter into all possible combinations with each other

(From *The Race Question in Modern Science*. Columbia University Press,
1961, pages 281–298. Copyright © 1951, 1952, 1953, 1954, 1960, 1961
UNESCO. By permission of the author and the publisher.)

and are not changed by this process. If we find persons of three genotypes such as *AA, Aa* and *aa* in certain proportions in a population at one time we should expect, other things being equal, to find them in the same proportions many generations later. The main reason for this is the constancy of gene reproduction. Whenever, in the process of growth and in the production of the sex cells (egg or sperm) one cell gives rise to a new one, each gene produces a replica of itself for the new cell; that is *A* produces a new *A*, *a* another *a*, *B* a new *B* and so on through the thousands of genes in each cell. They pass on unchanged from generation to generation except in the rare event that one changes by mutation to a new form in which case it reproduces in the new form and augments the variety. The proportions of *A* to *a*, *B* to *b*, etc., are not expected to change in the population if matings among all different genotypes occur at random, that is if *AA* persons are equally likely to marry *AA, Aa* or *aa* persons and similarly for all other genotypes. Then *AA* persons will always transmit *A* in all sex cells, *Aa* will transmit *A* in one half and *a* in the other half of the sex cells, and *aa* will transmit *a* in all sex cells. With persons choosing their marriage partners usually for reasons unconnected with genotype (which will usually be unknown to the prospective mate) all the genes in the population can be thought of as constituting one pool out of which two are drawn at each new birth. If 90 per cent of the alleles of one gene in the population are *A* and 10 per cent are *a*, then the following combinations will be found:

EGGS		SPERM		CHILDREN
0.9 *A*	×	0.9 *A*	=	0.81 *AA*
0.9 *A*	×	0.1 *a*	=	0.09 *Aa*
0.1 *a*	×	0.9 *A*	=	0.09 *Aa*
0.1 *a*	×	0.1 *a*	=	0.01 *aa*

In the population of children the proportion of *A* to *a* is also 9 to 1; it has not changed, and other things being equal, will not change. This extension of Mendel's rule is known as the Hardy-Weinberg rule from the English mathematician and the German physician who independently called attention to it in 1908. It tells us that in large populations in which mating takes place at random with respect to genotype, the relative frequencies of the different alleles of each kind of gene will tend to remain the same, provided also that mutation does not alter the frequency of one allele more than the other, that all of the genotypes have equal chances of marrying and leaving offspring, and that the gene proportions in the population are not altered by emigration or immigration.

If these conditions hold, a population will not change but will retain the genetic variety with which it began. In order to find out how populations become different and diverge from each other to produce the mosaic of different populations in the world today, we must ask whether the conditions responsible for constancy actually do hold. The most important clue comes from the observation that the populations in different parts of the world seem to be fitted for or adapted to the conditions under which they live. Certain hereditary characters such as black skins appear to have been more successful in Africa, others more successful elsewhere. Studies of animal and plant populations have shown that the proportion of a population having those combinations of characters which are advantageous in certain places, as for example in a desert, tend to increase there generation after generation until they constitute the bulk of the population. They gradually supplant the other combinations, although the latter may survive better in the forest or in the mountains. The chief means by which such changes occur is by differential reproduction, certain genotypes leaving more offspring than others. This is the process which Darwin called natural selection. It tends to produce local races and eventually species which are fitted or adapted for life in that locality. This means that all genotypes do not have equal chances of leaving offspring in all environments.

A specific example of the effect of natural selection on human populations is the recent discovery that normal persons who transmit a gene for sickle cell anemia (which is usually fatal in children who receive such a gene from both parents) have more children than persons without such a gene. This advantage of the carriers of this gene occurs only in areas where malicious (falciparum) malaria has been prevalent. In such areas as in the low coastal regions of British Honduras or in low areas in West Africa, natural selection tends to increase in this way the frequency of the gene. This is sufficient to counterbalance the adverse selection against those who get the gene from both parents for these usually die before they can transmit the gene. Consequently this gene is commoner in certain African peoples and their descendants elsewhere than in peoples whose ancestors have not been exposed to malaria. This produces great regional differences in the frequency of this gene. It is largely a peculiarity of Africans, whose ancestors it may have enabled to survive in malarial regions. Other traits common in Africans such as dark skins and certain of the blood group genes (cf. "A Biologist's View of Race" below) may also have been favored by natural selection in certain environments.

Natural selection, favoring some genes in certain places and others in other environments, has probably been the most potent factor in causing changes in gene frequency and thus in producing racial differences.

A second factor is sometimes involved in shaping the particular collection of genes which becomes a biological race. It may happen that the frequency of a gene may increase or decrease in a locality, not because it confers some advantage or the reverse, but simply because of accidental or chance fluctuations, which are much more serious in a small population than in a large one. The extinction or spread of family names which occur in small communities may be due simply to a run of luck in a family in the proportion of sons and daughters. In societies in which the name is transmitted through males only, a family with many sons would have its name spread in a small community, while one with no sons would have its name disappear, so that in neighboring villages a name would be common in one and absent in the other. In large cities such fluctuation would not be noticeable, but small populations may diverge from each other by such accidents. Differences among races in the proportions of persons with different blood group genes may have come about in this way. Such accidents must have been of great importance in earlier stages of human history when the human reproductive communities must have been very small. This risk which new variants or combinations run in small populations has been called random drift.

Finally, after these factors have acted, it is obvious that migration and mixing of different groups may lead to changes in old races or the formation of new ones. This can be seen going on today. New races are forming in the Hawaiian Islands, for example, by the mingling of Chinese and European immigrants with the native people; and in the United States and in South Africa by intermarriage among the descendants of marriages between Negroes and Europeans.

Since biologically races are populations differing in the relative frequencies of some of their genes, the four factors noted above as those which upset the equilibrium and change the frequencies of genes are the chief biological processes responsible for race formation. They are: (a) mutation or change in the elements of heredity, the genes; (b) selection, being differential rates of reproduction, fertility or survival of the possessors of different genes; (c) drift, or the accidents of gene sampling in small populations; (d) differential migration and mixing of populations.

None of these processes would result in hereditary differences among groups of people unless something interfered with the complete freedom of intermarriage among all persons which has been referred to as random mating, for otherwise all would be members of the same biological or reproductive group. Thus we must add a fifth factor of a different kind. This is isolation, geographical or social. Once the other factors are present, isolation is the great race-maker. If the whole population of the world constituted one marriage circle, in which any individual had an equal chance of marrying any other, then the great variety of people which is kept up by mutation and combination of genes would be distributed more or less evenly over the world. Obviously neither condition actually obtains.

The variety of the world's population is distributed in clusters. For example, most of the dark peoples are in one cluster in Africa, although another group occurs in Melanesia, most people with yellow skins are in north-east Asia, most light-skinned people in Europe or countries settled by Europeans, and so on.

Between these separated groups there is relatively little intermarriage. Choice of marriage partners is limited to those who live near, speak the same language, profess the same religion, and belong to the same class or caste.

These divisions of the world's populations did not always exist as at present. Once there was no human being in the American continents, nor in the islands of the South Seas, nor in Australia. There may even have been a time when the human race was actually one marriage community, because even today all races have many of their genes in common, as though they had all obtained them from a common source.

If it were not for the geographical and cultural barriers which separate people today, we could think of all of the genes in the human race as constituting one great pool.

But the world's population is obviously divided up into many different gene pools *within* which combinations occur more or less at random, but *between* which genes are less frequently exchanged because of the rarity of marriage between different groups. These different gene pools or marriage circles are likely to differ in the genes they contain, that is, different mutations may occur in different separated populations; selection may change the proportions of genes in different populations; the changes may occur by accident or by different rates of migration or intermixture. But however the original difference between two populations may have arisen, the difference will persist only if something makes intermarriage between them infrequent, and this is why isolation is so potent an influence in forming different groups of people. Isolation is often partial; it is anything which tends to cut down exchange of genes between groups. We all know the ways in which our choice of marriage partners is limited. They are not only geographical, but religious, social, economic, linguistic, that is to say, the isolating factors are largely cultural. Thus a common biological community tends to be broken up by non-biological factors into sub-communities, which may then tend to become biologically different.

Races form because of the operation of biological processes. These are determined by the nature of heredity, which provides for a variety of stable hereditary elements, genes, transmitted according to regular laws or principles; and by the nature of the environment, which is broken up into a variety of partially isolated habitats. Particular genes or groups of genes are more successful in (i.e., adapted to) certain environments, others in other environments. These views have been tested experimentally with a variety of plant and animal populations. They have only begun to be tested by observations on human populations, but the basic conceptions derived from experimental biology appear to be generally applicable to all bi-sexual animals including man.

A BIOLOGIST'S VIEW
OF RACE

The groups that become partially separated and different go by many names: races, hordes, tribes. All of them have this in common, that they differ from other groups by maintaining a different proportion of the same kinds of hereditary elements—genes.

This is nowhere more clearly shown than in the distribution of the genes which determine certain properties of the blood. There are four kinds of people, called A, B, AB, and O. These four kinds of persons differ in the substances they contain in their red blood cells.

It is well known that the red color of human blood is due to red particles which float in the transparent straw-colored fluid which forms the liquid part of the blood. As soon as blood is taken from the body and allowed to stand, it tends to congeal in a red mass which is called a clot. If the clot is allowed to stand for an hour or so, it contracts and a pale transparent yellowish fluid oozes out. This is called blood serum.

Blood has always played an important part in beliefs, not only about relationship but about the qualities of different persons. It turns out that some of these qualities of blood are quite specific. For example, it is possible to transfer blood from a strong healthy person to one who is ill or has lost a great deal of blood, but only if the transfer (transfusion) is made in specified ways. The rules governing blood transfusion were discovered 60 years ago, when it was shown that the presence or absence of certain substances in the red blood cells are responsible for the success or failure of blood transfusion. These substances in the red cells are called A and B substances, or A and B antigens.

In the serum are other substances which react with the antigens in the blood cells. These are called antibodies. For example, if serum is taken from a person in the A group, it will cause clumping of the cells of a B group person when these are placed in it. Consequently we say that the B persons have anti-A substances or antibodies in their blood. Therefore

if cells from an A person are transferred into the circulation of a B
person, the cells of the A person will form clots which clog up some of the
small blood vessels and this is likely to cause the death of the person who
was to have benefited by blood transfusion. When all these combinations
of cells and serum are carefully studied it is found that persons can give
and receive blood according to the diagram below:

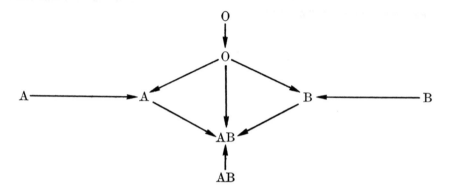

The blood group of each person is determined by his genes. The alleles
of this blood group gene are called A, B, and O. Every person can be
easily placed in one of the four groups, O, A, B, or AB (Table 1), and
we find that the genes responsible for these groups are present throughout the world, although the proportions of these different genes differ
somewhat from place to place and from race to race.

TABLE 1

PERSON OF BLOOD GROUP	HAS THIS SUBSTANCE IN HIS RED BLOOD CELLS	HAS THESE ANTIBODIES IN HIS BLOOD SERUM	HAS THESE ALLELES
A	A	anti-B	AA or AO
B	B	anti-A	BB or BO
AB	A and B	none	AB
O	none	anti-A and anti-B	OO

These different groups of people have the same kinds of antigens in the
blood, and the variety in the antigens is due to variation in the gene,
which probably arose by mutation.

Related people who probably got their genes from the same source
have similar proportions of the A and B alleles. This produces the great
cluster of blood group O in the American Indians, in whom B is rare or
absent, while A is generally also uncommon. There is a group of Indians
in Peru in which all persons tested were found to be of group O. Their
nearest neighbors are a tribe with 90 per cent group O. Probably A and

TABLE 2

The proportions of persons belonging to each of the four blood groups in different populations (per cent).

	O	A	B	AB
North American Indian (Chippewa)	87.6	12.4	0	0
South American Indian (Matto Grosso)	100.0	0	0	0
Australian:				
Aborigines West	48.1	51.9	0	0
East	58.6	37.8	3.6	0
Europeans:				
English	47.9	42.4	8.3	1.4
Swedes	37.9	46.1	9.5	6.5
Greeks	42.0	39.6	14.2	3.7
Russians	31.9	34.4	24.9	8.8
Asiatic:				
Japanese	30.1	38.4	21.9	9.7
Chinese	34.2	30.8	27.7	7.3

B were lost from the first tribe, either by accident when its ancestors migrated to a new home, or by some selective factor operating in the new environment.

Notice too the rise in the proportion of blood group B as we go east across Europe from England to Russia (Moscow).

There are some interesting situations in groups known to have split up by migration within historic time. The Icelanders are descended from Vikings from Scandinavia and "Westman" from Ireland who settled on the island in the ninth century A.D. Although the majority are supposed to have come from Scandinavia, and Iceland was politically united to Denmark until 1944, the blood types of the Icelanders are much closer to those of the Irish than of the Danes. The Basques, living near the

TABLE 3

Percentage of population in each blood group.

	O	A	B	AB
Icelanders	55.7	32.1	9.6	2.6
Irish	55.2	31.1	12.1	1.7
Danes	40.7	45.3	10.5	3.5

Spanish-French frontier, are unlike both their Spanish and French neighbors, who resemble each other more closely than either resembles the Basques.

TABLE 4

	O	A	B	AB
Basques	57.2	41.7	1.1	0
French	39.8	42.3	11.8	6.1
Spanish	41.5	46.5	9.2	2.2

As a final example, two groups of people living near each other in Hungary are very unlike each other in blood group distribution. One group is composed of gypsies with a large proportion of blood group B like some peoples of western India, whence the gypsies migrated long ago. The other is composed of "natives," long settled in Hungary with less than half the proportion of group B. Similar evidence exists for other groups who live near each other. The reason, of course, is found in the rarity of intermarriage between the different groups. This shows that a common environment does not by itself cause convergence, and that there are barriers other than geographical ones which cause peoples to remain distinct. Of course this would happen only if the genes retained their integrity and were passed on uninfluenced by the combinations in which they had taken part.

All these facts could be illustrated just as well by other human genes which can be classified objectively and accurately. The so-called M and N blood types, the varieties of the recently discovered Rh blood gene, genes for taste-blindness, color-blindness, and others all appear in their several varieties in nearly all human populations but in *different characteristic proportions*. It is important to emphasize that it is varieties or alleles of the *same* genes that are found in all races.

What has caused the separated populations of the world to diverge in this way in the proportions of different forms of the same genes is not known, but we may suspect that natural selection, favoring different alleles in different environments, has been an important factor. It is now known, for example, that in European populations persons who get ulcers of the intestine are much more likely to be of blood group O, than A or B or AB; those with a cancer of the stomach are more likely to be of blood group A than of O, or B. There may be other diseases to which persons of blood group B are more susceptible in certain environments. Research on connections between blood group genes and disease and other agencies which may act selectively is proceeding in many countries and may be expected to elucidate the part that natural selection plays in changing the frequencies of such genes.

Blood typing has certain obvious advantages over measuring or photographing in attempting to study the nature and origin of group differences. Blood typing immediately reveals the genetic constitution of the person tested, so that the distribution of these genes in a population is known from the blood group distribution. Description of a population by the genes found in it prevents the loss of the individual in the group because in general there is no "average" blood type. There are only characteristic proportions in which the same elements are mixed.

These differences in proportions are racial differences, that is, they indicate partial separation of the population in which the different proportions are maintained. The differences may be just as great between populations living in the same city as between populations living half a world away from each other. In Table 5 are shown the blood group varieties in two caste communities in Bombay, as determined by two Indian investigators.

The blood types of these groups are quite different, and differences like this were also found in six other gene-determined characters. They are in fact at least as different in these traits as American whites and American Negroes, who are separated by the low frequency of inter-marriage. These Indian communities are separated by customs which cause marriages to be contracted only between members of certain specified sections within the caste.

TABLE 5

	O	A	B	AB
Indians (Bombay C.K.P.)[1]	34.5	28.5	28.5	8.5
Indians (Bombay K.B.)[2]	51.0	24	20	5.0

[1] Members of the caste community Chandraseniya Kayasth Prabhu.
[2] Members of the caste community Koknasth Brahman.

These conditions permit the maintenance of gene differences between the groups. No one hesitates to call such differences "racial" as between Europeans and Negroes, everyone being aware that the ancestors of the Negroes now living in other parts of the world came from Africa a few hundred years ago where they had been practically isolated from the populations of other continents. But there would be a good deal of hesitation in referring to the two Indian caste communities as belonging to different races; the members of these two caste communities have lived together in peace and mutual respect for 2,000 years or more. This is good evidence that biological racial differences are not themselves the cause of race friction or prejudice. Probably the members of these castes do not recognize the biological differences which the scientists found, and after getting on well together for so long their behavior will probably not be influenced by this new knowledge.

The important thing is not to have an easy and certain answer for every question about racial classification, but rather to understand, from such instances, the nature of racial differences. Once these are seen to consist of collections of individual hereditary elements which do not blend even within the same population, then we can see in a different light the external differences from which we had earlier formed ideas about the fixity of "racial types." When we look around us from this second point of view, we find a good many facts which fit together into a consistent picture.

In the first place, no very radical changes in classification of the great branches of mankind are suggested when they are compared by the gene method.

Geographical isolation aided by natural selection has undoubtedly been the great race-maker, and this is clearly reflected in the differences in the frequencies of several genes as between European, African, Asiatic, American Indian and Australian racial stocks. Even these great branches are not discontinuously different, having most of their genes in common. European and Asiatic "intergrade" in eastern Russia and Siberia, Australian and Asiatic in the southern Pacific, and the other Pacific peoples show resemblances with, and no sharp differences from, Asiatics and Americans. Even the Australians and Europeans, separated so widely (except for the recent migration of Europeans) show clear evidence of common origin.

A racial classification of mankind based on the gene frequency method was that of Boyd who recognized five major races as follows: (a) European or Caucasoid, (b) African or Negroid, (c) Asiatic or Mongoloid, (d) American Indian, (e) Australoid. These can be characterized as groups by the relative frequencies of some eight genes, most of them concerned with blood antigens. It is obvious that they represent groups isolated geographically. The American Indians separated from their Asiatic ancestors only some 10,000 to 15,000 years ago, so they retain many mongoloid traits but still can be distinguished as a group. In addition to these, transitional groups are recognized, such as the peoples in the Pacific Islands, and in North Africa, and a hypothetical race not now in existence except as a small relic population, the Basques of Spain and France.

On the other hand, another study . . . by three American anthropologists, Coon, Garn and Birdsell, recognized 30 races, based largely on the classical criteria of physical type. Some of the 30 such as Neo-Hawaiian, American colored and South African colored are interesting as examples of races in the making. The authors thereby recognize that race is not something fixed and unchangeable, but a stage in the process by which human populations adapt themselves to special conditions. All of the 30 races above can be grouped into the same five categories recognized by Boyd and by anthropologists generally, since they are clearly based on geographical isolation.

It cannot be said at present that one classification is more correct than the other. The classification is in part a convenience and thus may be somewhat arbitrary, and should be determined by the purpose for which it is to be used. But it must be also a "natural" classification and express the evolutionary processes which have brought about the racial diversification of mankind.

The classification into a few large races is perhaps the one best justified. Races which have lived in one place for long ages seem to be fitted to live in just such a region. Biologists say they are "adapted" to the physical conditions, just as those plants which are best able to get along with infrequent rainfall or in extreme cold have survived in desert or mountain conditions.

Not much is known about the adaptive value of most physical characters in human races. Skin pigment appears to be advantageous where people are exposed to strong sunlight; great chest capacity and a large volume of the red blood cells which carry oxygen may be adaptations to high altitudes. Resistance to specific local infectious diseases must be an extremely important adaptative quality.

In man, ability to succeed in a great variety of environments is connected with the most important way in which he differs from lower animals, that is, his ability to learn and to profit by experience and especially to live in organized societies and to develop culture. The religious, moral and ethical traditions which all societies develop in some form, language which permits oral and written communication between generations and between different societies, the evolution of political and economic institutions and of literature, art, science, technology and industry—all of these reflect the peculiar mental adaptability and plasticity of man. All civilizations increase the selective advantage of genes for mental capacity and educability and these are found in all races.

No race is uniform with respect to mental traits any more than with respect to physical traits, or blood group or other genes. It is in fact this variety which permitted each race to adapt itself to a variety of environments. In the past, as today, persons must have been found to accomplish successfully all the varied tasks which are required in every human society. We may suspect that when the genes influencing the normal operations of the brain and nervous system are subjected to as extensive study as has been devoted to properties of the blood, a great variety of genotypes will be revealed. If there are, as reliably estimated, millions of different combinations of genes as expressed in the blood, not less should be expected in respect to genes influencing behavior and mental capacity and special abilities. It would be surprising if these were to be distributed uniformly in all environments in which natural selection has probably fitted different groups to cope with different conditions. We know relatively little now about the distribution of such genes; they are much more difficult to identify and to study objectively than genes which can be classified by physical or chemical means. Perhaps such methods must be used before the knowledge we need can be obtained. .

But much past experience should make us prepared to find that the biological capacities to absorb new cultural acquisitions are very widely distributed, however many local differences in the proportions of genes are found.

Peoples of ancient cultural traditions have been able quickly to adapt, as whole societies, to new technical and industrial methods; this has happened in Europe and in Asia and is now happening in Africa. Some of the peoples included in the Soviet State have in two generations changed from a hunting and gathering or a nomadic and pastoral way of life to operating an industrial economy based on machines.

In the light of the recent rapid development of similar technologies in all parts of the world the question may well be asked whether this growing uniformity in productive methods, with the greater ease of communication and consequent increase in the movements and migrations of peoples, and especially in the speed of urbanization, will tend to make all people alike. The best answer to this question comes from recalling the reasons for the existence of the enormous biological variety in all human populations. These reasons trace to the origination of gene differences by random mutation and the maintenance of these differences by the integrity of individual genes and the tendency to maintenance of variety as expressed in the Hardy-Weinberg rule. Other factors operating through migrations and changes in mating patterns will be discussed below under "Race Separation and Race Fusion."

RACE SEPARATION AND RACE FUSION

Two processes are clearly in evidence in our human species. One of these is race formation, by which distinctive collections of genes are gathered together; the other is race fusion, by which these collections are disposed. The essential condition for race divergence is always separation, partial or complete isolation, which reduces the frequency of marriage between two groups. We can call the group within which marriages are contracted the *marriage circle*. We can think of the population of the world as living within marriage circles of differing sizes. These circles overlap and permit some intermarriage between circles but less than within a circle.

Now anything which affects the size of the circle, that is, the number of people within the marriage circle, and the degree of separation between circles, will affect the distribution of genes. Every marriage circle is a potential race. I have already pointed out that members of two different caste communities in the city of Bombay are as unlike in the frequency of certain genes as are members of African and European marriage circles. Even if we did not know of the customs preventing marriage between members of these different castes, we should have to infer that they existed. Some of these caste communities are very large (several million) and others quite small (20,000 to 30,000).

The population of a large and geographically diversified area like that of Europe must perforce become broken up into smaller marriage circles. One such was based on caste, the royal families who married within their own circle. More circles were based on geographic isolation, for much of the population lived in villages and marriages were usually contracted between members of the same or nearby villages. If long continued this would lead to some biological divergence and the development of local peculiarities. City people too were partly isolated into different marriage circles, the barriers often being religious or social or linguistic. But such divergences never proceeded very far, for the history of Europe, in numbers of human generations, is a short one, and peoples in other parts of the world, although they could recognize Europeans, could seldom distinguish the different varieties. Whether one recognizes few or many races in Europe is a matter of taste about which anthropologists do not agree.

The important fact for us in the present connection is that the marriage circles tended to change as economic, social, and political conditions changed. The movements from country to city which the development of industry greatly accelerated, resulted in a very great enlargement of the marriage circles. Now boys met girls from different parts of the country and wherever other barriers were absent the expected took place. The incipient peculiarities of separated communities were merged in the larger group. The development of cheap transportation had an important effect, especially as between different countries. Most important for Europe, connection with America became very close, and in the American cities members of different European marriage circles met and became members of the same circle. Moreover, the social and economic class barriers tended to get lower as political democracy spread.

These considerations show only that the conditions tending to change gene distribution may be responsive to external factors of many kinds. They do not explain why one group should spread and another contract. Sometimes this is due to pure luck, just as whether we are exposed to a fatal disease may be a matter of chance. Sometimes factors which are only secondarily biological will be decisive, such as customs of early or late marriage, decreed for religious or economic reasons, which determine the rate of natural increase of the group. Sometimes the conjunction of great military or religious leaders will cause one group to expand or migrate at a fortunate time while another disappears for no apparent biological reason.

These are cultural changes, and yet they have greatly affected the distribution of genes. The net effect of industrialization in Europe and the Americas has been to increase the size of marriage circles, and thereby to reverse the tendency to isolation by which races tended to diverge. Genes in the European world now have a much greater mobility and will tend to spread themselves more evenly. One effect is to make it less likely that members of this large community will marry relatives and thus bring to expression those hidden recessives, many of them deleterious, which nearly everyone conceals. In this sense enlargement of the marriage circle is beneficial.

Such effects are of course not peculiar to Europe. They accompany urbanization wherever it occurs and the history of the world is replete with other movements of peoples and minglings of races. We often hear it said that intermarriage between races has had biological consequences. There is no good or extensive evidence of this and much to be said on the other side. It is true that the immediate offspring of mixed marriages often have a hard time, falling between two racial communities without belonging to either of them. But the effects in such cases are usually of a social and economic and psychological nature rather than biological. That populations with new biological combinations of traits may arise in this way may be seen in the American Negroes, in the Cape colored of South Africa, in some of the populations of Central and South America and the Caribbean in which genes from European, American Indian and sometimes from African ancestors are mingled. Race fusions of this sort have been going on ever since bands of people acquired the means of mobility and migration. Its effects are reflected in the variety found within all human races. Whether the mixture was remote or recent, the result is that all human beings are hybrids or mongrels containing genes from a wide variety of different ancestors.

At times the mingling of races may tend to break up adaptive combinations of genes assembled under the influence of natural selection over long generations of living in one set of environments. This becomes of less importance as man learns to control his environments. He now begins to adapt his environment to his needs rather than the reverse which is the only way open to other creatures. Today he gets rid of malaria by inventing and using DDT to destroy the mosquitoes which transmit it and consequently need not depend upon the slow process by which natural selection builds up inherited resistance to the disease.

One result of recent studies of plant and animal populations suggests a possible biological reason why the genotypes of most human individuals contain unlike alleles in most of their genes. Such hybrids (heterozygotes is the technical phrase) frequently have greater vigor and biological efficiency. The great success of hybrid corn is due to this, and in many animal populations natural selection appears to favor unlike combinations of alleles in preference to the pure or homozygous state. Perhaps man too may owe his position as the most successful and adaptable of animals to his mixed genetic nature.

However this may be, it is in any case clear that the evolutionary processes by which man adapted himself to the varied environments of this planet did not include the formation of pure or uniform races since these do not exist anywhere. Rather the process by which he was able to colonize all the habitable parts of the world was first by the assembly of varied combinations of genes formed under the influence of natural selection and other natural forces. These differed in proportions as different natural conditions required. Race is a stage in this process, always as a flexible means rather than as a fixed or determined final stage. Second, he developed culture and a great variety of techniques by which he bent his physical environments to his human needs and purposes. Cultural acquisitions are transmitted by language and written records, a form of inheritance separate from and independent of biological heredity. This second mode of adaptation is now the most important one by which he conquers new environments such as Antarctica yesterday, and outer space tomorrow. Race is not a stage in this process and its biological function is now a secondary one.

The persistence of race prejudice where it exists is a cultural acquisition which as we have seen finds no justification in biology. It serves no biological function in a world which is now progressing beyond the need of race formation as a means of adaptation. The conditions of modern life, deplorable as they are for the many peoples over whom hangs the threat of insecurity and war are nevertheless those which will tend further to reduce the importance of the conditions which formed biological race differences. This does not mean that biological race differences will disappear; the effects of thousands of generations of human evolution will not be more quickly altered. But they may now be viewed in proper perspective and based on knowledge rather than prejudice. The knowledge of the operation of heredity which we now have should lead also to better understanding of the nature of the biological diversity of individuals which lies at the basis of group diversity. The emphasis on the uniqueness of individuals which this new knowledge promotes should thus improve relations within as well as between human groups.

Men are social beings and religious beings as well as biological ones, and they must depend upon their immediate fellows however close they may be drawn to others in the world community. Attachments to place, to neighbors, to members of the same community of thought and spirit have values which all men need and this is true in spite of all the abuses perpetrated in the name of communities based on race. These need not be given up when the tolerance and sympathy with which we regard members of our own group are extended to all others.

21

RACIAL DIFFERENCES
IN HEAT TOLERANCE

Paul T. Baker

*The features that distinguish clusters of human populations
from one another have probably arisen through the action
of natural selection. If so, the question may be asked: selection
for what? Are the climatic differences in various earth zones
the environmental factors to which human populations have
become adapted in the course of time? What is the relation between environments and adaptive differences under
varying thermal conditions? Pigmentation (which will be discussed in a later article by Harold F. Blum) is one difference that may have adaptive significance.*

*A possible line of approach to these questions is to
determine whether humans do differ in their capacity to perform work under varying climatic conditions and whether
the differences are distributed differently among populations. The careful research represented by Paul T. Baker's
work will convey some idea of the experimental approach in
studies of human differences. Baker is Professor of Anthropology at Pennsylvania State University. The paper reprinted
here is one of a number that he has written about human
resistance to heat stress.*

INTRODUCTION

The science of genetics has emphasized the importance of natural
selection in the formation of taxonomic races. This in turn indicates
the desirability of a re-evaluation of human races in terms of the possible sources of selective forces. Such a re-evaluation may be based on

(From *American Journal of Physical Anthropology*, Vol. 16, September
1958, pages 287–305. By permission of the author and the publisher.)

ecological inferences from the distribution of modern races; or specific hypothesis may be tested by experimental means.

It is the purpose of this study, using the experimental approach, to compare the heat stress resistance (heat tolerance) of Negroes and Whites. The development of this type of knowledge will eventually permit us to define some of the role of climate in the selection of certain morphological characteristics.

The American Negro, as a racial group, is certainly a mixed genetic population with considerable White admixture. Some authorities have claimed there is also a high percentage of Indian admixture, but recent blood studies dispute this claim. For these reasons it should not be assumed that the heat stress resistance of the American Negro is identical with any other group. Comparison between American Whites and American Negroes has value primarily as an estimate of the variation in resistance which is related to genetic factors. The American Negroes as a group have a genetic inheritance drawn from a tropical population, while American Whites have lived almost exclusively in temperate climates for many generations. If there is a genetically controlled difference in the heat stress resistance of these groups, it would strongly indicate the presence of a genetic difference in heat tolerance between temperate and tropical populations; however, the extent of the potential genetic difference cannot be ascertained by studying these groups alone.

Past studies on racial differences in heat tolerance are inadequate in light of our present knowledge of acclimatization and human temperature regulation. Most of the comparative work was performed under differing environmental conditions. Caplan and Lindsay studied Indian mine workers under saturated hot-wet conditions and compared their results to those of Mackworth's on English Whites. Wyndham studied South African and Tanganyikan Negroes under hot-wet conditions. He compared his results with those obtained on Whites by Eichna et al., McArdle et al., and others. He also compared his results with those of Robinson et al. on Mississippi sharecroppers. In both studies a difference between racial groups was claimed. Rectal temperatures and pulse rates were slightly lower in the non-White groups; sweat loss was much lower in the non-Whites.

Two aspects of these studies qualify interpretation of the results. First, the experiments were not designed for direct racial comparisons. Consequently, neither the level of acclimatization nor the climatic exposure conditions were the same for the White and non-White groups. Thus, the comparisons are subject to possible variations in responses caused by the level of acclimatization, small differences in heat stress levels, climatic conditions during non-test periods, and even differences in diet.

Second, in both studies the average body weight of the non-Whites was much lower than the Whites with whom they were compared. From the data of Adolph relating body weight to sweat loss, it may be assumed that most of the sweat loss difference between groups in the above studies was a function of the difference in body weight. Of course, even if the group differences in sweat loss were a function of body weight, they could still be considered a genetically determined racial difference since weight is partially under genetic control.

The racial comparison study of Robinson et al. remains the best study so far, despite the limitations of some of the conclusions reported in the same article. His study was made before acclimatization was a well-known phenomenon, and his effort to acclimatize the men brought from the North before comparing them to the Southern Whites was not adequate. However, for a racial comparison, Southern Negro and White sharecroppers were studied. By using groups with similar environmental background, cultural and acclimatization factors were reduced. Fortunately, weights for the two groups were also quite similar. The most important difference noted was in post-stress rectal temperatures. Under identical workloads the Negroes had a mean rectal temperature of 100.9°F as compared to 101.6°F for the Whites. Robinson concluded that the racial differences in heat stress resistance could probably be attributed to racial differences in the surface-area-over-weight index and mechanical efficiency. His second conclusion was based on an assumed racial difference in oxygen consumption per unit of surface area. It has been demonstrated that surface area is not the best reference for oxygen consumption; and it is quite possible that the presumed extra efficiency of the Negro sharecroppers is attributable to a racial difference in body composition.

In summarizing the published evidence it has been possible to find experimental omissions in all the studies, but it cannot be said in any case that the total results have been explained by inadequate experimental or environmental controls. Instead, the published material, particularly Robinson's work, strongly supports the conclusion that there is a genetically determined racial difference in resistance to hot-wet heat stress.

EXPERIMENTS IN HEAT TOLERANCE

Because of the differences between hot-wet and hot-dry climates, two separate experiments were performed; one under moderate hot-wet conditions in Virginia and the other under hot-dry conditions in the Yuma Desert. The experiments were designed to test whether American White and Negro soldiers showed any difference in their ability to withstand heat stress.

HOT-WET CONDITIONS

Procedure and Methods. Potential strain differences due to racial differences in body size and composition were controlled by selection. One hundred American Negro and 100 American White soldiers were measured at Fort Lee, Virginia. From these 200 men, 40 pairs were matched as closely as possible for per cent of fat in the body, fat-free weight and stature.

These 40 pairs were then subdivided into 4 groups of matched pairs, each of which contained 10 Negro and 10 White soldiers matched for body size and composition. Each group followed the experimental procedure twice and an average of the strain measurements for both days was used for the analysis of the men measured.

Each matched pair was exposed to equal heat stress, and the strain responses of the men were measured. The strain measurements were sweat loss, rectal temperature and pulse rate per minute. In detail, each group reported to a walking course at 12:45 P.M. They stripped and weighed nude on a gram scale accurate to plus or minus 10 grams. They then inserted rectal catheters which contained thermocouples for reading rectal temperatures. All men wore the same style and quantity of clothing which consisted of Army uniforms, caps and boots.

After each pair had weighed and dressed, rectal temperature was recorded on a potentiometer. These temperatures have a reproducibility of plus or minus 1/10 of a degree Fahrenheit. The men were dispatched in pairs at 5-minute intervals. They walked around a half-mile course at a rate of 3½ miles per hour. To insure that a constant pace was held by all men, two timekeepers were posted, one at the starting point and one at the halfway mark. At the end of one hour the men stopped at the observation tent, where pulse was immediately counted. Rectal temperatures were again read from the potentiometer. Each pair then undressed, wiped off all sweat, and were weighed. Identical procedure was followed for all groups all days.

TABLE 1

A comparison of body composition measurements on matched American Negroes and Whites

MEASUREMENT	WHITE MEAN	N = 40 S.D.	NEGRO MEAN	N = 40 S.D.	MEAN DIFFER-ENCE
Per cent of fat in the body[1]	5.3	3.2	5.2	3.4	0.1
Fat-free weight (lb)[1]	145.7	13.8	145.7	13.2	0
Stature (cm)	175.1	6.5	172.9	5.7	2.2

[1] Per cent fat and fat-weight were estimated using the QMC caliper described by Newman.

Sweat loss was calculated in the following manner: sweat loss equaled initial weight minus final weight. Water intake and urine output were prevented so that no corrections were required. It was considered unnecessary to correct for respiratory loss of weight since this constitutes a negligible source of error under these conditions.

Results. Field work always has one uncontrollable variable: weather. In this study we were unfortunate, since the weather was cool for Virginia in August. Within the test hours the temperature averaged 84.3°F while the relative humidity averaged 44%. As shown in Table 2 the low stress level was reflected in low strain levels.

Negro-White differences in heat stress responses are also shown in Table 2. As measured by a paired T-test, there was a significant difference at the 0.05 level or better between the rectal temperatures of the Negroes and Whites both before the walk and afterwards. The difference was increased by the exercise. There was no significant difference at the 0.05 level for pulse rate or sweat loss.

Eighteen Whites, but only 4 Negroes in this study came from Northern States. There was, therefore, the possibility that the difference in rectal temperatures was a function of the Northern origin of the Whites. Eighteen Southern Whites were selected who had been studied on the same days as the Northern Whites and who had comparable body compositions.

TABLE 2

A comparison of American Negro and White heat stress responses

MEASUREMENT	WHITE MEAN	N = 40 S.D.	NEGRO MEAN	N = 40 S.D.	MEAN DIFFER-ENCE	SIGNIFI-CANCE OF DIFFER-ENCE
Pre-test rectal temp. (°F)	99.6	0.38	99.4	0.42	0.2	>0.05
Post-test rectal temp. (°F)	100.4	0.45	100.0	0.45	0.4	>0.01
Pulse rate (beats per/min)	122.4	12.9	119.4	14.6	3.0	<0.05
Sweat loss (gm per/hr)	912	139	873	137	39	<0.05

The strain measurements of these 18 Southern Whites were compared to the same strain measurements for the Northern Whites. The slight differences that were found indicated the Southern Whites were lower in heat tolerance. However, these differences were in no case statistically significant and were probably a function of the size of the sample. This comparison seemed to indicate that the locale from which the subjects were drawn did not influence their heat tolerance.

There still remain several possible non-genetic explanations for the difference between the racial groups. Probably some differences exist in the childhood nutritional patterns of the two groups. However, body composition was controlled by selection, and differences in responses cannot be attributed to the Negro's lower fat or greater linearity.

Differences in physical conditioning might also effect resistance. For this reason an effort was made to obtain racial groups in the same state of physical training. The men participating in this study came from the same Army units, and as the Army no longer separates Negro and White troops, these men had, for at least the last 6 months, performed similar duties.

There may be other potential sources of difference which have not been considered, but the data strongly suggest that under similar mild wet heat stress loads American Negroes have lower rectal temperatures than American Whites and that this difference is probably not attributable to post-conception environment. The data do not indicate the nature of the genetic difference. That is, it cannot be determined whether the lower rectal temperatures in the Negroes are related to greater cardiovascular output (which would increase internal to peripheral heat flow), greater mechanical efficiency, or more effective performance in other temperature regulatory mechanisms such as sweat salinity or distribution.

Because the Negroes and Whites in this study were selected for similar gross morphologies, neither group is necessarily representative of its respective population in terms of body composition. From studies of Army populations it is known that U.S. Army Negroes have body compositions considerably different from Whites. The American Negro population is lower in body fat and has slightly more fat-free weight. If representative samples had been chosen the results would probably have reflected greater racial differences in heat strain measurements. On the basis of work in previous experiments on White soldiers, a fatter group would have had higher rectal temperature, pulse rates and sweat losses. Thus, in typical samples not matched for body composition, the Negro-White differences in strain responses would have been greater. However, it cannot be concluded that the relationship found for Whites (between gross morphological characteristics and heat strain indicators) holds for Negroes.

The differing daily weather conditions made it necessary to analyze each daily subsample of Negroes and Whites separately. The multiple subdivision of the group left a maximum sample size of 10, which was small for correction analysis. Rectal temperatures were significantly correlated with fat in only one of the subsamples. This is to be expected because of the low stress level. As shown in Table 3, there was consistent and significant correlation between sweat loss and fat-free weight for both Negroes and Whites.

TABLE 3

Correlation coefficients for sweat loss and fat-free weight

	WHITES		NEGROES	
SAMPLE GROUP	N	Correlation Coefficient	N	Correlation Coefficient
August 4 and 5	10	0.64	10	0.51
August 6 and 9	10	0.94	10	0.60
August 10 and 11	10	0.58	10	0.86
August 12 and 13	10	0.66	10	0.71

The regression equations of sweat loss on fat-free weight indicated a considerable between-group variation in regression slopes. Most of this variation is attributable to the small sample sizes, but some part of it may be related to the between-group differences in heat stress levels.

While weather conditions may have affected the regression slopes, no significant differences were found between the regressions of sweat loss on weight for Negroes and Whites. These results make it more probable that the regressions of fat-free weight on sweat loss found for Whites may be validly applied to American Negroes. Assuming that there is no difference in the regressions, in representative racial samples, there would not only be a significant difference in rectal temperature which may under heat stress be genetically determined but also a significant difference in sweat loss, determined by racial differences in body composition.

HOT-DRY CONDITIONS

Procedure and Methods. For the study under desert conditions a sample of 8 White and 8 Negro subjects was chosen from a group of approximately 50 men. These two samples were matched for body composition and proportions as the group for hot-wet conditions had been matched.

Measurements were also made of skin color reflectance on both groups. A Photovolt reflectometer was used to make the measurements. The readings with an amber tristimulus filter were made weekly at 5 sites; the cheek, the chest over the nipple, the inner arm, the outer arm, and the back over the inferior angle of the scapula. The measurements were repeated three times at each site, and an average was calculated.

After thorough heat acclimatization in the desert, a Latin square experimental design was implemented so that each man was studied under 8 different desert conditions for 2 hours. Negroes and Whites were paired so that in each day's study there were 8 pairs, one under each condition. Each man repeated each condition 4 times for a total of 32 exposures. The conditions were combinations of: sun, shade, nude, clothed, walking and resting. Shade was obtained from a large assembly tent. Walking was around a small rectangular course at the rate of three miles per hour, and rest was sitting inactive on a foot locker. A more complete description of the experimental design and conditions will be published in a forthcoming Quartermaster Research and Development Technical Report.

The physiological measurements made were: rectal temperature (initial and final)—by means of a clinical thermometer; total sweat loss—by weight change corrected for water intake; evaporated sweat loss—by total sweat loss minus sweat retention in the clothing; pulse rates—counted for 20 seconds at the wrist.

Results. Analysis of the effects of the experimental variables showed that most conditions had significantly different effects on the men. The Negroes and Whites showed significant differences (by variance analysis) in their initial and final rectal temperatures but not in total sweat loss, evaporated sweat loss or pulse rates. Table 4 shows the absolute values and the difference in rectal temperature between Negroes and Whites.

The Negro-White difference in initial rectal temperature is, of course, in no way affected by the condition to which they were later exposed but is important in calculating the total heat storage during the experimental condition. Prior to the experiment, the men rested on cots for one hour in their tents in the desert. The racial difference found in the initial rectal temperatures must, therefore, be attributed to this condition as there is no difference under neutral climatic conditions.

The final rectal temperature differences seem to show a very definite pattern related to the condition to which the men were exposed. When the men were in the shade or protected from the direct sun by clothing, the Negroes had a slightly higher rectal temperature than the Whites. However, when the nude skin was exposed to the sun the differences between the groups increased so that when walking nude in the sun, with a maximum of skin exposed, the difference amounted to almost four-tenths of a degree Fahrenheit. This pattern is exposed even more clearly when the rectal temperature rise from initial to final is examined.

When the Negroes were protected from the sun, their rise in rectal

TABLE 4
Rectal temperature for Negroes and Whites

TEMPERATURE DEGREES F.	CONDITION							
	Shade Clothed Rest	Shade Nude Rest	Sun Clothed Rest	Sun Nude Rest	Shade Clothed Walk	Shade Nude Walk	Sun Clothed Walk	Sun Nude Walk
Initial								
Negroes	99.19	99.21	99.21	99.21	99.27	99.20	99.23	99.22
Whites	99.00	99.02	99.01	99.00	99.02	98.99	98.96	99.08
Difference	−0.19	−0.19	−0.20	−0.21	−0.25	−0.21	−0.27	−0.13
Final								
Negroes	99.19	99.26	99.32	99.54	100.15	100.17	100.31	100.40
Whites	99.11	99.18	99.30	99.30	99.92	99.98	100.07	100.02
Difference	−0.08	−0.08	−0.02	−0.24	−0.23	−0.19	−0.24	−0.38

TABLE 5
Rectal temperature rise from initial to final readings

	CONDITIONS							
	Shade Clothed Rest	Shade Nude Rest	Sun Clothed Rest	Sun Nude Rest	Shade Clothed Walk	Shade Nude Walk	Sun Clothed Walk	Sun Nude Walk
Rectal rise degree F.								
Negroes	0.00	0.05	0.11	0.33	0.88	0.97	1.09	1.20
Whites	0.11	0.16	0.29	0.30	0.90	0.99	1.11	0.94
Difference	+0.11	+0.11	+0.18	−0.03	+0.02	+0.02	+0.02	−0.26

temperature was the same or even lower than that of the Whites. Only when the two groups were walking nude in the sun did the Negro rectal temperature rise substantially more than the White.

Although the sweat losses were not significantly different between the two groups, at the 0.05 level, the differences reflect very closely what was found in rectal temperatures.

Again the major difference is found when the two groups are exposed nude to the sun although a fairly large difference also appears when the two groups are walking clothed in the shade.

The effect of the *nude* exposure in establishing racial difference in responses, very strongly suggests that greater heat absorption by the Negro skin may be the major factor determining the observed differences. By utilizing the skin reflectance reading an estimate was made of the difference between the two groups. The amber tristimulus filter used to measure skin color transmits light in the approximate wavelength of 600 millimicrons, which falls near the middle of the visible sunlight spectrum, thus, skin reflectance reading with this filter offers a rough estimate of the heat absorption from the sun. From the 4 areas exposed to the sun (cheek, chest, arm and back) an average reflectance during the study was derived. It was found that the Negroes absorbed approximately 84.6% of the light received while the Whites absorbed approximately 69.7%.

The average radiation of the sun was measured with a pyroheliometer in a horizontal position. For the total experimental period the radiation averaged 846.5 kilogram Calories per square meter per hour (kg Cal. per m^2 per hour). If this is corrected for the normal incidence, then the radiation intensity was 977.5 kg Cal. per m^2 per hour. Woodcock has shown that at the angle of the sun encountered under these conditions the seated and walking man has about 20% of his surface area exposed to the sun. The Negroes and Whites had identical surface areas of 1.90 square meters as calculated by the DuBois formula from height and weight. This means they both had about 0.38 square meters of skin exposed to the sun. From these figures we calculated the approximate heat absorbed from the sun by the two groups by means of the following formula:

$$\text{Kg. Cal. of heat absorption} = (\text{Two-hour radiation in kg Cal. per } m^2) \\ \times \text{ surface area exposed} \times \text{skin absorption}$$

It was found that the Negroes absorbed 628 kg Cal. during the average two-hour exposure while the Whites absorbed only 518 kg Cal. or a difference of 110 kg Cal.

Although rectal temperatures were significantly different for the two

TABLE 6

Total sweat losses for Negroes and Whites

	CONDITION							
	Shade Clothed Rest	Shade Nude Rest	Sun Clothed Rest	Sun Nude Rest	Shade Clothed Walk	Shade Nude Walk	Sun Clothed Walk	Sun Nude Walk
	Sweat loss in grams							
Negroes	963	1255	1393	2010	2143	2221	2582	2796
Whites	961	1219	1407	1857	1997	2166	2502	2656
Difference	−2	−36	+14	−153	−146	−55	−80	−140

TABLE 7

Evaporated sweat loss for Negroes and Whites

	CONDITION							
	Shade Clothed Rest	Shade Nude Rest	Sun Clothed Rest	Sun Nude Rest	Shade Clothed Walk	Shade Nude Walk	Sun Clothed Walk	Sun Nude Walk
	Sweat loss in grams							
Negroes	922	1229	1326	1982	1953	2181	2350	2780
Whites	923	1195	1344	1823	1822	2121	2286	2608
Difference	+1	−34	+18	−159	−131	−60	−64	−172

racial groups, the total heat storage difference was very small. This means that there should have been a fairly large difference in evaporated sweat loss to account for a large difference in solar radiant energy absorption. Assuming water evaporation to have an equivalent of 0.58 kg Cal. per gm, the Negro theoretically should have evaporated 190 more grams of sweat than the White. As shown in Table 7 the difference was not this great.

If these theoretical calculations are nearly correct, then it must be assumed that in some manner the Negro was able to dissipate more heat than the White without proportionately greater sweat loss.

The greater solar radiation absorption of the Negro is primarily a function of the melanin deposited in the epidermis and most of the solar energy is presumably converted to heat in this surface layer. The assumption is supported by the work of Laurens and Foster who showed that at 6 mm depth Negro and White skins had the same temperature when exposed to visible infra-red radiation. If the additional Negro radiation absorption is converted to heat in the epidermis, the Negro's exposed skin must have a higher temperature. This in return means that during this test, where the ambient temperature was higher than skin temperature, less long wave radiant heat was received. As skin temperature was not recorded during this study, the hypothesis cannot be checked; however, it forms a very logical explanation for the discrepancy between expected and found heat losses. It would mean that when Negro and White skin is exposed to solar radiation, although the Negro skin absorbs more of this energy, it warms more on the surface and thus loses more long wave radiation to an environment which has a temperature below that of the skin and gains less from an environment above skin temperature.

DISCUSSION AND CONCLUSIONS

Until recently the human species was taxonomically divided into races based on what were assumed to be adaptively "neutral" characteristics. At first these were body measurements and attributes, later blood factors such as the ABO antigens. In turn each of these characteristics was proven to have selective or adaptive aspects so that they could no longer be considered "neutral." This has led the modern geneticist and physical anthropologist to postulate a system of races which is based on geographical population isolates which conform more closely to genetic units. Classification of this nature certainly is genetically sound since it fulfills most of the requirements for the group to be considered a breeding isolate. The most important criticism which can be leveled against the geographical concept of race is that it is only a functional system without time depth or proof of genetic affinity. This is not so much a criticism of the system as it is a comment on the present state of our knowledge about the genetic and adaptive aspects of human morphology. Even though the geographical system appears to be the best that can be formulated at this time, we should not be satisfied with it. Instead, as pointed out by Garn, we must seek to define the adaptive nature of morphological characteristics.

Until the mass population shifts of the late eighteenth and early nineteenth centuries, African and European populations were restricted to separate climatic zones. Evolutionary theory suggests that some of the morphological differences that separate these groups may be based on the selective survival of genes which were adaptive to these differing environments. However, climatic zones vary in many ways and surveys of the native populations do not tell us which environmental isolates have exerted selective pressure on the morphological characteristics. One of the best documented factors in the environment is climate; given this single factor, it has been possible to apply an experimental approach and thus investigate the relative tolerance of two racial groups to a given environmental stress.

In the present studies the experimental approach has been applied to investigate the possible role of climate in creating the differences in American Negroes and Whites. The results of these experiments fit the spatial distribution of present day populations, since the Negroes of the world do not predominate in desert areas but are found in hot-wet areas. Distinctive groups such as Nilotics, Bushmen and Australian aborigines are the only Negro-like men found in the desert. These groups have been variously described as race mixtures, hybrids and even separate races. While any of these descriptions is a possibility, the experimental evidence indicates the morphologically typical Negro would be selected against by the climatic conditions, and the alternative possibility, therefore, remains that these groups came from the same ancestral genetic pool as the hot-wet area Negro, but were modified by climatic selection.

Once quantitative relationships have been established between environmental elements, (e.g., air temperature, solar radiation) and racial characteristics, it should be possible to apply these relationships to data on previous climates. In this way critical attention can be focused on those areas and times at which climate was exerting strong adaptive pressure. This will permit us to construct a racial classification with time depth as well as inferred genetic unity.

SUMMARY

The physiological responses of American White and Negro soldiers were studied under hot-wet and hot-dry conditions.

Under hot-wet conditions 40 pairs of men matched for body fat, weight and stature were walked around a course at 3½ mph for one hour.

Under hot-dry conditions 8 pairs of men also matched for body fat, weight and stature were studied under 8 different conditions which included combinations of clothing, sun, shade, walking and sitting.

The results of this series of experiments indicated:

1. Under hot-wet conditions with both Negroes and Whites clothed and walking, the Negroes had a higher physiological tolerance.

2. Under hot-dry conditions with both groups clothed, walking, or sitting they had about equal tolerance.

3. Under hot-dry conditions with both groups nude and exposed to the sun, sun-tanned Whites had the higher tolerance.

These results further suggested that the differences found were not a function of transient environmental effects and may be mostly genetic in origin. The results are discussed in relation to racial taxonomy systems and the distribution of human morphological attributes.

22

DOES THE
MELANIN PIGMENT
OF HUMAN SKIN
HAVE ADAPTIVE VALUE?

Harold F. Blum

Students of human differences have disagreed sharply over the significance of human skin pigmentation as an adaptation to different climates. Those who believe that it is an adaptation have suggested that the differences in skin color among human populations have risen as different groups moved into areas of greater or lesser solar radiation, and that natural selection acted to adapt them to such conditions. Harold F. Blum takes forceful issue with this position in the following article. Blum is the author of a classic in biology, Time's Arrow and Evolution.

"It is unnecessary to point out my admiration in general for the great modern synthesis which the science of evolution represents, but I may venture to observe that some examples of adaptive mechanisms are being paraded where the physiological interpretations are taken much too lightly."—P. F. Scholander.

Melanin pigment plays a predominant role in giving the brown and black color to the skin, which provides some of the most striking differences in outward appearance of human races. This would seem a very superficial difference, yet there has been an attempt to find adaptive significance in the presence of the pigment itself. It is quite generally accepted, without qualification, that the pigment constitutes a protective barrier against injurious effects of sunlight. Reasoning on this basis, Negroes have been thought to be better adapted than white-skinned peoples to life in the tropics, and this has been attributed to natural selection. Charles

(From *Quarterly Review of Biology*, Vol. 36, March 1961, pages 50–63. By permission of the author and the publisher.)

Darwin himself made this suggestion, although he hedged it with characteristic caution. The argument has been expanded since, and the idea has come to be widely accepted. This is sometimes cited today as a definite example of natural selection in Man.

In Darwin's day very little was known about the effects of sunlight on the human body or their relation to the spectrum of sunlight, or about the geographical distribution of sunlight; and although a good deal has been learned since, the knowledge does not seem to have been widely disseminated. There are still many things to be explained, but enough is known for a reasonably critical examination of various aspects of the above thesis. When one attempts such an examination he cannot but be surprised that such far-reaching conclusions, based on such tenuous evidence, should have received so much credence.

MELANIN AND ITS POSITION
IN HUMAN SKIN

The term melanin is applied to a type of finely granular, dark-colored substances in skin, hair, and some other organs of animals. While there is basic similarity in chemical composition there is a good deal of variety among the types of melanins. The color, which ranges through various shades of brown to black, is strongly affected by scattering of light by the pigment particles. The latter factor makes it difficult to relate the color to chemical composition, because of the difficulty it introduces into the measurement of absorption spectra.

In human skin the melanin is normally contained in the *epidermis*—a thin outer layer ranging from about 0.07 to 1.2 millimeters in thickness. The relationship of the epidermis to other structures, and some approximate dimensions, are indicated in Fig. 22–1B. In discussing the optical properties of skin, which concerns us here, it may be necessary to oversimplify the details of structure, which are quite complex. To this end I shall treat the epidermis as composed of two layers: the *malpighian*, made of living cells; and exterior to this the *corneum*, a dead layer which is produced from the living malpighian. The optical properties of these two layers differ greatly, although it would be difficult to demonstrate a sharp boundary between them, either optically or biologically. The distinction is useful, however, because the corneum obviously serves as an efficient barrier to ultraviolet light, greatly diminishing the amount that reaches the viable cells of the malpighian. Beneath the epidermis is the dermis, where are found a variety of structures, including the hair follicles, sebaceous glands, and sweat glands. The most superficial blood vessels are located in the dermis just underneath the epidermis. The

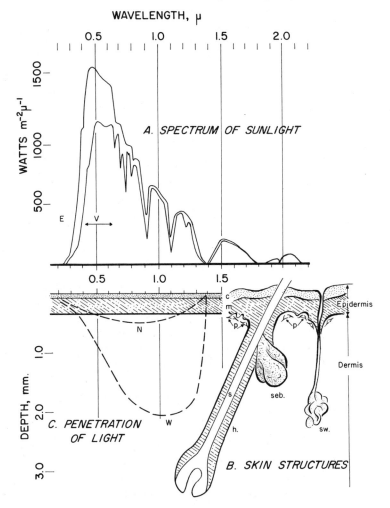

FIGURE 22–1—(A) Spectral distribution of sunlight at the surface of the earth. Curve 1, with sun at zenith. Curve 2, with sun at 60° (four hours) from zenith. V, spectral limits of human vision. E, spectral limits (within sunlight) for sunburn, antirachitic action, and cancer induction. (B) Diagrammatic representation of skin structures. A schematized conception in which the dimensions should not be taken as generally representative, since the skin may vary widely in its thickness. c, corneum, that is, horny layer of epidermis. m, malpighian layer of epidermis. sw., sweat gland. seb., sebaceous gland. p, the most superficial blood vessels, arterioles, capillaries, and venules. h, hair follicle. s, hair shaft. (C) Penetration of light into human skin as a function of wavelength. The curves N and W indicate for Negro and White skin, respectively, *rough estimates* of depths at which radiation of the corresponding wavelengths is reduced to 5 percent of its incident value. There are insufficient data to make more than rough estimates, and these curves should be regarded as suggestive rather than in any way exact. (Adapted by Jacquelyn Hetrick.)

melanin is produced in specialized cells, the *melanocytes;* but passes into neighboring cells of the malphigian, and may be carried up into the corneum. For a discussion of the melanocytes and the general histology of the epidermis the reader is referred to the excellent review of Billingham and Silvers (1960). In the white races the corneum and upper part of the malpighian may be relatively free of melanin except after injury —including the action of ultraviolet light which results in the familiar suntan. Negro skin, on the other hand, not only contains more melanin, but this is more evenly distributed throughout the epidermis, including the corneum.

The distinction made here between ''Negro skin'' and ''white skin'' is perforce somewhat arbitrary. With few exceptions neither optical nor histological studies specify exactly the race or origin of the subject; and one can only assume that these terms apply to some reasonably well distinguished extremes of pigmentation. There seems to have been little or no optical study of skins of intermediate color, beyond reflectance measurements, which are not very instructive in the present regard.

While the study of evolution of races is one of separation of genotypes, the role of natural selection in such a process must depend upon interrelationships between phenotype and environment, and it is at this level that we find ourselves in the present discussion. Thus the mechanism of inheritance of the melanin of human skin need not enter directly here. This is fortunate because of the complicated nature of the problem, into which many facets of the phenotype may enter. For example, a matter of first importance is the penetration of light into the skin, and while one may measure this directly with some success the contributing factors might be very difficult to analyze. They include the absorption and light scattering properties of the various layers; and to what extent melanin is concerned in this must depend upon such factors as dispersion and distribution of the pigment, its chemical composition and spectral absorption, and the character of the other components. To disentangle the genetics pertinent to all these factors, some of which we do not understand at all clearly, would be a difficult matter indeed. For the recent status of genetic studies on melanin of mammal skin, the reader is again referred to Billingham and Silvers.

SUNLIGHT AND ITS PENETRA-TION INTO SKIN

Fig. 22–1A shows the spectral distribution of sunlight at the surface of the earth, when the sun is at two different angles; curve 1 for the sun at zenith, and curve 2, for the sun at 60° (four hours) from zenith. The lower wavelength limit (i.e., in the ultraviolet) is set at about 0.29 μ by absorption of the shorter wavelengths by ozone in the upper atmosphere. The serrated appearance in the infrared part of the spectrum is due principally to spectral absorption bands of water vapor. The human eye detects only a small part of this spectrum, as the line labelled V indicates —normally a range from about 0.4 μ to 0.65 μ. Thus the eye is a poor judge of total sunlight, and no judge at all of the ultraviolet or infrared parts. The very short wavelengths of sunlight are those which cause sunburn, that is, a range from the lower limit at 0.29 μ to about 0.32 μ, as indicated at E in the figure. This is a very tiny fraction of the total (less than 0.1%) under the maximal conditions represented by curve 1; and is reduced to a negligible amount when the sun moves a few hours from zenith, as indicated by curve 2. On the other hand, total sunlight varies much less with zenith angle, that is, with season, latitude, and time of day, as is easily seen by comparing curves 1 and 2 for the whole range of wavelengths.

In order to interpret the various physiological effects of sunlight on Man, it is necessary to have some idea of the extent of penetration of the different wavelengths into the skin. But this is not an easy matter to determine, and although a number of dependable measurements have been made for limited spectral regions these cannot be put together into more than a rough composite picture. Skin is made up of optically in-homogeneous layers, having different properties and varying in thickness and structure from one part of the body to another, and since different investigators have measured different samples of skin the results cannot be fitted together accurately. Even with more complete measurements no universal values for skin transmission could be assigned which would apply to skin from all parts of the body. The curves drawn in Fig. 22–1C, which purport to show the depth of penetration of 5 per cent of the incident radiation, for Negro skin (N) and for white skin (W), cannot therefore be accepted as more than rough estimates; but I think they will be useful and not misleading if they are employed only as approximate guides.

Referring to these curves, it is seen that the sunburning radiation (wavelengths shorter than 0.32 μ) is nearly all absorbed in the epidermis —it is here, then, that this radiation must have its effect. Penetration increases toward longer wavelengths—reaching the superficial blood vessels and other structures of the epidermis—until a maximum depth is reached around 1.0 μ in the infrared. The penetration then decreases rapidly as wavelength increases, there being little of importance beyond 1.4 μ, within the spectral range of sunlight. While some investigators have claimed greater transmission of some wavelengths in the visible and infrared, it seems clear that no portion of the radiation of sunlight penetrates in important amount below a few millimeters. General discussions often fail to recognize the great importance of differences in penetration of different spectral regions of sunlight, and that different regions have different physiological effects.

Faulty measurements have led from time to time to misconceptions regarding the depth of penetration of sunlight into skin. Important errors may enter in two ways: (1) low measurements are obtained when scattering is neglected, this error being increased by drying out of the skin sample; (2) if care is not taken to minimize heating of the skin by absorbed radiation, or proper shielding is not provided, the measurements may indicate too great penetration. In preparing the curves in Fig. 22–1C, the measurements of Hardy and Muschenheim, of Kirby-Smith, Blum, and Grady, and of Thomson have been relied upon. . . .

The curves in Fig. 22–1C neglect the specific absorption bands of hemoglobin, carotenoids, and other substances. Hemoglobin in the superficial vessels absorbs the shorter wavelengths of the visible spectrum quite strongly, so that light reflected back is predominantly red, thus giving the ruddy tint to many complexions. The curves indicate that Negro skin is less transparent in the visible spectrum than white skin, and this is no doubt due chiefly to the difference in melanin content. But Negro skin also has a thicker corneum than white skin, an important factor with regard to sunburning radiation (see below).

PHYSIOLOGICAL EFFECTS OF SUNLIGHT ON MAN, AND FACTORS AFFECTING THEM

Sunlight has several physiological effects on Man, which may be separated into two general categories on the basis of the spectra involved: (1) the effect of adding the energy of sunlight to the heat load of the body; and (2) specific effects of those wavelengths that cause sunburn, which also have carcinogenic and antirachitic action. The latter are classed together, not because of physiological similarity, but because they are produced by the same spectral region of sunlight, since this factor is of basic importance if we are to relate them to geographical distribution.

At least one other, minor, effect will be mentioned below, and there are certain pathological conditions brought about by parts of the solar spectrum which are so rare that they are of no interest in the present discussion. There are also diseases of domestic animals in which sunlight is the precipitating factor; but which, for physiological or dietetic reasons do not have their counterpart in Man.

THE SOLAR HEAT LOAD

In the standard resting state the human body produces a certain amount of heat by its own metabolism, which must be dissipated in some way. If the body becomes active this heat production increases, and in case of severe exercise may rise several fold above the resting condition. The human body has several means of getting rid of this heat load. The blood, heated internally, comes to the surface to pass through the vessels of the skin, and a certain amount of heat may be *conducted* to the surrounding air. The rate of dissipation is increased by movement of air over the skin, that is, *convection* is a factor. Another important means of dissipating heat is by *evaporation* of water from sweat at the surface of the skin. A factor less commonly recognized and more difficult to assess is the loss to cooler surroundings by *radiation*.

All bodies emit radiation according to their temperature and size. In the ordinary range of temperatures, all this radiation is in the infrared spectrum and hence invisible, although it may be detected through the sense organs of the skin as a sensation of coolness, warmth or, if intense, of pain. The human body radiates to its surroundings and receives radiation from them; it may gain or lose in the exchange, for example, it gains heat from a hot radiator or loses heat to a block of ice, even though these objects are at some distance. But there is also a constant imperceptible or barely perceptible exchange with objects nearer the temperature of the body—indoors with the walls of the room, outdoors with hot soil or rocks or the cool foliage of plants. It is clear that the effective temperature of the environment, with respect to the human body, is a complex matter, and is not to be measured adequately in terms of the temperature and humidity of the ambient air alone.

Out-of-doors one may receive an important amount of heat from direct exposure to the sun; that is, the total spectrum of sunlight impinging upon the body adds a certain amount of heat load. On the other hand, the body may lose a considerable amount of heat by radiation to the clear sky, which, is effectively, at a lower temperature than the body, the amount of loss through this channel being largely determined by the quantity of water vapor in the atmosphere. This radiation to "space" may be an important factor in desert areas, where the atmospheric water vapor is low. . . .

It is clear that the human body is constantly exchanging heat with its environment in a number of ways. Hence the amount of heat lost, and the means of losing it, must vary according to the particular environmental conditions, and some of these may be difficult to evaluate. The radiation factor is among the most difficult to assess because it involves both the geometry of the human body and that of the surroundings, since the amount of heat exchange by radiation must depend upon the profiles which the radiating masses present to each other. The heat dissipation is modified by clothing, which may prevent the conduction of heat away, and may absorb or reflect the incident radiation according to the wavelengths concerned. Thus, dissipation of the heat load—which is essential if the man is going to live—becomes quite a complicated matter, and one that can be treated only with reference to the particular complex of environmental conditions that may obtain.

If the conditions are such that the man cannot adequately dispose of his heat load the temperature of the body must rise, but there are no climatic conditions in the world inhabited by Man where death is likely to result directly from raising the body temperature—the body is not likely to be "cooked" by coagulation of its proteins. Even under maximum conditions, the energy of sunlight is not nearly sufficient to burn the skin by heating unless concentrated by means of a lens, sunburn being caused by ultraviolet light acting in a very different way. Contrary to common impression, there is no evidence that the brain may be unduly heated by exposure of the head to direct sunlight.

A man may, however, suffer collapse due to circulatory failure under environmental conditions that lead to excessive water loss, as, for example, in desert climate, and sunlight may be a factor in this. If the intake of water is not sufficient to compensate for the loss by evaporation and through other channels, the blood volume may fall so low that the heart can no longer maintain sufficient blood flow. The resulting collapse may be sudden, although the condition of low blood volume has accumulated for hours. Being usually associated with high environmental temperature, such collapse has been called "heat stroke," or—since it often occurs when the person is exposed to the sun—"sunstroke." The factors contributing to the depletion of water may be complex. They are most easily analyzed, perhaps, in the case of desert conditions where the temperature of the air is above that of the body, so that loss of heat by conduction and convection is virtually nil, and cooling must be accomplished almost entirely by evaporation of water from sweat. Such conditions may be exaggerated by the solar heat load, coming both directly from sunlight impinging on the body and also from reflection and reradiation from heated surroundings. Walking under these conditions, a man may lose as much as one liter of water per hour, and if this is not adequately replaced the blood volume must be eventually reduced, with ultimate collapse.

Under such conditions the radiant energy absorbed from sunlight may constitute a critical increment of heat load, and the man who can most readily reduce this increment would have an advantage, and might survive longest. In this case the man whose skin reflected more of this

TABLE 1

*Estimated relative absorption of sunlight by White and Negro skin,
based on Heer; values for color temperature 6000°C, which is
approximately that of the photosphere of the sun.*

WHITE		NEGRO	
Untanned (inner forearm)	Tanned (forehead)	Untanned (inner forearm)	Tanned (forehead)
1.00	1.16	1.36	1.46

load should be better off. Table 1 indicates that Negro skin absorbs roughly 30 per cent more sunlight than white skin; but it is to be remembered that this figure applies to only a part of the total heat load. Thus, if a Negro and a white-skinned man walked side by side, naked, in direct sunlight, across a desert where the temperature of the air was above that of the body, the Negro might be expected—other things being equal—to collapse before the white man. But these particular competitive conditions are not likely to be often met. If the bodies of both men were similarly clothed or otherwise covered any advantage would, of course, be largely lost.

It has been suggested that the melanin of the Negro, because it brings about greater local heating of the skin, leads to more profuse sweating, and that this is of advantage to him in the tropics. Thomson has recently shown that sunburn tends to reduce sweating in white skins to a greater degree than in Negro skins, and this might conceivably give the Negro a certain advantage in this regard. But while profuse sweating may confer a somewhat greater degree of comfort under conditions where water is rapidly evaporated, it could only increase the water loss, and this would seem to be the factor of real importance—a disadvantageous one—with regard to survival.

Taking all things into consideration, it seems necessary to assume that the possession of a dark skin should be a disadvantage to the Negro, as regards heat load and life in hot desert areas, but that the disadvantage is not a very great one, and probably of little importance under his usual conditions of life. It would seem that, if anything, his melanin pigment might be of some, although limited, advantage to the Negro in a cooler climate where it was important to conserve rather than to lose heat.

EFFECTS OF ULTRAVIOLET LIGHT

We now come to consider some other effects of sunlight in which melanin may also play a role. These are: (1) *sunburn*, a phenomenon with which everyone is acquainted; (2) *carcinogenesis*, i.e., the induction of cancer of the skin; and (3) *antirachitic action,* the prevention of rickets, a disease of bone. All three effects are caused only by wavelengths shorter than about 0.32 μ, which, as we have seen, constitutes a very tiny fraction of sunlight. The fact that all three effects have the same long wavelength limit does not mean, however, that all are closely related. The first and last are very separate entities; the second is probably related to the first but this cannot be said with complete assurance.

SUNBURN

To most readers sunburn means an unpleasant blistering of the skin following exposure to sunlight. I use the term, however, to include a complex of related effects, ranging from a mild reddening of the skin, or *erythema,* to the severe blistering just mentioned. As a result of any degree of sunburn, melanin may increase in the epidermis—this we recognize as *suntan.*

The erythema is the manifestation of dilation and consequent increased blood content of the minute vessels lying just beneath the epidermis. The photochemical reaction bringing about the dilation of the vessels has its locus in the epidermis, however, principally in the viable malpighian, where histological examination shows that cells may be injured or killed. The dilation of the vessels in the dermis is presumably due to substances which diffuse down from the injured epidermis. The corneum or outer horny layer of the epidermis protects against sunburn by absorbing a large proportion of the incident sunburning radiation before it reaches the malpighian—it is a very effective absorber.

While it seems safe for our purposes to consider the malpighian to be the locus of the principle changes underlying sunburn, the overlying corneum serving only a protective function, certain factors should be mentioned in this regard. Studies by Rottier and by Mullink and Rottier indicate that photochemical changes brought about in the corneum may contribute to the erythema. But the eliciting wavelengths are, at least for the greater part, shorter than those found in sunlight, so this finding can have little or no concern in the present context. The sunburning radiation is absorbed in greatest part in the epidermis; but, at least in some white skins that have not been exposed for some time the longer wavelengths may penetrate to a small extent below, particularly in unexposed areas. The small fraction which reaches the minute vessels of the dermis may cause damage there, as shown by the inhibition of erythema; and it is possible that this may contribute to the blistering that occurs in some cases after severe exposure to sunlight.

The brownish color, or *suntan,* which develops some days after exposure of white skins to sunlight, involves the production of new melanin in the epidermis, although the earliest stage may represent migration of melanin that is already present, to a more superficial position. The formation of new melanin seems to be a response to injury—it also follows other kinds of insult to the epidermis. The color begins to fade after a time, but traces may persist for years. The fading is not all the result of removal or destruction of the melanin, but represents in part bleaching of the pigment by reduction, and the pigment may be subsequently darkened again by oxidation. It was shown just before the second World War by Henschke and Schultze, that the bleached pigment may be caused to darken by exposure to longer wavelengths than those that elicit its formation. These wavelengths—0.3 μ to 0.44 μ—are much more plentiful in sunlight, and much less affected by the angle of the sun, than are those that produce the suntan. Darkening of preformed pigment may also be brought about by endocrine secretions, and probably by other influences mediated by the circulation. The pigment-darkening reaction seems to have no physiological significance in itself; but it is interesting to us, because it shows that the color of the skin cannot be taken as a reliable quantitative index of the amount of melanin present in the human epidermis. The degree of bleaching and darkening seems to vary widely in white skins.

It is common knowledge that the development of suntan is generally accompanied by a decreased sensitivity to sunburn, and it is perhaps natural to relate the two events—the eye tells us that the skin has darkened, and we may jump to the conclusion that it transmits less light of all wavelengths, including those we do not detect. About 1899, Niels Finsen performed a simple experiment which he supposed to prove this point. He painted areas of his arm with India ink before exposing it to sunlight. When he scaled the ink off later he found that the areas it had covered had not been sunburned. He reasoned that the melanin in the skin has the same protective effect as the India ink. Very little being known about sunburn at the time, he did not recognize that while India ink is opaque to ultraviolet light, he had no evidence that the same was true for melanin. Nevertheless Finsen's interpretation was accepted for 20 years without question, and still is by the majority of people.

About 1920, however, doubts began to arise as the result of observations by several investigators. It was noted that the immunity to sunburn disappears much more rapidly than the suntan—the immunity is usually gone in two months, whereas the tan may persist for years. And it was found that vitiliginous and albino skins, which do not form melanin, may develop a degree of immunity to ultraviolet light. An explanation was given in 1926 by Guillaume, who found that after exposure to ultraviolet light the epidermis, particularly the corneum, becomes thickened, and attributed the accompanying immunity to the enhanced absorption of the sunburning radiation in the latter layer. His findings were soon confirmed, and somewhat later it was shown by direct measurement that albino mouse epidermis increases its absorption of ultraviolet light after repeated exposures. As a result, it was generally accepted by those actively working in this field that the relative immunity to sunburn which follows exposure is due to a resultant thickening of the outer horny layer, although the acceptance of the role of melanin pigment in this regard persisted, generally, outside this small group. After all, there seemed no good reason to think that melanin should be a better absorber of ultraviolet light than the protein which makes up the greater part of the corneum.

But Negro skin is very refractory to sunburn, and if this could not be accounted for by high melanin content, some other explanation was needed. The epidermis of Negro skin had been reported to be thicker than that of white skins, and it seems to have been generally assumed by those working in this field that it was the thicker corneum which made the Negro skin less susceptible to sunburn—at least I accepted this explanation myself. A few years ago, however, Thomson made a comparative study and found that Negro corneum was indeed thicker than that of white skins, but also that the former was more opaque to the sunburning radiation per unit thickness. It seems reasonable to attribute the greater opacity to the higher melanin content, although this may not be fully established. The corneum is composed principally of protein which absorbs the sunburning radiation strongly; but its effectiveness as a protective light-filter is greatly enhanced by its flake-like structure, which scatters the light and thus increases the path-length through which the light rays must travel in the absorbing medium. The amount of melanin is much less than that of the protein, and it is unlikely that it is a much better absorber of the sunburning radiation; but because it is made up of small particles it is an effective scattering agent, and this may make it an important additional factor in the absorption of the sunburning radiation by the corneum. Thus, after all, the melanin may play a considerable protective role, as regards sunburn—but all we know definitely is that the horny layer of the epidermis of Negro skin is a more effective shield against the sunburning radiation than is the epidermis of white skins. Thus, while it is reasonable to assume that melanin plays a role in protection against sunburn—and this assumption will be made in the following discussion in this paper—it should be kept in mind that the point is not definitely proven.

But can immunity to sunburn be regarded as having survival value? Sunburn is essentially an acute effect, which while it may be briefly debilitating in severe cases involving a considerable area of the body, does not cause prolonged, systemic damage. It is seldom disfiguring, although it may cause deterioration of complexion after many years of exposure—this coming late in the lifespan is not likely to play a role in sexual selection. In many white societies suntan is looked upon today as a sign of health and beauty. As regards the female sex, fashion reversed itself in this regard about half a century ago, but the survival of the societies concerned does not seem to have been seriously affected thereby.

Cancer of the Skin

Although it does not seem to be a matter of common knowledge, clinical, experimental, and geographical evidence converge to indict the sunburning portion of sunlight as a principal cause of cancer of human skin. The cancers involved grow from the malpighian layer of the epidermis—many of them are not very malignant and mortality from this cause is relatively low. In white-skinned people these cancers are limited almost exclusively to the exposed parts, particularly the face. They are very rare in Negro skin, and when they occur show no preference for the exposed parts. There seems every reason to draw a parallel with the Negro's immunity to sunburn, attributing his low incidence to skin cancer likewise to the opacity of his corneum. Negroes do not show comparable immunity to other types of cancer, and indeed it is reported from the Kenya region of Africa that cancers of the skin occur not infrequently among natives in association with parasitic infection.

Skin cancer does not, so far as we know, result from a single bout of sunburn, no matter how severe, but is a cumulative, "chronic" effect of exposures to sunlight repeated over a long period. Since these cancers are usually not lethal, and not very disfiguring except in late stages—as a rule they do not appear until late in life, well after mating—it would seem unlikely that cancer due to sunlight could have any great effect on racial survival in the sense of biological evolution.

Clear distinction should be made between these cancers and the very dangerous, though fortunately very rare, malignant melanomas which are cancers of a different type. The latter occur largely on parts of the body not exposed to sunlight.

Antirachitic Action

The same wavelengths that cause sunburn bring about an entirely different photochemical reaction—transformation of precursor substance into vitamin D. The site of the reaction can hardly be deeper than the epidermis, where these wavelengths are principally absorbed. It is difficult to estimate the effect of melanin on the efficiency of sunlight in producing Vitamin D—it might decrease formation by absorbing some of the effective radiation, or it is conceivable that by scattering in the corneum and consequent increase in path length, it might even enhance vitamin production in that layer.

Vitamin D is required for bone development and if it is lacking, the bone disease, rickets, results. Exposure to sunlight may prevent or cure this disease; but Man is not strictly dependent on sunlight in this regard, since vitamin D may also be introduced in the diet, and under most conditions of life the role of sunlight is probably not very great. Rickets is most frequent under crowded urban conditions where both diet and sunlight are limited. The disease most often affects children, and, since it is of crippling nature, its prevention could have survival value. But because of the complicating factor of diet, it would be difficult to estimate just how important sunlight might be as regards a given population living under natural conditions.

A TENTATIVE BALANCE SHEET

It is clear that the part played by melanin in the physiological responses of the human body to sunlight has aspects which require analysis in different ways, with regard not only to sunlight but to other environmental factors as well. Any classification of these aspects with regard to their advantages or disadvantages must be a very rough one. Still, it may be worth while to draw up a tentative balance sheet at this point in our discussion. In the one that follows, plus or minus ratings indicate estimated relative advantage of the high melanin content of Negro skin as compared to the low melanin content of white skin.

PHYSIOLOGICAL EFFECT	NEGRO SKIN	WHITE SKIN
Solar heat load at high environmental temperature	−	+
Sunburn	+	−
Cancer of the skin	+	−
Prevention of rickets	±	±

Presented in this way the result seems equivocal, Negro skin having an advantage as regards sunburn and skin cancer, but a disadvantage as regards heat load at high ambient temperature. The advantage or disadvantage as regards antirachitic action is uncertain, but the latter seems the more probable. The balance sheet avoids the question of whether the advantages listed have significant survival value or not, and also how they might be related to the distribution of sunlight with latitude, that is, between the tropic zone and other zones. The latter question must now be taken up.

DISTRIBUTION OF SUNLIGHT
WITH LATITUDE AS REGARDS
PHYSIOLOGICAL RESPONSES
OF MAN

On the whole, those who have assumed that Negroes inhabit the tropics because their skin pigment adapts them to the conditions of insolation in that zone, seem to have given little attention to the spectral character of sunlight and its distribution with latitude. It seems to have been generally assumed that since the tropics are hot there is more sunlight there, but the problem is not so simple as this. Reference to Fig. 22–1A will show that total sunlight decreases less rapidly as the sun moves away from the zenith than does the sunburning portion. Obviously the solar heat load, being related to total sunlight, must vary differently with latitude than does the sunburning radiation.

Fig. 22–2 gives a rough, general idea of the distribution of sunlight with latitude. Represented on the left of the map are distributions, with latitude, of the total energy of sunlight at noon under three conditions: (W) with the sun at its northernmost excursion (summer solstice), when it is over the tropic of cancer (23° 44′ N); (S) with the sun at its southernmost excursion (winter solstice) when the sun is over the tropic of capricorn (23° 44′ S); and (E) with the sun over the equator (equinox). On the right of the figure are represented the distributions of the sunburning fraction of sunlight at the same respective positions of the sun. It is noted that the sunburning radiation is much more "concentrated" in terms of latitude than total sunlight; the amounts of energy are, of course, very different in the two cases.

It is clear from the diagram (see page 378) that at some times of the year a part of one temperate zone may receive more total sunlight than does a part of the tropic zone; indeed, the difference in this regard between the temperate and tropic zones is not so great as is commonly conceived. Even the Arctic and Antarctic zones receive a considerable amount of solar energy during parts of the year. So it is seen that the effect of the solar heat load in exacerbating collapse due to water loss should not be restricted to the tropics—at the time of the summer solstice, for example, other things being equal, it should be just as likely to occur at 47° N (about the latitude of Zürich or Quebec) as at the equator. The fact that the sun crosses the equator twice during the year, but reaches the tropic of cancer only once, should not be of importance in this regard, since "heat stroke" is an acute effect, that is, one that involves, at most, a few days' exposure to the sun. Much more important would be other aspects of the environment such as desert conditions, which are to be

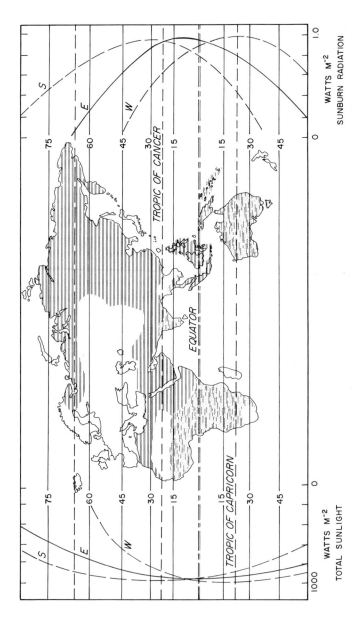

FIGURE 22–2—Map of the distribution of brown skin color. On the left, distribution of total sunlight with latitude. E, at equinox; S, at summer solstice; W, at winter solstice. On the right, distribution of sunburning radiation (wavelength shorter than 0.32μ) with latitude. E, at equinox; S, at summer solstice; W, at winter solstice; The curves on the right and left are based on values from Moon. Note that the curves for summer and winter solstices are distorted by the Mercator projection. These curves, based on light incident upon a surface normal to the sun's rays, neglect scattering from the sky, which may be very important in the case of the sunburning radiation, and also neglect geometrical relationships of the human body profile with respect to the radiant environment. They are thus to be considered only as rough guides. (Adapted by Jacqueline Hetrick.)

found in the temperate zones as well as the tropics. As has been said, high melanin content of the skin should be a slight disadvantage under those conditions. But it could be of limited advantage in a cooler climate where heat gain might be desirable.

In a recent paper, Cowles stresses the advantage of black or brown pigment in reducing visibility, and suggests that this might have had survival value for Man, in the role either of predator or pursued, at some time in his evolution. Whatever the importance of this factor in natural selection, it would seem to be one which should be related more to local environmental situations than to a global distribution such as has been supposed as regards adaptation of Negro skin to life in the tropics. From the curves in Fig. 22–2 it may be seen that the visible portion of sunlight, which is that part pertaining to Cowles' thesis, varies relatively little in its maximum intensity, from Tropic to Temperate zones, or even the Arctic, where summer sunlight is bright. On the whole it would seem that Cowles' argument should apply more to nocturnal vs. diurnal life, than to geographical distribution.

It is to be noted from the curves on the right of Fig. 22–2 that the sunburning radiation varies more with latitude than does the total solar heat load. But, nevertheless, part of the temperate zones receive relatively high amounts at certain times of the year. At summer or winter solstice the chances of being sunburned should be about as great at 47° N or S, respectively, as at the equator, and with sufficient exposure sunburn may occur above the Arctic Circle. Of course, sunburn is an acute effect, and the situation should be somewhat different as regards the "chronic" effects, carcinogenesis and antirachitic action—because these depend on the total exposure to the sunburning radiation throughout the year, and the sun is near zenith in the tropics for a greater part of the year than it is in the temperate zones. But, nevertheless, parts of the temperate zones receive a relatively high annual incidence of the sunburning radiation.

In the United States the occurrence of skin cancer within the white population shows a north-south distribution which fits reasonably well with estimates of the distribution of the sunburning radiation, within the latitude range (32° to 41° N). But at most the incidence of these cancers is small, and, as has been said, probably could have little effect on racial survival. The Negro population has a very low incidence of skin cancer, but I think no one would venture to say that this in itself has played a significant role in the relative distribution of the Negro and White populations in our country. Fairly recent historical events have been obviously much more important in determining this distribution than has natural selection. Would it not seem reasonable to think that, correspondingly, at a much earlier time events not directly related to the environment played a dominant role in determining the distribution of the Negro and White races in the eastern hemisphere rather than biological adaptation to the climate of the particular areas they now inhabit?

As regards historical factors in the distribution of races, the Bushmen of Southern Africa offer a most interesting example. These people, at present restricted to the region of the Kalahari Desert, occupied a much greater area, including quite different terrain and climatic conditions, at the time of the entrance of Europeans into this region. Subsequently the Bushmen have been pushed gradually out of other areas and have taken refuge in the Kalahari. Here the remnants of the race live under very difficult conditions in an arid land with relatively sparse vegetation. They appear to have adapted themselves to a precarious existence under these conditions by learning to take advantage of what corners of the environment they may grasp, rather, so far as we know, than by any particular physiological adaptation. If we read the record right, they have lost at least one remarkable facet of their previous culture in doing this, the making of the rock paintings that have been attributed to them —not a surprising loss considering the complete preoccupation with survival which seems to be their present lot. A cultural change resulting from recent historical events imposing a new habitation area would thus seem to account for the Bushmen's present adjustment to a rigorous environment, rather than selection on a biological basis. May a similar situation not affect other distributions and cultures where the history is unknown, being farther in the past?

My information regarding the Bushmen has been greatly increased since this paper was first written, by conversations with Dr. B. Kaminer, who has studied these people at first hand in the Kalahari, and has taken color photographs of them. Dr. Kaminer pointed out to me by means of his photographs, the great amount of dirt and desert soil which these people, who have no opportunity to bathe, carry about on their skins. Even without physical measurements one can be quite sure, I think, that the amount of sunburning radiation that reaches the skin is greatly reduced, and consequently the importance of melanin as protection in this regard. Seeing these photographs one might conclude that the solar heat load should be determined more in terms of the reflectance of the soil from the local terrain, than in terms of that of the uncoated skin. The fact that the Bushmen tend to be brown rather than black would not seem of great importance. This observation seems still further to confuse the question of the adaptive value of melanin in "feral" Man or his ancestors, making its importance even more questionable.

Finally, we may ask whether the distribution of the dark-skinned races really fits very well with the distribution of sunlight. The comparison in

Fig. 22–2 does not seem to give very strong support. The map shown there is drawn after Fleure, who has attempted to explain the distribution of skin color in part in terms of local climatic conditions, but his argument does not take into account the nature of the physiological factors concerned. Actually, the comparisons made in the present paper, regarding melanin pigment and physiological effects of sunlight, are based on what is known about White and Negro skins, since applicable data are only available regarding these; to what extent the brown-skinned peoples may fall into an intermediate position with regard to the physical and physiological factors that have been discussed we do not know.

A HISTORICAL NOTE

In 1871, Darwin wrote in his *Descent of Man* . . . as follows: "Dr. Sharpe remarks, that a tropical sun, which burns and blisters a white skin, does not injure a black one at all. . . . I have been assured by a medical man that some years ago during each summer, but not during the winter, his hands became marked with light brown patches, like, although larger than, freckles, and that these patches were never affected by sun-burning, while the white parts of his skin have on several occasions been much inflamed and blistered. . . . Whether the saving of the skin from being thus burned is of sufficient importance to account for a dark tint having been gradually acquired through natural selection, I am unable to judge."

The complete passage is of interest, but to conserve space I have quoted only those parts that seem particularly cogent here. It is to be noted that Darwin was properly cautious about his attribution of dark skin to natural selection. The evidence of association of relative immunity to sunburn with pigmentation we need not question, although, as is not infrequently the case, Darwin is using information at secondhand. But one may question the interpretations, while remembering how little was known at the time about the action of sunlight.

> The case of apparent immunity of pigmented patches on white skin to sunburn, is intriguing in the light of present knowledge. Was this, perhaps, a case of *vitiligo?*

Although Ritter had shown the existence of ultraviolet light in the sun's spectrum in 1801, only about the middle of the century was it realized that sunburn is caused by such radiation. This came about with an observation by the physicists Foucault and Despretz who were accidentally sunburned by the radiation from an electric arc with which they were experimenting; the matter was reported in a brief note by Charcot. It had been thought before that time that sunburn resulted from heating the skin, and Darwin may still have been under this impression when he wrote. A more definitive demonstration that sunburn is due to ultraviolet light was reported by Widmark in 1889. Some of the more recent developments have already been noted.

Another early suggestion that skin color favors the residence of Negroes in the tropics is of interest. In 1887, Wedding presented, in a brief note before the Berliner Gesellschaft für Anthropologie und Urgeschichte, what appears to have been the first account of buckwheat poisoning in sheep, giving proof that sunlight is a precipitating factor. He showed that animals fed on the buckwheat plant developed lesions of the skin when subsequently exposed to sunlight, but that areas of the skin which he covered with tar did not display the lesions. We know today that this condition is brought about by a substance present in the buckwheat plant. When the plant is ingested, this substance gets into the blood stream and is carried to the skin, which it photosensitizes to wavelengths in the visible spectrum. Man seems never to eat enough buckwheat to become photosensitized in this way, and the basic photochemical mechanism is not related to sunburn. Clearly, the phenomenon observed by Wedding has nothing to do with the normal responses of human skin to sunlight, but he was unaware of this—very little being known about such responses at that time, particularly with regard to spectral relationships. He suggested that the pigment in the Negro skin offered protection in the same way as did the tar he painted on his sheep, and that this was of advantage to the Negro in the tropics. He even went so far as to suggest that a ship be sent to the tropics with half the crew painted with walnut stain, for the purpose of studying the effects of tropical sunlight. His paper makes no mention of Darwin or natural selection.

I have often wondered how Wedding's paper came to be presented to an anthropological audience rather than to veterinary scientists. It described a discovery of first importance to the latter, but introduced only a misconception with regard to the study of Man.

GENERAL REMARKS

In examining the interrelations between certain physiological responses of Man and a particular facet of his environment—sunlight—we have found the situation more complex than it is generally thought to be. This particular environmental factor has more than one separate physiological effect on Man, and other environmental factors may play important roles in the overall result. The specific thesis examined—that high melanin content of the skin adapts to life in the tropics because it offers protection against sunlight—seems to have little to recommend it. The melanin might provide a degree of protection in some cases but could be detrimental in others. On the whole, one may doubt that the possession of melanin pigment makes very much difference one way or the other, and that it could serve as an important "handle" for natural selection seems most unlikely. And when we examine the distribution of sunlight, we find that the geographical distribution of skin color really does not correspond at all well with the suppositions of the thesis.

The particular point may not seem worth the laboring I have given it, and the removal of the notion from our thinking might not, in itself, affect very greatly our concepts of races and their origins. But certain doubts may be raised. We may be led to ask whether there are not other instances where survival value has been attributed to anatomical or physiological factors which it would be difficult to substantiate, or where pertinent aspects of the environment are not well understood. The case of adaptation of warm-blooded animals to cold climates, where Scholander has pointed out that the physiological and environmental factors concerned do not coincide with commonly accepted ecological and evolutionary ideas, seems another cogent example. Surely we may question the evidence in such cases without challenging the basic role of natural selection—I believe no one who has read my writings on evolution would accuse me of making such a challenge.

What we really deal with here is the relationship between phenotype and environment, as I have said earlier, selection depending upon the closeness of fit between the two. Complete fitting is not to be expected in the complicated situations that prevail in nature. Rather, one may think of the over-all agreement as the algebraic sum of many positive and negative values, representing advantageous and disadvantageous facets of the phenotype with respect to corresponding facets of the environment. If the sum of these values is positive, the phenotype, and consequently the genotype, should have selective advantage. The total balance sheet could contain many plus and minus values, large and small; the relationship of melanin to sunlight seems one of minor weight in the survival of human races. It might be extremely difficult to analyze the situation accurately, and one could go badly astray by underestimating the complexity of the factors concerned.

If a somewhat facetious illustration is permitted, I may point out that if we consider only the role of melanin pigment with regard to sunlight, Negro skin would seem to be highly adaptive to life on one of the snow-capped mountains near the equator. Here the sunburning radiation should be high, being enhanced by reflection from the snow field, and the protection afforded against it might be assigned a high positive value.

The low reflectance of total sunlight from the skin could be also advantageous in this situation in maintaining body temperature by increasing the solar heat load. The importance of antirachitic action, whatever its sign, would seem to be minor compared to the general problem of maintaining adequate nutrition. The negative factor of concealment might also be slight because there would be so little wild game anyway. I am afraid that in spite of the positive values assigned to melanin, the overall fitting between phenotype and environment would have a rather high negative value in this case.

It seems so easy to read adaptive value into almost any aspect of an organism, particularly if our understanding of both physiology and environment is incomplete, as must so often be the case. If we yield to the temptation to find adaptive value in every racial or specific characteristic, do we not run the risk of reaching a position not unlike that of Dr. Pangloss—in spite of Candide's observations, and our own?

23

RACE
AS AN EVOLUTIONARY
EPISODE

Frederick S. Hulse

The traditional view of races as stable groups of people with
similar biological characteristics has proved useless in under-
standing how populations have come to differ from one another
and in analyzing the ways in which populations do differ. To
make thinking about human differences congruent with our
knowledge of evolutionary process, it is more useful to view racial
differences as differences in the frequencies of hereditary char-
acteristics in populations and to concentrate our attention on the
dynamics of differentiation. It is in this light that Frederick S.
Hulse discusses raciation, rather than race, in the following
article. Hulse is Professor of Anthropology at the University of
Arizona and has specialized in population studies.

An examination of living human groups shows that we have not been
exempt from the normal processes of local evolutionary change. It would
be difficult to mistake a Chinese for a Dane, or a Hottentot for a Sioux.
Genetic differences between these groups have accumulated throughout
the thousands of generations during which they have shared only a
minute portion of their ancestry. Certain constellations of characteristics
have become typical of the people of East Asia, others have become just
as typical of Europeans. It is a matter of interest and importance that
evolutionary diversification has not proceeded still further among
humans, and that by all biological criteria, we remain members of a
single species.

Since we are all members of a single species today, and since the human
fossils from very early times are, in many respects, so different from any

(From *American Anthropologist*, Vol. 64, October 1962, pages 929–945.
By permission of the author and the publisher.)

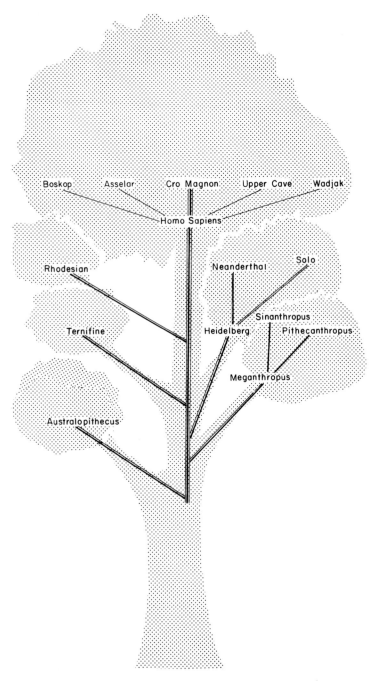

FIGURE 23–1—Phylogenetic tree. (Adapted by Jacquelyn Hetrick from drawing by S. M. Nagoda.)

modern skeletal material, it has become a very common opinion that racial diversity postdates the appearance of Homo sapiens. The phylogenetic tree which has been most popular among anthropologists is shown in Figure 23–1. In this type of arborization the various fossils antedating those of the Upper Paleolithic are ordinarily shown as side branches which suffered termination through extinction rather than through evolution. As a rule, they have been given specific or even generic status, at least by their discoverers. Only one central line ascends triumphantly to the very peak of the tree, upon which twigs represent whichever racial stocks suit the fancy of the designer. It would appear from an examination of such a diagram that we have never succeeded in digging up our grandfathers, but only our great uncles, who were childless.

Not all students of human evolution, of course, have accepted this scheme in all details. Hrdlička, for example, maintained that Neanderthal man was ancestral to ourselves. Hooton could not bring himself to believe that hybridity had not taken place between our unfound ancestors and at least some Neanderthaloids. And a few authors, going to the opposite extreme, assumed a total separation between the so-called major racial stocks dating back to the Pliocene or earlier. This extreme opinion, however, has no evidence of any nature to support it. The different sorts of people whom we find in the world today just are not that different.

At the same time there is an inherent improbability in the notion that only a small proportion of the earlier populations of men left any offspring at all. It would seem strange that the bones of our direct ancestors elude us, while we continue to find those of their close relatives. Perhaps the standard design of the ancestral tree, so useful in representing the descent of different species, has misled us. Is such a design appropriate as a representation of sub-specific diversification? Do all the Middle and Lower Paleolithic human fossils differ enough from one another to deserve separate specific names?

In my opinion, the answer to both questions is: No. Weidenreich, a number of years ago, proposed a design to represent the immediate phylogeny of Homo sapiens, not in the form of a branching tree, but of a grid or trellis, similar to that shown in Figure 23–2. Hooton showed a vine of which the branches coalesced, as well as separating, to indicate what he believed to be the relationship between the living human races. Both of them realized that, within a species, genetic continuity exists, and that any diagram which does not show this fact is bound to be misleading. Weidenreich even pointed out certain characteristics of Sinanthropus, especially in the teeth, which he believed foreshadowed some of the characteristics of the living inhabitants of eastern Asia. Many of his colleagues refused to see any significance in these resemblances, but on grounds of chance alone one would expect to find a greater concentration

SOUTH AFRICA   AFRICA   EURASIA   EAST ASIA   AUSTRALIA

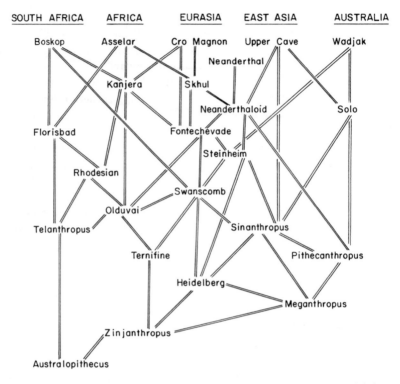

FIGURE 23–2—Phylogenetic trellis. (Adapted by Jacquelyn Hetrick.)

of genes derived from Sinanthropus in East Asia than in Europe or Africa. This does not mean, of course, that Sinanthropus, when alive, looked like a modern Chinese. An examination of the fossil remains of this early type demonstrates that he did not. Mankind as a whole has evolved to a very considerable degree during the last five hundred thousand years, and we have no evidence to suggest that any contemporary of Sinanthropus could be mistaken for any contemporary of ours. Although, except for Sinanthropus and Pithecanthropus, the fossil evidence from this period is slim, we find all taxonomists agreed that the human beings of that time should be classified in another species than our own. Confirmed splitters speak of different genera. Indeed, until a generation ago, Sinanthropus and Pithecanthropus were given separate generic status. It is interesting to note that Ashley Montagu, who denies the existence of races within Homo sapiens, was a fervent advocate of generic distinction between the Chinese and Javanese forms, on the basis of the diastema found in the latter, but absent in the former.

Since we are fortunate enough to have several individuals from both of these groups, it is possible, and therefore necessary, to say that they do appear to represent separate populations. The available remains of their western contemporaries, found at Heidelberg and Ternifine, are so scanty as to demand great caution in our conclusions concerning them, yet the small size of the teeth in the large Heidelberg jaw is suggestive, at least, of a certain degree of difference between this form and the others. Would it not be more reasonable, however, to think in terms of population differences in different parts of the world during the lower Paleolithic of the same order of magnitude which we find among populations living in different parts of the world today? It may well be that the accumulation of evidence in the future will lead us to the conclusion that mankind was then divided into separate geographic species; or that, on the contrary, people then resembled one another much more closely than is now the case. The evidence which we have at present, however, leads me to infer that then, as now, human populations living in various parts of the world could reasonably be classified as races, but not as species.

What is implied by the term "race"? To some people it is just another nasty four-letter word, not to be uttered in decent company, with the hope that it may thus be conjured out of existence. This abhorrence is easy to understand, for the word has been badly misused in many ways and has carried varied implications. But so has another four letter word: Love. In neither case does banning the word appear to be the type of action which will assist in solving the problems connected with its use. Ashley Montagu raises a more serious problem in stating that the word does not correspond to any reality in the actual world and is therefore dangerously misleading. To him, the word race contains the implication of eternal unchangeability, so that it cannot be made to fit into an evolutionary framework. It is true, of course, that the use of the term is rather older than the demonstration by Darwin of how evolution is brought about. But Darwin does not appear to have felt it necessary to avoid the use of the word species, which in earlier days had carried the implication of eternal unchangeability as well as separate creation. No matter what the origin and destiny of species may be, the word represents a valid taxonomic category. In the same way, recognizable sub-specific categories are known to exist within many, but not necessarily all species. According to Simpson, the recognition of subspecific taxa is appropriate if this happens to be useful to the taxonomist, which it will certainly be if there is some nonarbitrary element in the definition of the groupings concerned. A grouping may be considered as real, and as existing in nature rather than in the taxonomist's mind, if three-quarters of the individuals in adjacent subspecies are unequivocally determinable.

Subspecific categories, whether we call them races, breeds, varieties, subspecies, demes, breeding populations, isolates, or anything else, are likely to lack the sharp boundaries which characterize species. In the absence of artificial hindrances, genetic communication between any one of them and its neighbors is open and is likely to be frequent, in direct contrast to the lack of genetic communication between adjacent species. Breeding between members of separate species, although often technically possible, is likely to take place only when artifically encouraged, as for instance in the case of captive animals which have no other sexual partners available. Hybrids between valid species are therefore as rare, in the natural world, as hybrids between subspecific categories are common.

Despite this fact, it is sometimes easier to distinguish members of one breed of a species from members of another breed of the same species than it is to distinguish members of one breed within that species from members of another species. An Alsatian, for example, looks more like a wolf than it looks like a Dachshund. Variety within a species, clearly, can proceed to a remarkable degree with no break in the chain of genetic continuity. So long as this chain is not broken, the subspecific taxa are always capable of merging with one another, and vanishing: animal breeders must exercise constant care to maintain those genetic characteristics which they happen to favor. In the wild, only geographic isolation can be depended upon to keep naturally existing subspecies distinctive from one another. One would expect then, in the history of any species, that subspecific taxa should be evolved from time to time within it, but that most of them would eventually disappear, as such, because of random mating, as the opportunity arose, between the members of the various natural groupings.

Dobzhansky in his article, "Species after Darwin," states that "Races are sometimes referred to as incipient species . . . it does not, however, follow that every race will at some future time be a species. . . . When the interbreeding of populations does not lower the fitness, the stimulus for the development of reproductive isolation is lacking." He is writing, in this instance, about genetic mechanisms enforcing, or at least promoting, reproductive isolation; he is not writing about external circumstances, such as geographical barriers, which may lead to such isolation for a certain period of time. Among living human populations, all the evidence at our disposal would indicate that interbreeding between populations whose ancestors had long been isolated from each other does not lower the fitness. Europeans, after their invasion of the Americas, interbred freely with the Indians, producing offspring who appear to be at least as fit as either parental stock. Our knowledge of prehistory would suggest that these two groups had shared no ancestry whatever for at least one thousand generations. A great many millions of Latin Americans today are of such mixed ancestry, and the birthrate in that part of the world indicates adequate fertility. Scientific studies of European-Hottentot hybrids in South Africa and of European-Polynesian hybrids in the South Pacific demonstrate that fitness has been preserved, and perhaps even enhanced, by such mixtures. It would certainly seem that human races show no signs whatever of being incipient species. On the contrary, some of the populations which are classed as races by Coon, Garn, and Birdsell have come into existence as a result of mixtures which took place within the last few score generations. Within the genetic continuum of any species, the genesis of a new race by means of hybridization may be anticipated whenever the circumstances are opportune. Human fossil remains indicate that this sort of diversification between contemporary populations took place during quite remote as well as more recent times.

It is also clear, however, that long continued free interchange of genes on a random basis must result in the complete merging of such previously distinctive populations as may have existed earlier. In the absence of historic documentation, whether in the form of written records or of skeletal remains, any attempt at description of the biological characteristics of such now submerged racial groupings is hazardous at best. It is often alleged, for instance, that separate races such as Nordics, Alpines, and Mediterraneans once existed in Europe. At present, there are clines of frequency for such characteristics as blondness of hair and eyes, various series of blood-types, brachycephaly, stature, and numerous other items within that continent. It must be noted at once, however, that clines divide frequencies of characters, not sorts of organisms: the clines which we find in Europe are not racial boundaries in any sense. Blondness is most frequent in the north, red hair along the Atlantic Coast, brachycephaly in the east, short stature in the south, and so on. If we draw clines for the frequency of as many as half a dozen characteristics on a map of Europe, a crazy-quilt pattern is seen, and nothing more. To reconstruct racial history on the basis of such data would be out of the question, and the notion of separate races within this region was exploded by Huxley and Haddon. Fortunately, for this continent historic and prehistoric documentation does exist. Some, but far from all, of the data concerning living people can be made to fit with what we learn from a study of European history. But to all intents and purposes, breeding in Europe has been random enough to submerge any previously existing distinctive populations. Any classification of Europeans, purporting to show subspecific or racial differences, is really arbitrary rather than natural and would have to be abstracted from such a diagram as is shown in Figure 23–3, derived from Simpson's *Principles of Animal Taxonomy*. As can be seen, any one of a number of groupings would appear to be equally valid. Of course, different types may be rather more frequent in some

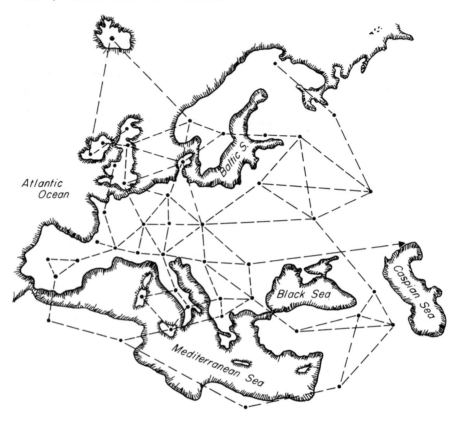

FIGURE 23-3—Lines of genetic communication in Europe. (Adapted by Jacquelyn Hetrick.)

areas than in others. Individuals of so-called Nordic type—tall, leptor-rhine, dolichcephalic, and blond—are rare in Italy, Greece, and Spain; whereas, in Norway and Sweden as much as 10 percent of the popula-tion of some valleys may combine all of these features. But types within a breeding population are by no means races, and the inclusion of such types among the 31 races listed by Coon, Garn, and Birdsell is incon-gruous with the rest of their seminal book, *Races*. Only a few minor populations, such as the Basques and the Lapps, appear to differ at all sharply in gene-frequencies at several loci from their neighbors. In-deed, as far back as the Upper Paleolithic, the range and variety among the European skeletal remains which are available for study indicate the lack of racial divisions among them.

Yet these early skeletons do appear to be those of Europeans rather than those of Orientals or Negroes. They closely resemble skeletal re-mains from North Africa and the Middle East, but are much less similar to those from Boskop, Asselar, Kanjera, and others from Africa south of the Sahara. At the same time, as Weidenreich has pointed out, the Wadjak specimens have strong affinities to modern native Australians, and those of the Upper Cave at Choukoutien show some characteristics typical of the present inhabitants of northeastern Asia. The earliest remains from the Americas do not differ to any great extent from much later or even recent American Indian skeletons. Unfortunately, our data from places other than Europe and the Mediterranean area are still far too scanty. Yet what is available would suggest that during the Upper Paleolithic, as during earlier times, different parts of the world were inhabited by populations having different bodily characteristics. Most, but not all, of these ancient specimens are more rugged in build than is the bulk of the world's population today. Since modern Europeans are, on the average, distinctly less pedomorphic than are most non-Europeans, this fact tends to obscure the extent of divergence, among early populations, which would otherwise be apparent. Evolution within the various populations has certainly been proceeding since, just as it had been before, and differing circumstances have led to selection pressures in different directions.

The South African Bushmen and the aboriginals of Australia are among the few living peoples who still pursue their livelihood in a manner reminiscent of that which characterized all peoples five or six hundred generations ago. Selection (or drift?) among the former has led to the still further development of the pedomorphic qualities foreshadowed by Boskop. Among the latter, however, the contrary has been the case. Many of their skeletal characteristics have remained similar to those which most men possessed in earlier times, with the result that numerous skeletons from as far apart as Lagoa Santa and Afalou have been misleadingly labeled Australoid. Why the Australians have remained conservative while the Bushmen have not we do not know. It is interesting to note that the Bushmen and the Australians are divergent in such characteristics as blood-types and dermatoglyphics as well as in skeletal structure and general hirsuteness: gene-flow between their ancestors must have been infinitesimal for a very long time indeed.

In Paleolithic times communication between widely separated parts of the world was certainly difficult and probably slow. Hunters and collectors may range over a considerable territory, but for sound practical reasons are reluctant to move beyond the range to which they are accustomed. There is ample evidence that some migrations did take place, but to extrapolate from this and jump to the conclusion that our Old Stone Age ancestors were busy milling around all over the world is quite unjustified. As an explanation of assumed similarities between populations in different parts of the world, the hypothesis of widespread migration is to be received with profound skepticism, unless it is accompanied by supporting data from archeology and linguistic distribution. It seems more cautious to assume gene-flow by means of mating between adjacent groups as the more ordinary means for spreading hereditary characteristics. From Ajit's study of the Juang, an aboriginal tribe in Orissa, we learn that the average distance of movement in marriage is, at present, only three kilometers. He has calculated that, at this rate, a new mutation might be expected to travel about 50 kilometers in one hundred generations. From Peking to Paris is more than ten thousand kilometers, so that four hundred thousand years might be expected to elapse before a mutation in one place reached the other. Doubtless settlements were much further apart during the Paleolithic, so that, with an equal degree of deme exogamy, genetic transmission would have been very much speeded up, but it would certainly have been very slow during the time when walking was the only available means of transportation. It is not, therefore, strange to find that the Swanscombe skull is so different from those of Sinanthropus, although both of them date from the Mindel-Riss interglacial. Distances within Europe are minimal compared to distances between France and China, or either of these with South Africa. It would be perfectly reasonable to expect that such natural geographical barriers as oceans, glaciated mountain ranges, or deserts would channel such gene-flow as existed along specific routes. If this indeed took place, the proper diagram to represent the relationships between peoples in the world after the end of the Würm Glaciation would be one such as is shown in Figure 23–4, also modified from Simpson.

This is in sharp contrast to the European-Mediterranean situation, since it shows a natural rather than arbitrary set of divisions into subgroups within the genetic continuum. At other times during human history, existing lines of communication would certainly alter: old ones might vanish and new ones appear. But at all times some barriers would be bound to exist to channel gene-flow. Thus the conditions which might be expected to promote the evolution, and the fluctuation, of perfectly valid sub-specific taxa have been in existence during most, if not almost all of human history. A number of things should be noted in the clustering of populations which is apparent on this chart. In the first place, not all are of equal dimensions: racial groups need not be equal in population, or even of the same order of magnitude. Population size is totally irrelevant to the degree of genetic distinctness: small groups are not necessarily branches of big ones. In the second place, some are intermediate between other clusters: racial groups may be intermediate in gene-frequencies between other such groups. Nor need this be the result of hybridity: it may be a response to intermediate

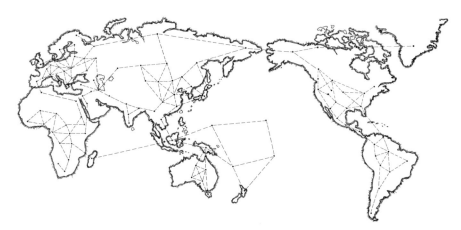

FIGURE 23–4—Lines of genetic communication in the world. (Adapted by Jacquelyn Hetrick.)

conditions. In the third place, some clusters are in communication with only one other, some with two, and some with even more than that. This chart does not represent a neatly ordered filing system: it simply attempts to represent lines of genetic communication.

Within this framework, of course, selective pressures have been at work since the beginning. The necessity to adapt to the circumstances of the time and place, and natural selection of those best fitted for survival and reproduction, continues among humans as among nonhuman organisms. But as time has gone on, our ancestors, in developing culture, have succeeded in modifying the surrounding circumstances to a greater and greater degree. The ability to do so has of course proved advantageous in all parts of the world and at all times, with the result that orthoselection has tended to develop the mental abilities of mankind to an equivalent degree in all populations, as was pointed out by Dobzhansky and Ashley Montagu. Adaptation to the requirements of culture must have become necessary at a very early time among all proto-human populations, and since these requirements are similar in all societies, parallel evolution towards increased intelligence, increased emotional adjustability, and increased motor skills in dealing with tools presumably took place. Adaptation to the requirements of culture is very probably dependent upon the well-known plasticity of man, which is one aspect of his individual versatility: a characteristic which has had high survival value for our species. As Thoday points out, a high degree of heterozygosity within any population tends to enhance this useful characteristic, which is often considered to be a sign of evolutionary progress.

Furthermore, at some time, perhaps rather early in the development of human culture, an idea concerning sexual behavior arose which has, since then, become a cultural universal and had a universal effect. This idea is the incest taboo, and its effect has been to promote gene flow. We do not know to what extent other primates mate outside their group of origin, but during his careful and prolonged studies of baboons, Washburn observed only two successful cases of intergroup migration. Since they lack ideas, there is no abhorrence among them to mating within such a group. All field studies of nonhuman primates agree on this point. Insofar as any close kinfolk become unavailable as sexual partners, however, gratification must be sought elsewhere. Rules concerning availability vary a great deal among different peoples today, but there are always rules of some sort, so that there is a greater amount of pressure favoring the exchange of genes between different human groups than exists among nonhuman creatures. The lines of genetic communication within the human species have been kept open, because of this universal habit, to a greater extent than is true of any other species, and the result must always have been to minimize the differences which would otherwise have developed between populations.

As time went on and technology improved, our ancestors began to build—although very slowly at first—a new environment within which they lived, sheltered to some degree from the conditions of the outside world. The division of labor, tools, fire, language, and many other aspects of culture began to form a protective screen which reduced the effect of differences in natural circumstances existing in different parts of the world. These aspects of culture also have tended to result in orthoselection and the minimization of divergent evolutionary trends within the species. During the last few thousand years technological revolutions have taken place earlier among some societies than among others, so that among some populations the protective screen of culture has become much more effective, but by far the greater part of human evolution took place before this divisive influence came into existence. Thus, for many thousands of generations, the influence of culture must have tended to guide the course of human evolution in the same direction wherever men lived, even though not necessarily at the same speed in all places.

A few aspects of culture may have tended in the other direction, and these should certainly be mentioned. For instance, the division of labor in itself should have made the emphasizing of secondary sexual characteristics easier than it would otherwise have been; and we find in all peoples that differences in appearance due to sex are of the same sort. However, ideals of desirability differ from one society to another, and Darwin suggested that, as a result of this fact, racial characteristics began to develop by means of sexual selection. This is a dubious proposition, but it is possible that existing differences may have been reinforced in this way. Linton believed that he had found evidence of this among the Tanala in Madagascar. Even if all adults in preliterate societies marry, not all of them produce or raise the same number of offspring. Among civilized peoples, Spuhler and Clark have found in Michigan a higher fecundity among males with large heads and women with narrow noses. Henriques has found that, in Jamaica, females having some approximation to physical characteristics of Caucasians are able to attract males who will assume more responsibility for their offspring. Elston has found definitive positive correlations in physical features such as eye color and lip thickness between mates in Sweden, but has not indicated whether their marriages are more or less fecund than are others. Unfortunately, no one has bothered to collect data concerning possible relationships between fecundity and physical characteristics among preliterate peoples.

Furthermore, human culture makes it possible for very small groups indeed to maintain an existence, and to do so even when completely out of contact with the rest of the species. Under such conditions genetic drift can become effective in determining the relative frequency of alleles in future generations. Examination has shown that peoples in remote places, and those who are known to have had a relatively high number of their ancestors in common, are the ones most likely to have unusual gene-frequencies. It is perfectly possible that a number of the ways in which races differ from one another are, under these circumstances, nonadaptive in so far as biological survival value is concerned. This idea, which used to be considered orthodox, has recently become a bit unfashionable. It should not for that reason be discarded.

At the same time it is clear that climatic and other factors of the environment have played a great part in guiding the evolution of human races. Correlations between nasal index and climate were documented on a large scale more than a generation ago. More recently, Roberts has demonstrated correlations between climate and both weight and basal metabolism. The peculiar utility of Mongoloid facial features for hunting under frigid conditions was noted by Coon, Garn and Birdsell. Marrett suggested iodine economy as an explanation of the hair-characteristics of Mongoloids. The function of heterozygosity at the sickle-cell locus, as a protection against malaria, has been demonstrated by Allison and others. Brues has pointed out that the greatly skewed distribution of ABO blood-types must indicate some selective advantage for heterozygosis at this locus as well. The studies of Vogel suggest that the relative frequency of blood-type O in different parts of the world may be due to the fact that the bubonic plague bacillus contains the H antigen; he also finds that smallpox is more severe among persons of type A, at least in India. Selection by contagious disease has obviously become increasingly important since the Neolithic, and it is possible, at least in the case of pulmonary diseases, that this might have resulted in some depression of stature by eliminating those who were growing most rapidly during adolescence.

Body build which, together with pigmentation, is among the most obvious ways in which various populations differ from each other, appears also to be among those traits which can most plausibly be explained as a climatic adaptation, and climate is clearly an aspect of the environment which has been important from the very beginning, and in all parts of the world. All of our ancestors have had to adapt to climatic stress, whereas most other stresses have been less universal. At the same time, we must remember that different adaptations to similar forms of stress may come into existence. The Neanderthal people of Europe during the Würm Glaciation do not seem to have had a Mongoloid facial appearance at all. Deep orbits may have served to protect their eyes from freezing, and their enlarged maxillary sinus— a feature lacking in all living races—may have served to warm the air they breathed in. Among living peoples, the natives of Tierra del Fuego do not have the same mechanisms to protect their bodies from chilling as have the natives of Australia, though both appear to get along equally well in cold, but not constantly frigid, weather without clothing. The Papago and other Indians of the southwestern desert in the United States are far from skinny, as many other desert-dwellers tend to be, but their limbs are frequently long. As Baker points out, climate must always be considered in relation to culture. Melanesians are alleged to suffer fewer ill effects from malaria than do their Polynesian neighbors, yet they lack the abnormal hemoglobins which appear to confer some immunity against this disease among Africans. It is not unlikely that blondness among northwest Europeans is an adaptation to the necessity of synthesizing vitamin-D in a rather sunless climate, but the Northwest Coast Indians, under the same conditions, have much darker skins: their diet includes plenty of oil from the fish which has been their staple food.

Selection can only work on the material which is available, and the conditions under which the remote ancestors of any racial group lived are bound to affect the way in which such a group adapts to new conditions. We all have ancestors as well as necessities. American Indians, most if not all of whose ancestors arrived via the Arctic, tend to retain some characteristics which are best explained as Arctic adaptations, even though they now dwell in the Amazon Valley. All too many of us, no matter what our racial origin, are capable of storing up excess fat when food is plentiful; this must have been a useful ability when meals were less easily available. Light eyes and fair skin have by no means been eliminated from the gene pools of the middle Eastern and North African peoples. During the Würm Glaciation, this part of the world apparently had a climate somewhat similar to that of northern Europe today, so that selection for blondness ought to have taken place among the populations which lived there at the time, if indeed blondness is adaptive in such a climate. It may be noted that there is no archeological evidence of the consumption of sea food in this part of the world until rather late in this period.

Racial characteristics are not eternally unchangeable, but neither does the selection which causes evolution take place over night. Race is an evolutionary episode, and racial evolution proceeds at a slow pace. As conditions change, no matter how the change may be brought about, new selective forces replace old ones, and individuals who might earlier have been successful now die. But the constant flow of genes from one population to another may either speed up or slow down any shift of gene-frequencies due to local adaptation. Travel to great distances has become so rapid and so easy by now, that such gene flow is a more important factor in human evolution than is adaptation to purely local circumstances. During most of human history, however, this cannot have been the case. Even when racial mixture takes place, one cannot expect that gene-frequencies among the resulting offspring will be predictable without taking selection into account: and, in the present state of our knowledge, this will be difficult to do. If, in fact, the smallpox virus contains the antigen of blood-type A, which is frequently found among Europeans, and if Europeans introduced smallpox among American Indians, as well as mating with them, would one expect an increase of blood-type A in American Indian populations? We do not know the answer. But among several tribes in the Northwest the degree of intermixture calculated from RH frequencies is much higher than that calculated from ABO frequencies.

Many of the barriers which impede gene flow between adjacent populations, or populations sharing the same territory, are man-made, the products of our imaginations. This is another of the objections raised by Ashley Montagu against the use of the word race. His contention is that the only lines of division separating mankind today are cultural ones: he therefore comes to the conclusion that we should speak and think only in terms of castes and ethnic groups. Yet the power of the human imagination is such that the barriers which it raises against gene-flow are as much a part of our environment as is the incest taboo which acts in the opposite direction. Xenophobia, religious prejudice, caste snobbery, and linguistic diversity may well be even less amenable to our efforts at amelioration than are deserts, oceans, malarial swamps, high plateaus, and contagious diseases. Any psychiatrist knows that few cures are affected by telling a patient that his delusions are imaginary. All of these factors, the man-made, the man-modified, and those as yet unchanged by man, have had effects upon the fluctuating pattern of racial diversification and resubmergence. Gene frequencies have changed, and are changing, in response to selective pressures, some of which tend towards separation and others which do not. All the evidence available to us suggests that the differences in gene-frequencies between human populations living in different parts of the world have been of the same order of magnitude in prehistoric as in historic times. We cannot devise a neat filing system in classifying these populations, but we cannot avoid observing that some of them have highly distinctive gene-frequencies: such groups are valid subspecific taxa. Some of them may be ethnic groups as well: this will depend upon whether or not they are distinguishable by cultural as well as biological characteristics. The Andaman Islanders, for instance, might be considered both as a race and as an ethnic group. The Jews, on the other hand, although they have shared a common cultural tradition and so are properly thought of as an ethnic group, are so internally diverse in a biological sense that they could scarcely be classified as a race. Others may be castes as well: this will depend upon their social status. The Ghetto-based Jewish population of Europe was certainly a caste, as is the American colored population today. The latter, however, may properly be called a race because of its distinctive gene-frequencies.

Races are populations which can be readily distinguished from one another on genetic grounds alone. They are not types, as are a few of the so-called races within the European population, such as Nordics and Alpines. It is the breeding population into which one was born which determines one's race, not one's personal characteristics. Central Africans are equally Negroes whether or not they have the sickle-cell trait; Hopi are equally American Indians whether or not they are albinos or have shovel-shaped incisors. One cannot change one's race, but, by mating with someone of another race, one can produce offspring who may fall into a different classification: only the future can tell. Populations with distinctive gene frequencies tend to be more long-lasting than political and other social units: perhaps it is this fact which has given the illusion of permanence to racial groups.

But in fact, races are simply episodes in the evolution of a widespread species. Without the ability to diversify in response to existing circumstances over a wide range, a species could scarcely be considered successful. Such diversification is useful insurance against environmental changes which are bound to occur; it enables the species to become numerous; it promotes the heterozygosity which appears to confer added vigor to its members. Whether our improving ability to modify our environment will abolish the advantages of diverse racial adaptations remains to be seen: such adaptations have certainly been useful in the past.

24

ON THE NONEXISTENCE
OF HUMAN RACES

Frank B. Livingstone

*The previous articles in Part Six have accepted the race
concept, and each author has attempted to utilize this concept
to redefine it, or to suggest how the dynamics of population
differentiation may substitute for the traditional view of
race as type.*

*The validity of any set of categories is related to its
utility in organizing data, in showing similarities and distinctions, and in helping to explain these similarities and distinctions. But in anthropology, as well as in fields of biology
that investigate evolutionary processes as they affect non-
hominid species, the validity of the race concept has been
called into question.*

*Frank B. Livingstone is one anthropologist who has chal-
lenged the utility of the race concept in understanding human
differences. It is his view that the investigation of population
differences can only proceed through the study of the frequencies
of genes controlling single traits. Comparing Livingstone's
extreme position on race with the opinions of Dunn and Hulse
can give us some idea of the major disagreement that exists
among students of human biology over a term whose meaning
appears so obvious to so many people.*

*Livingstone is celebrated for his work in demonstrating
the relationships between the sickle-cell gene in Africa and
the introduction of agriculture. He is at present a member
of the Anthropology Department of the University of
Michigan.*

In the last decade there has been a remarkable increase in our knowledge of the complexities of human genetic variability. To an increasing number of anthropologists the concept of race seems to be losing its usefulness in describing this variability. In fact, for the human populations among which some of us have worked, it seems impossible even to divide these populations into races. At the same time a growing minority of biologists in general are advocating a similar position wth regard to the usefulness of the concept of subspecies for classifying such diverse organisms as grackles, martens, and butterflies. Although there appears to have been a minimum of communication between anthropologists and biologists on this common problem, many of the arguments of the two groups are quite similar. It should be pointed out that the two similar positions on subspecific variation do not imply that there is no biological or genetic variability among the populations of organisms which comprise a species, but simply that this variability does not conform to the discrete packages labeled races or subspecies. For man the position can be stated in other words: There are no races, there are only clines.

The term, race has had a long history of anthropological usage and it can be generally defined as referring to a group of local or breeding populations within a species. Thus, it is a taxonomic term for subspecific groupings greater than the local population. Most anthropologists today use a genetic definition of races as populations which differ in the frequency of some genes.

The term, race, or its newer synonym, geographical race, is used in a similar way with reference to biological species other than man. Where the term is used, it can be considered as approximately synonymous with the term, subspecies. In 1953 Wilson and Brown first suggested discarding the concept of subspecies since it did not accord with the facts. Their main argument was that the genetic variation among the local populations of a species was discordant.

Variation is concordant if the geographic variation of the genetic characters is correlated, so that a classification based on one character would reflect the variability in any other. Such a pattern of variation is almost never found among the local populations of a wide-ranging species, although it is usually found among related relatively allopatric species.

Thus, although it is possible to divide a group of related species into discrete units, namely the species, it is impossible to divide a single species into groups larger than the panmictic population. The causes of intraspecific biological variation are different from those of interspecific variation and to apply the term subspecies to any part of such variation is not only arbitrary or impossible but tends to obscure the explanation of this variation. If one genetic character is used, it is possible to divide a species into subspecies according to the variation in this character. If two characters are used, it may still be possible, but there will be some "problem populations," which, if you are an anthropologist, will be labelled composite or mixed. As the number of characters increases it becomes more nearly impossible to determine what the "actual races really are."

In addition to being a concept used to classify human variability, race has also been overworked as an explanation of this variability. When a particular blood group gene or hair form is found to be characteristic of the populations of a particular region, it is frequently "explained" as being a "racial" character. This type of explanation means, in other words, that this particular set of human populations possess this character, while it is absent in the rest of humanity, because of the close common ancestry of the former. At times many characteristics which were thought to be racial have been found in many widely separated populations, so that the explanation in terms of race required the assumption of lengthy migrations. In this way race or common ancestry and migration have been used to explain much of the genetic variability among human populations. Unfortunately such explanations neither accord with our knowledge of the population structure and movements of hunters and gatherers, nor take into consideration the basic cause of biological variation, natural selection.

The incompatibility between race and natural selection has been recognized for a long time; so that if one's major aim were to discover the races of man, one has to disregard natural selection. Thus, nonadaptive characters were sought and, in some instances, considered found. But the recognition of the role of natural selection has in the past ten years changed the course of research into human variability; or at least it has changed the thinking of the "aracial ultrapolymorphists."

Recently there have been two somewhat different attempts to resolve the dilemmas created by our new knowledge and outlook and still retain the term, race. On the one hand, Dobzhansky appears to want to apply the term, racial variability, to any differences in gene frequencies among human populations, a usage which accords with the genetic definition of race as stated above. Since all human populations most likely differ in the frequency of some gene this position implies that each population would be a separate race; but to Dobzhansky it is a matter of convenience as to how many we call races. Such a usage also implies that any number of racial classifications of the same populations but based on different gene frequencies are "equally valid" or useful. It should be noted that this is a quite different concept of race than previous usage and seems as unfortunate to Hiernaux as it does to me. But if applied rigorously to the human populations of the world it would result in much the same description of human genetic variability as the clinal analysis advocated in this paper but with the description in words and not in numbers as a clinal analysis would be.

On the other hand, Garn, although paying homage to the genetic definition of race, has attempted to demonstrate the existence of nine specific geographical races, but the question of whether there are nine or nineteen such races is not arbitrary or up to the classifier or dependent on the genetic character used in the classification. These are taxonomic races, but "taxonomic races must bear correspondence to natural races, mirroring nature rather than lecturing her," which I think it is fair to say, Garn thinks his geographical races do. Also some of these geographical races "approach true subspecies," and these races, and not others, exist because "the first and foremost fact governing the existence of a geographical race is that it has distinct geographical limits coinciding with major reproductive barriers," which Garn's races presumably do. Thus, according to Garn, there are natural races to which our taxonomic races should correspond, and although the number of races may vary through time, it is still fixed at any one time. Since the existence, validity, or utility of this racial classification is almost entirely dependent on the existence of these major reproductive barriers to gene flow, it seems to me that Garn should present a careful, detailed analysis of these barriers to demonstrate the existence of his geographical races. Aside from a few vague references to the "scarcely inhabited uplands," in Western Asia or the deserts of Africa, however, such a demonstration is not forthcoming. Thus, it is rather difficult to contest the existence of the nine geographical races, but I think it can be argued that at present these "major reproductive barriers" do not exist and most likely have existed even less in the past. For example, an analysis of the populations and/or genes in the Sahara Desert certainly indicates that the desert is not a major reproductive barrier, although there may be fewer people or populations inhabiting it. In addition, the utter wasteland which characterizes most parts of the Sahara today is a rather recent phenomenon and due in large part to human occupation. A short 5000 years ago pastoralists occupied much of the Sahara, and it was perhaps one of the most populated parts of Africa. Prior to these pastoralists, the rich African fauna inhabited most of the Sahara and North Africa and provided probably the best hunting in the whole continent, as the great numbers of archeological finds attest. The concept of race seems to me to be of no use in describing or explaining human genetic variability in this region today. The retention of this obsolete concept has caused a recent analysis of the genetic variability among Saharan populations to label the Teda as having "Berber blood in Negro bodies" and the Moors as having "negroid blood in morphologically Berber bodies.'' Such a description only confuses the issue and hence is worse than useless.

Such a description of the bodies and blood of a human population also implies an explanation of their particular characteristics, which is based on common ancestry and/or mixture with the race involved. The advocates of the validity of the concept of race recognize the great genetic variability which occurs among the populations of the Sahara, Sudan, and Ethiopia, and even refer to these areas as a ''clinal zone.'' The usual explanation of these clines in terms of race and mixture is so widely accepted—even among cultural anthropologists and the general public—that Murdock can state baldly with respect to Ethiopians, ''The Cushites have long since incorporated a not insubstantial infusion of Negroid blood. This reveals itself in different ways in different tribes. Thus the lowland Somali are much darker than the peoples of Highland Ethiopia but have hair that is wavy or occasionally straight and only rarely kinky, whereas this typically Negroid form prevails in sixty to seventy percent of the plateau population.'' This statement clearly indicates that the clines in these characters are discordant. For this reason it is impossible to explain these clines or this genetic variability solely in terms of race and mixture. If a population is X per cent Negro in one characteristic it must be X per cent in all characters for this to be an adequate explanation. If it is not, other factors of evolutionary change must be involved. One could invoke random genetic drift but the more likely explanation is natural selection. I think this analysis of human genetic variation in racial terms aptly illustrates the inadequacy of this kind of analysis. As an illustration of how our increasing knowledge of biochemical genetics increases this inadequacy, I refer the reader to a recent series of papers on Ethiopian populations. Furthermore, this increase in knowledge clearly contradicts Coon's statement that ''To me, at least, it is encouraging to know that biochemistry divides us into the same subspecies that we recognize on the basis of other criteria.'' It is discouraging, to me at least, that anyone would make such a statement.

Garn also seems to regard some biological characteristics as having a similar racial explanation. Garn states that while ''Certain human differences transcend geographical race, and are more meaningfully distributed with respect to climate or disease. . . . A geographical race is a collection of populations whose similarities are due to long-continued confinement within set geographical limits.'' Although these similarities are not outlined in detail, Garn does imply that some biological characteristics are due to natural selection through climate and disease, while others—the racial traits—are not. Natural races thus only reflect variability in certain traits, and any racial classification can only describe a part of human genetic variability and seemingly explain it.

For animal populations other than man, Mayr has also considered the problems associated with the concept of subspecies, although Mayr feels that "These questions are of little evolutionary interest." He gives a definition of subspecies as "an aggregate of local populations of a species, inhabiting a geographic subdivision of the range of the species, and differing taxonomically from other populations of the species." Mayr thinks that the subspecies category is such a convenient taxonomic device, this accounts for the great reluctance to abandon it. Although it is still convenient, Mayr warns "It must be realized at all times, however, that in many cases the subspecies is an artifact and that it is not a 'unit of evolution.' Nor should the subspecies be confused with phenomena of a very different nature, such as character gradients (clines)." I think it is fair to say that both Garn and Coon conceive of human races as "units of evolution," in fact the major units of human evolution, which is the major source of confusion as Mayr says.

Mayr continues his discussion of genetic variation within a species by separating this variation into three categories: 1) clinal, 2) geographic isolates, 3) hybrid belts or zones of intergradation, which he further divides into primary and secondary zones of intergradation. According to Mayr, "Whether a subspecies is part of a cline or is isolated completely by geographic barriers is, however, of decisive influence on its evolutionary potential." Thus, some genetic variation within species is subspecific, some clinal, and some associated with primary or secondary zones of intergradation, which, however, might exist between subspecies.

In addition to being a method of describing genetic variability among the populations of a species, each of Mayr's concepts implies an explanation of the variability which it labels. This seems to be particularly so when such variability is said to be associated with primary or secondary zones of intergradation. Mayr's different concepts of the way in which to explain genetic variability among the populations of a species accord with the mathematical theory of population genetics, which is advocated here, but again, like Dobzhansky, Mayr's analysis attempts to apply words or labels to different kinds of variability or "phenomena." However, the major argument of this paper is that at present we can be much more precise and, further, that these obsolete labels are inhibiting scientific advances in this field.

I do not think these arguments or the problems they face are of "little evolutionary significance" but quite the opposite. The explanation of the genetic variability among human populations is a central problem of physical anthropology, and there are other methods of describing and explaining this variability which do not utilize the concept of race or which simply attempt to label different kinds of genetic variability. Human genetic variability can be described in terms of the concepts of cline and morphism or polymorphism which is becoming more widely used to denote the same thing. The variability in the frequency of any gene can be plotted in the same way that temperature is plotted on a weather map, and this description of genetic variability can describe all of it and implies no explanation whatsoever. Then one can attempt to explain this variability by the mathematical theory of population genetics. This is a very general theory and is capable of explaining all racial or gene frequency differences, although of course for any particular gene the exact magnitudes of factors, mutation, natural selection, gene drift, and gene flow, which control gene frequency differences are not known. All genes mutate, drift, flow, and for a given environment have fitnesses associated with their various genotypes. Hence differences in the frequency of any gene among a series of populations can be explained by these general factors which control gene frequency change. Gene frequency clines can result from many different types of interaction between the general factors which control gene frequencies. For example, a cline may be due to: (1) the recent advance of an advantageous gene; (2) gene flow between populations which inhabit environments with different equilibrium frequencies for the gene; or (3) a gradual change in the equilibrium value of the gene along the cline. The theoretical analysis of clines has barely begun but there seems to be no need for the concept of race in this analysis.

I want to emphasize that in contrast to racial analysis, clinal analysis is a method which can describe all gene frequency differences. Even if one or several genes are completely absent in one population and 100 per cent in the next adjacent population, these differences can still be described as clines albeit very steep ones. But if the variability of a particular gene is continuous from Cairo to Capetown, its variability cannot be described in terms of race, or if two genes vary discordantly, the races set up on the basis of one do not describe the variability in the other. Just as Galileo's measurements and experiments paved the way for Newton's laws of motion, which totally replaced the Aristotelian laws of motion concerned as they were with describing the nature of bodies and their "essences," our newer genetic knowledge and the measurement of gene frequencies will replace the studies on the nature or essence of race and the mathematical theory of population genetics will replace the Linnaean system of nomenclature. Newton's laws can describe and explain all motion, just as clines can describe all genetic variability and coupled with the modern theory of evolution explain it. Linnaeus was given a medal 200 years ago for "discovering the essence of genera" which I think is an apt expression of the Aristotelian mode of thought and concept of the universe. In 1963 Newman and Dobzhansky are still attempting to discover the nature of race or as Dobzhansky says "defining the essence of race. . . ." Dobzhansky has characterized my position as having "discovered that races of man do not exist," but I have never "discovered" anything. The concepts of a culture are primarily a function of the level of measurement and observation within the culture. "Races" of man unfortunately exist in the United States, and race as a concept of Western Civilization exists just as much as God or the $\sqrt{-1}$. Much of the discussion on the existence of race reminds me of the obituary in *Time* Magazine of Arthur O. Lovejoy. When the late Professor Lovejoy was asked at a government investigation if he believed in God, he promptly rattled off thirty-three definitions of God and asked the questioner which one he had in mind. But of course it really didn't matter to the questioner. To avow a belief in the existence of God simply assured one's participation in the socio-cultural system, in which everyone knows that God exists out there but we humans are just too ignorant to perceive or define Him accurately. It is likewise with races; they exist but we haven't discovered or defined them yet.

Just as races do not exist but are only part of a general theory concocted by human beings to explain or render intelligible their observations, so the concepts and theorems of the mathematical theory of population genetics do not exist in the same sense. Any scientific theory can be considered as a mathematical or logical system with no reference to reality. It consists of certain basic or primitive terms and axioms from which are derived the major statements or content of the theory, the theorems. Such a theory is fitted to reality by operational definitions of the basic terms so that there are rules to measure random mating or the mutation rate just as there are rules to measure mass or acceleration. In this way the application of any scientific theory is a function of the measuring instruments and experiments of the culture at that time. According to this particular view, I don't think it is legitimate to say that anthropologists and geneticists have "discovered" breeding populations in the last twenty years.

The concept of breeding population when considered as part of the mathematical theory of population genetics pertains to nothing in reality. But when combined with concepts of gene frequency, random mating, etc., further concepts such as the Hardy-Weinberg Law or the principle of random gene drift can be logically derived. The latter are more or less the theorems of population genetics and are the logical outcomes of the more basic concepts or axioms. The science of population genetics then attempts to apply this theory to bodies of data and to attempt to determine which group of individuals in a particular area fits most closely the concept of breeding population, but the function of this concept of the theory is not to divide up or label reality, but to explain it. Of course, the concepts of the mathematical theory of population genetics have been developed from the data and findings of a particular sphere of reality and are approximations to these data. But they can also be considered solely as logical concepts and studied as a formal system with no reference to this reality. As Medawar has remarked, this theory has great generality in biology and in that science occupies a position analogous to Newton's Laws in physical science. An infinite population randomly mating without selection, mutation, or gene flow is analogous to Newton's body moving without friction at a constant velocity.

In applying the theory of population genetics to humanity, the species is divided into breeding populations although for any area or group of people this concept may be difficult to apply. It is likely that each breeding population will prove to be genetically unique, so that all will be racially distinct in Dobzhansky's terms. But this is not the general use of the concept of race in biology, and the concept has not in the past been associated with this theory of human diversity. Race has instead been considered as a concept of the Linnaean system of classification within which it is applied to groups of populations within a species. To apply a concept of the Linnaean system to a group of populations implies something about the evolutionary history of these populations, and it also implies that these populations are similar in whatever characters were used to classify them together because of close common ancestry.

For years such racial traits were considered to be relatively non-adaptive and were the property of the physical anthropologists, while at the same time the geneticists were concerned with characters which were due to the presence of a single gene and which were for the most part deleterious. Much of the early work in human genetics was done on such characters as achondroplasia, albinism, alcaptonuria, and brachydactyly. Most of these deleterious genes occur in low frequencies in most populations and their explanation seems to be a balance of mutation to them and selection against them. These were considered "bad" genes but once in a great while a "good" gene would appear and completely replace its allele. Although the sickle cell gene has changed the outlook of geneticists, the idea that there are different kinds of inherited traits which require different explanations persists today. Coon has even introduced a new division into racial and evolutionary characters. But to use an overworked cliché, a gene is a gene is a gene, and all genes are subject to the factors outlined previously which control gene frequencies. Hence the mathematical theory of population genetics applies to all genes, racial, deleterious, evolutionary, etc.

But science progresses. Just as the theory of population genetics is gaining acceptance, the pace of biological research is such that our measuring instruments are beginning to reach beyond the concepts. Newton's Laws when first accepted were considered to be "truth" or "facts," but when the measuring instruments began to get above and below their sphere of application, Einstein's equations replaced them. Similarly the mathematical theory of population genetics evolved around and was based on the concept of a gene as a bead on a chromosomal string. It was the unit which mutated, recombined, and functioned—at first to produce one enzyme but now one poplypeptide chain. And it was a satisfactory unit for the experimental genetics of the day which consisted of animal breeding and observation of hereditary characters. But now as these discrete units have become a rather continuous strand of DNA, the question can be asked, do these units with the aforementioned properties exist? Obviously not, and it has been suggested that we discuss mutons, recons, and cistrons in place of genes. It would appear that any unit above the individual base pair is arbitrary. Hence the mathematical theory of population genetics is almost obsolete before it begins to be accepted. But to me this is only one vivid example of the maxim that "Yesterday's science is today's common sense and tomorrow's nonsense." For the concept of race and the intraspecific application of the Linnaean system of classification, tomorrow is here.

SELECTED READINGS

Allison, A. C., 1955, "Aspects of Polymorphism in Man," *Cold Spring Harbor Symposia on Quantitative Biology,* 20:239–255.

———, 1956, "Sickle Cells and Evolution," *Scientific American,* 195: 87–94.

Baker, P. T., 1958, "The Biological Adaptation of Man to Hot Deserts," *American Naturalist,* 92:337–357.

Barnicot, N. A., 1959, "Climatic Factors in the Evolution of Human Populations," *Cold Spring Harbor Symposia on Quantitative Biology,* 24:115–129.

Birdsell, Joseph B., 1953, "Some Environmental and Cultural Factors Influencing the Structuring of Australian Aboriginal Populations," *American Naturalist,* 87:171–207.

Boyd, William C., 1950, *Genetics and the Races of Man, an Introduction to Modern Physical Anthropology.* Boston: Little, Brown.

Coon, Carleton S., 1955, "Some Problems of Human Variability and Natural Selection in Climate and Culture," *American Naturalist,* 89:257–279.

————, 1961, "Man against the Cold," *Natural History,* 70:56–69.

————, S. M. Garn, and J. B. Birdsell, 1950, *Races: A Study of the Problems of Race Formation in Man.* Springfield, Ill.: Charles C Thomas.

Dobzhansky, Th., and M. F. Ashley Montagu, 1947, "Natural Selection and the Mental Capacities of Mankind," *Science,* 105:587–590.

Garn, S. M., ed., 1960, *Readings on Race.* Springfield, Ill.: Charles C Thomas.

Hunt, Edward E., Jr., 1959, "Anthropometry, Genetics and Racial History," *American Anthropologist,* 61:64–87.

Johnson, Francis E., 1964, "Racial Taxonomies from an Evolutionary Perspective," *American Anthropologist,* 66:822–827.

Klineberg, Otto, 1935, *Race Differences.* New York: Harper & Row.

Lasker, G. W., ed., 1960, *The Processes of Ongoing Human Evolution.* Detroit: Wayne State University Press.

Montagu, A., ed., 1964, *The Concept of Race.* New York: Free Press.

Morton, N. E., and C. S. Chung, 1959, "Are the MN Groups Maintained by Selection?" *American Journal of Human Genetics,* 11:237–251.

Mourant, A. E., 1959, "Human Blood Groups and Natural Selection," *Cold Spring Harbor Symposia on Quantitative Biology,* 24:57–63.

Pollitzer, William S., 1963, "Hemoglobins, Haptoglobins and Transferrins in Man," *American Anthropologist,* 65:1295–1313.

Roberts, D. F., 1953, "Body Weight, Race, and Climate," *American Journal of Physical Anthropology,* 11:533–558.

Roberts, J. A. Fraser, 1959, "Some Associations between Blood Groups and Disease," *British Medical Bulletin,* 15:129–133.

Roe, Anne, and George G. Simpson, eds., 1958, *Behavior and Evolution.* New Haven, Conn.: Yale University Press.

Spuhler, J. N., ed., 1959, *The Evolution of Man's Capacity for Culture.* Detroit: Wayne State University Press.

Washburn, S. L., 1963, "The Study of Race," *American Anthropologist,* 65:521–531.

PART SEVEN

IS MAN
STILL
EVOLVING?

We are fairly certain that man, as we know him today, has been essentially the same kind of animal for over thirty thousand years. He has been at a plateau of evolution for at least a thousand generations. At this point in his history, it is not speculative to assert that there is a greater likelihood of man's next evolutionary step being his extinction rather than morphologic change. If any major change were to occur in the course of time, he would no longer be *Homo sapiens,* so closely have anthropologists defined the species. As the object, then, of large-scale evolutionary change, man probably is finished. But evolutionary factors continue to operate on human populations. The conditions of life within which humans operate, the human ecological niche, include not only the physical environment, but, as we have seen, the requirements imposed by culture-building, culture maintenance, and culture transmission. This means that the conditions under which people work together, live together, or fail to live together have implications for the direction in which future human evolution will alter.

In the following readings, we take a new theme, the evolution of the emotions and also study another determinant of evolution, the density of human population numbers.

The questions implicit in this section are whether man can evolve (or invent by other means) the emotional equipment that will enable us to live together as post-Pleistocene human beings.

The inclusion of these articles is as close as the editors of this collection are willing to approach the sticky problem of predicting the future course of human evolution.

25

EMOTIONS
IN THE PERSPECTIVE
OF HUMAN EVOLUTION

David A. Hamburg

Is it premature for scientists to attempt to construct an evolutionary psychology? Do we have enough data about the behavior of infrahuman primates and about the behavior of hominids of the past, as well as enough comparative data about modern humans, to reconstruct, in outline at least, the evolution of the human psyche? Certainly the lack of data has not prevented past generations of philosophers, sociologists, psychologists, and anthropologists from making statements about the "innate" nature of man, nor from drawing elegant chronologies of the progressive changes in human thinking, feeling, and aspiring— despite the fact that much less substantive information was available then than scientists have today.

David A. Hamburg of the Stanford University School of Medicine believes that certain formulations are possible today. Speaking as a psychiatrist whose background includes study of human evolution and cultural evolution as well as medicine, he explores here the changes in feelings and expression of emotions that must have accompanied the successive changes in man's relation to his environment as well as the relations among men as tool-making and the capacity for using symbols evolved.

"The most general principle of all in biology is evolution." In spite of this fundamental fact, and the demonstrated power of an evolutionary view in relation to a wide variety of biological problems, students of human behavior have so far paid little attention to the evolution of living organisms or of man himself. Anthropology alone among the behavioral sciences has taken evolution seriously and made it a major focus of research. This neglect applies as much to the emotional aspects of behavior as to any other, and is remarkable in this context since Darwin was so strongly interested in emotions and pointed the way for future investigators. It is therefore quite appropriate that this Symposium, through its title and some of its papers, should again establish a link between human emotions and evolutionary processes.

In recent years, there have been very important advances in research on the evolution of living organisms. The most basic of these has been the modern synthesis of evolution, a powerful theory which has led to a variety of significant new observations and experiments, and has been able to integrate effectively an extraordinary variety of data from all fields of biology. Moreover, the heretofore sketchy record of human evolution has been substantially filled in, although it is by no means complete. The evidence bearing on human evolution is much more abundant and penetrating than it was even ten years ago, and the implications of this evidence are now being carefully worked out.

Within the past few years, biologists in various fields have shown increasing appreciation of behavior in relation to natural selection and, in keeping with the development of population genetics, have drawn attention not only to individual behavior but to the organization and function of groups.

At this point, I believe it will be helpful to sketch very briefly a few central concepts of the modern evolutionary synthesis and indicate their linkage to behavior. In order to do this, I have chosen excerpts from recent publications of three distinguished biologists: a geneticist, a paleontologist, and a zoologist.

Dobzhansky delineates the concept of natural selection as follows:

> Modern versions of the theory of natural selection are in a way simpler than the classical. *In any one generation, the carriers of different genotypes make, on the average, unequal contributions to the hereditary endowment of succeeding* generations. The fit genotypes, and, by extension, the fit phenotypes, are those which transmit efficiently their genes to future generations. The less fit genotypes transmit their genes less effectively; the unfit ones leave little or no surviving, reproductively competent progeny. . . . Countless *genotypes with different reaction patterns* are formed in every species by *mutation* and *sexual reproduction. Natural selection perpetuates the genotypes which react to promote survival and reproduction in the environments which the species encounters more or less regularly in the territory which it inhabits* [italics by Hamburg].

George Gaylord Simpson presents a penetrating statement on reproductive success and its relation to behavior:

Reproductive success may be comparatively simple in asexual organisms . . . in biparental populations the matter becomes highly intricate. (1) Male and female must occur in proximity or must find each other. (2) In many, especially the more complex, animals they must be sexually acceptable to each other and must mate. (3) Fertilization must occur. (4) The gametes must be genetically compatible. (5) Normal embryological development must occur. (6) Offspring must survive to breeding age and become successful reproducers in their turn. Relatively greater or less success may occur at any one of these stages and at substages within them, and selection depends on the total outcome. . . .

A central problem of evolutionary theory has always been the explanation of adaptation, and the synthetic theory maintains . . . that *adaptation is a result of natural selection.* But it also demonstrates that *natural selection always favors reproductive success of a population,* and nothing else. It might be suitable to redefine adaptation as such reproductive success, but some confusion might arise from the fact that *reproductive success of the population involves all phases of individual life cycles and will incomparably more often than not be favored by individual adaptation to the environment.* Such adaptation will therefore almost always be favored by natural selection. Nevertheless the possibility remains that selection, as here defined, could favor population reproduction at the expense of individual adaptation. . . .

An aspect of the synthetic theory especially pertinent here is that it again brings in behavior as a central element. It not only points the way to *evolutionary, historical explanations of existing behavior patterns* but also involves *behavior as one of the factors that produce or guide evolution. Some phases of selection, as in zygote and embryo, are not directly behavioral, but aspects of breeding, care of young, and subsequent survival are pre-eminently so and are obviously crucial elements in selection* [italics by Hamburg].

Scott emphasizes social behavior in adaptation:

The evolution of any species, and particularly of a highly *social* species, cannot be understood without studying its behavior and social organization. *Evolution is one of the fundamental theories of biology. Its basis is adaptation, and one of the important kinds of adaptation is behavior* [italics by Hamburg].

Where does emotion come into this? Interestingly, basic reference works on evolution rarely mention emotion, and similar works on emotion rarely mention evolution.

Why are emotional phenomena so universal in man and so important in behavior if they have not served some adaptative functions in evolution? I believe that emotional processes have served motivational purposes in getting crucial jobs done. What crucial jobs? Finding food and water, avoiding predators, achieving fertile copulation, caring for the young, training the young to cope effectively with the specific requirements of a given environment. In the case of man, we may go further and emphasize, as Julian Huxley has done, his increasing independence of and control over the environment, his growing ability to exploit a wide range of environmental opportunities.

Selection favors those populations whose members, on the whole, are organized effectively to accomplish these tasks. This is where emotion comes in. Let us consider for a moment the sexually aroused mature adult. We say readily enough he is quite emotional. By this, we usually mean that he feels strongly a particular kind of inner experience. From an observer's view, we can also say that in this state the likelihood of his achieving fertile copulation is greater than when he is not in this state. From an evolutionary viewpoint, we can further say that he now *wants* to do what the species needs to have done, whether he is aware of it or not. His emotion reflects a state of heightened motivation for a behavior pattern that is critical in species survival.

Thus, the emotion has several components: a subjective component, an action component, and a physiological component appropriate to the action. Emotion as usually considered emphasizes the subjective component—but this is in fact the subjective aspect of a motivational pattern. On the whole, these are motivational patterns that have had selective advantage over a very long time span. There is substantial genetic variability in every aspect of structure and behavior. Selection has operated on this variability, preserving those motivational-emotional patterns that have been effective in getting the tasks of survival done.

I want to add an important qualification here. I am *not* saying that emotional responses occur *only* in connection with behavior that facilitates reproductive success of *contemporary* human populations. For one thing, contribution of an individual to reproductive success of his species may be difficult to tease out in the very large and complex human societies of recent times. Some nonreproducers may contribute much to the reproductive success of the *species;* e.g., the many bachelors who have made contributions in disease prevention. Moreover, as every clinician knows, the human is quite capable of learning motivational-emotional patterns that are maladaptive by any reasonable standard.

Any mechanism—structure, function, or behavior—that is adaptive *on the average* for populations over *long time spans* has many exceptions, may be "fooled" by extraordinary environmental circumstances, and may even become largely maladaptive when there are radical changes in environmental conditions. When we consider the profound changes in human environmental conditions within *very recent* evolutionary times, it becomes entirely conceivable that some of the mechanisms which evolved over the millions of years of mammalian, primate, and human evolution may now be less useful than they once were. Since cultural change has moved much more rapidly than genetic change, the *emotional response tendencies* that have been built into us through their suitability for a long succession of past environments may be less suitable for the very different *present* environment. In this sense, there may be some respects in which modern man is obsolete; and this seems to me an important area for research in human biology.

In the remainder of this paper, I would like to illustrate this evolutionary concept by returning to the theme mentioned by MacLean early in this Symposium, i.e., the emotional experiences associated with interpersonal bonds—the feelings and actions referred to by terms such as attachment, affection, respect, and love. I believe this to be an important area for such illustration because these experiences were crucial in human evolution, are seriously neglected in behavioral and biological sciences, and have recently been clarified to a significant extent by research in several fields. The principal points I want to make are as follows: primates are group-living forms; the primate group is a powerful adaptive mechanism; emotional processes that facilitate interindividual bonds (participation in group living) have selective advantage; the formation of such bonds is pleasurable for primates; they are easy to learn and hard to forget; their disruption is unpleasant and precipitates profound psychophysiological changes that tend to restore close relations with others of the same species.

Since behavior, unlike physical structure, does not leave fossils, the behavior of early man must be reconstructed inferentially from a variety of sources. Some inferences regarding behavior can be drawn from the fossil record; as the richness of that record increases, which is in fact currently happening, such inferences will become increasingly dependable. Some inferences regarding behavior of early man, in its most general features, can be drawn from the study of living forms—the more complex nonhuman primates and the most primitive humans. In doing so, we must be cautious because: (a) the living nonhuman primates are not our direct ancestors—rather, the contemporary old-world primates and *Homo sapiens* has come from some common ancestor; (b) all the living humans are *Homo sapiens*, they have had some contact with European culture, and many of them have been driven into marginal subsistence areas by more technologically developed peoples. Nevertheless, they have something to teach us.

Sahlins has recently published a provocative analysis of the most rudimentary of documented human social systems, based on an extensive survey of available data. I have selected a few excerpts from his paper that are relevant to my main theme.

We include in our comparison the following primitive societies: Australian Aborigines, Tasmanians, Semang, Andamanese, Philippine and Congo pygmies, Bushmen, Eskimo, Great Basin Shoshoni, Naskapi, Ona and Yahgan. It is assumed that these societies parallel early cultural society in general features. This is simply an assumption of order and regularity. The technologies and low productivity of modern hunters and gatherers resemble the archeologically revealed productive systems of early cultures. Granting that a cultural social system is functionally related to its productive system, it follows that early human society resembles rudimentary, modern human society. This reasoning is supported by the large degree of social similarity among the present hunters and gatherers themselves, despite the fact that some of them are as historically distant from each other, as separated in contact and connection, as the paleolithic is separated from modern times. Further, simply because many food gatherers have been driven into marginal areas, they are not thereby disqualified from consideration. There still remain strong social resemblances between marginal peoples, such as Bushmen, Ona, and Eskimo, and those found in isolated, but otherwise not ecologically marginal areas, such as many Australian groups and the Andaman Islanders. . . .

Hunters and gatherers live in relatively open groups between which relations are usually friendly. . . . It is the kinship ethic of mutual aid that permits populations of hunters and gatherers to shift about according to the distribution of resources. Kinship is thus selectively advantageous in a zoological sense; it permits primitives to adjust to more variable habitats than subhuman primates. . . .

Given the division of labor by sex and the formation of domestic units through marriage, it follows that sharing food and other items, rather than being non-existent, as among monkeys and apes, is a *sine qua non* of the human condition. Food sharing is an outstanding functional criterion of man. In the domestic economy of the family there is constant reciprocity and pooling of resources. And, at the same time that kinship is extended throughout the band of families, so are the principles of the domestic economy. Among all hunters and gatherers there is a constant give and take of vital goods through hospitality and gift exchange. Everywhere, generosity is a great social virtue. Also general is the custom of pooling large game among the entire band, either as a matter of course, or in time of scarcity. Where kinship is extended beyond the local group by interband marriage, so are reciprocity and mutual aid. Goods may pass over great distances by a series of kinship transactions. Trade is thus established. Hunters and gatherers are able to take mutual advantage of the exploitation of distant environments, a phenomenon without parallel in the primate order.

Goldschmidt has quite recently published a stimulating work of synthesis on the evolution of human societies, drawing from diverse sources chiefly in the field of cultural anthropology. I wish to quote a few passages pertinent to the present discussion.

There is no reason to suppose that the earliest man had anything but a nomadic hunting and food-gathering system. In every major land area a few of these still exist. . . . The common and recurrent elements in their social system offer us the closest approximation to the earliest form of human social life that can be reconstructed on the basis of ethnographic data. . . .

The general characteristics of nomadic hunting and food-gathering societies are these: they are formed into bands of from twenty to fifty persons who camp together, share a territory which they protect from enemy invasion, and interact with other coequal bands inhabiting contiguous but separate territories. . . . The band is subdivided into families or hearth groups, a marital couple . . . and their immature and unmarried children. The individual family (or sometimes groups of closely related families) may split off into separate units under dire economic circumstances, but the band usually remains together throughout the year . . . most characteristically the band is the core of social unity and action. . . .

Values remain personal and direct. Where a population is close to subsistence, as is usually the case, the knowledge necessary for finding food, skill in hunting, and the requisite energy and industry to do so are likely to loom large.

[On the basis of his exhaustive review of the ethnographic evidence, Goldschmidt draws this important conclusion:] . . . man is by nature committed to social existence, and is therefore inevitably involved in the dilemma between serving his own interests and recognizing those of the group to which he belongs. Insofar as this dilemma can be resolved, it is resolved by the fact that man's self-interest can best be served through his commitment to his fellows. . . . *Need for positive affect* means that each person craves response from his human environment. It may be viewed as a hunger, not unlike that for food, but more generalized. Under varying conditions it may be expressed as a *desire for contact*, for *recognition* and *acceptance*, for *approval*, for *esteem*, or for *mastery*. . . . As we examine human behavior, we find that persons not only universally live in social systems, which is to say they are drawn together, but also *universally act in such ways as to attain the approval of their fellow men* [italics by Hamburg].

Margaret Mead has recently contributed an important paper on cultural determinants of behavior. She says:

. . . each cultural system which survives has to meet the same set of minimum requirements for maintenance and for survival. Each human language—highly diversified though languages appear to be—must be one which every normal member of the group can learn to speak; each culturally patterned dietary must provide for human growth; each family and community system must provide for the care of human children during their long dependency and for their education, must regulate the patterns of mating and of competition, and must pattern the behavior of members of the social group. As each variant of culture must meet the same basic requirements, cultural systems have a regularity which makes it possible for human beings, of whatever level of culture, to recognize and borrow from the cultural behavior of members of other cultural systems.

. . . only those cultural behaviors which are shared by every group of human beings are irreversible gains . . . these irreversible patterns would include language; the family (including a sexual and an age-graded division of labor); tool using; selective exploitation of the environment to provide food, shelter, and protection; the idea of a group organization which unites a group of families and determines their relationship to other like groups; some idea of the elaboration of ornamentation . . . and some system of relating man to the perceived universe.

Thus, the past few years have seen substantial progress in the integration of a great variety of observations on technologically primitive human populations. The available evidence strongly indicates that, throughout the long course of his evolution, man has been a group-living form—probably characterized by intense and persistent attachments between individuals within an organized, cohesive small society. Moreover, it is very likely that the human group, throughout the history of the species, has been a powerful problem-solving tool, coping with all sorts of harsh and taxing environmental contingencies. It has been an adaptive mechanism *par excellence.*

Another field of research that has a significant bearing on human evolution is the observation of behavior of the more complex nonhuman primates under natural conditions. The past few years have seen a burst of activity in this direction, with six species being carefully, systematically, and extensively observed under free-ranging conditions. These species are: baboon, gorilla, howler monkey, Indian langur, Japanese macaque, and rhesus macaque (the usual laboratory monkey). Most of the studies have not yet been reported in detail, but some important features are emerging.

The one fact that I wish to emphasize here is that all of these species are pre-eminently group-living forms. They do not come together in some minimal fashion that simply permits reproduction. They are not loosely associated herds. Rather they are intensely and persistently bound up with each other, living usually in cohesive troops, organized in a fairly complex way. Bourliere has recently made an extensive review of available field observations on social organization of primates including the most primitive ones. While field observations are very limited for many species, the evidence to date suggests that practically all living primate species are intensely and persistently group-living forms. Only a few of the most primitive Prosimians species may turn out to be exceptions. So far as the more highly developed primates are concerned, it seems clear enough that strong interanimal bonds are highly characteristic of them.

Washburn, from his extensive baboon observations, points out that the troop is a survival mechanism. The competence of the troop as a whole far exceeds that of any individual. For example, Washburn and DeVore put considerable emphasis on protection of the entire group by the powerful adult male baboon. DeVore says:

> Once a monkey group begins living on the ground, the much greater danger from predators would alone be sufficient to account for a more strictly organized social system, one which, e.g., placed a premium upon male specialization in group defense. . . . While observing free-ranging baboons, Washburn found that the adult males were continually solicitous of the wel-

fare of the young baboons, especially, e.g., when a troop was moving (a situation of more than usual danger) . . . the females with infants, not necessarily those in estrus, stayed nearest the protective, dominant males.

Altmann's observations of rhesus macaque and Carpenter's of howler monkeys also indicate the role of the adult males in policing the group internally as well as protecting it from outside danger.

All of this recent work—both the field observations of nonhuman primates and the synthesis of observations on preagricultural human groups—suggests that group living has conferred a powerful selective advantage upon more highly developed primates. This includes: (1) protection against predation; (2) obtaining food and water supply; (3) dealing with climatic problems; (4) coping with injury and illness; (5) facilitating reproduction, especially in care and training of the young. Indeed, it is likely that a wide range of adaptive functions have been facilitated by the evolution of primate social organization. The selective advantage of such organization must lie not only in the impressive extension of sensorimotor equipment which the group provides over that available to any individual, but also in the greatly increased possibilities for generating, storing, and mobilizing alternative coping strategies for dealing with a wide variety of environmental contingencies. The latter point seems to be particularly important in the case of early man.

Shultz has pointed out a high incidence of injury and illness among living primates in the wild. In this connection, one of Washburn and DeVore's baboon observations is especially pertinent:

> When the troop moves out on the daily round, *all* members must move with it, or be deserted. We have seen sick and wounded animals making great efforts to keep up with the troop, and finally falling behind. At least three of these were killed, and the only protection for a baboon is to stay with the troop, no matter how injured or sick. In wild primates injuries are common . . . and animals which are so sick that they can be spotted by a relatively distant human observer are frequent. For a wild primate, a fatal sickness is one which separates it from the troop.

This observation suggests one of the many ways in which selection pressure may have operated in favor of those individuals having strong motivation for group membership. In a situation such as the one described, those individuals having powerful attachment to others in the troop would be more likely to stay with the troop, in spite of the difficulty, and so be more likely to survive and pass their genes along to the next generation.

The adaptive function of primate groups should alert us to look for processes in the individual that facilitate the development of interindividual bonds. In seeking such processes, we may find useful guidance in the principle that *individuals seek and find gratifying those situations that have been highly advantageous in survival of the species.* That is, tasks that must be done (for species survival) tend to be quite pleasurable; they are easy to learn and hard to extinguish. Their blockage or deprivation leads to tension, anger, substitutive activity, and (if prolonged) depression. Such blockage is often accompanied by emergency-type physiological responses that support actions necessary to correct the situation. In the postinfancy human, a remarkable variety of coping behavior may be mobilized by such blockage or deprivation, determined in substantial part by cultural patterning.

In view of the extreme dependence on learning in the human species, such bonds would most likely be greatly strengthened through learning. Selection may operate on *differential readiness for learning responsiveness and attachment to others of the same species.*

Harlow's work gives us one important lead as to how the development of such motivational systems may be analyzed experimentally. He found that infant monkeys form attachment for an object that provides contact comfort. This attachment is very persistent—exceptionally difficult to extinguish. More recently, Harlow has shown that in the infant rhesus macaque, the clinging response even takes precedence over the postural righting reflex. When this fact is related to observations of macaques and baboons in the wild, its significance is clarified. When the troop moves, the mother moves, and the infant can only stay with the mother by clinging securely to her. There is no alternative: cling or perish. The mother's hands are not free to hold the baby; she must use them for locomotion. Those infants born with weak clinging responses do not get a chance to pass their genes along to the next generation.

This situation provides a nice illustration of the evolutionary concept of emotion I am trying to delineate. The monkey infant must cling to survive; apparently the infant likes to cling and forms attachment to an object that provides the opportunity for clinging; he wants to do what in fact he has had to do over the course of many generations.

But the human mother is practically hairless, and in any event the motor equipment of the human infant does not permit effective clinging. Yet the human infant is even less capable of fending for itself than monkey infants. How is this adaptive problem resolved? Simple—the mother must hold the baby: sometimes for long periods, under very difficult circumstances. In that event, the mother must *want* to hold the baby, must find pleasure in it, must seek out the opportunity, must experience some unpleasant feeling if she is deprived of the opportunity. This, in fact, turns out not to be so simple. It is a remarkable evolutionary achievement which, like so many other important phenomena, only seems simple when we take it for granted.

Since the mother's motivation for holding the child probably has so much adaptive significance, it is worth examining the factors that affect such motivation. There are several mother-infant transactions which probably serve to strengthen the motivational-emotional bond between the two. Among these transactions are: (1) close bodily contact; (2) nursing; (3) smiling; (4) stroking, patting; (5) rhythmic movement. All of these are situations in which most mothers in most human cultures find considerable pleasure. The likelihood is that some or all of these situations strengthen the mother's motivation to care for her infant. Indeed, it is reasonable to surmise that selection has favored infants whose behavior most effectively elicited caretaking motivational patterns in the mother. Those babies who evoke pleasure in the mother are more likely to survive under harsh conditions. Thus, future developmental research may find it profitable to analyze such transactions, seeking the characteristics in each of the participants that tend to strengthen the attachment of the other. This is one way in which an evolutionary view may suggest fresh observation and experiment in unanticipated directions.

Another side of the evolutionary coin may be stated in the principle that *individuals avoid and find distressing those situations that have been highly disadvantageous in species survival.* Applied to the specific issue of interindividual bonds, it seems reasonably clear that disruption of such bonds in primates is perceived as seriously threatening. It is usually felt as unpleasant and is often associated with emergency-type physiological responses. Such disruptive events usually mobilize coping behavior that tends toward restoration of strong bonds.

There is a great mass of human experience and clinical observation that bears on these questions, but I will limit myself here to mentioning briefly a few recent studies, carried out in a relatively systematic and critical way, that go a little beyond our previous impressions.

The classic investigations in this field are those having to do with the developmental consequences of mother-child separation in early childhood. Newer research has generally supported the earlier work indicating that prolonged mother-infant separation tends to produce damaging long-term aftereffects in intellectual, emotional, and social development. However, it has become clear that such effects are not a necessary result of separation; many factors have a bearing on the long-range outcome, one of the most important being the adequacy of substitute mothering during the period of separation. Further work is needed to clarify what constitutes adequacy of mothering under these circumstances.

For some years, psychoanalytic and psychosomatic observations have suggested that threat of separation and loss in deeply meaningful personal relationships is one important factor in precipitating depressive reactions; and that the problem of loss and grief may be one significant class of precipitating factors in psychosomatic disorders.

Significant work in this area has been going on during the past decade under the leadership of George Engel. A recent report from this group by Schmale has been especially intriguing. He carried out a systematic survey of the medical (not psychiatric or surgical) services in a university hospital and found a remarkably high incidence of major interpersonal separation and loss accompanied by feelings of helplessness and hopelessness—occurring shortly before onset of the symptoms leading to hospitalization. A variety of medical disorders were involved, not just the ones usually regarded as psychosomatic disorders. If this survey finding holds up when put to rigorous tests, it would have important implications for a wide gamut of medical problems.

Another line of recent research, in which I have been actively engaged for some years, has begun to work out the endocrine responses to disruption of personally crucial relationships. In the behavior-hormone investigations, one approach has involved the study of patients hospitalized because of profound depression, often following the disruption of a very important interpersonal bond. In such patients, there is now abundant evidence of substantial increase in adrenocortical activity over extended time periods—manifested by persistent elevation in plasma level and urinary excretion of 17-hydroxycorticosteroids. The extent of these elevations roughly parallels the severity of the clinical syndrome. Another approach has examined the effect of experimental probing interviews, chiefly concerned with jeopardy to respect and affection in close personal relationships, on emotional and adrenocortical responses. These interviews evoke transient, mild-to-moderate affective responses—principally anxiety, anger, and depression. In these experiments, a linear relation between intensity of emotional distress and tendency to hydrocortisone elevation has been demonstrated.

Three other adrenal hormones—all of great biological significance—have been similarly implicated in emotional responses to jeopardy in acceptance by significant other people. These are epinephrine, norepinephrine, and aldosterone. While the evidence is not as decisive as in the case of hydrocortisone, it is certainly suggestive that a similar linkage exists.

Thus, disruption of interindividual bonds may have profound consequences in carbohydrate, protein, fat, electrolyte, and water metabolism, and on crucial functions of the circulation. Such disruption is felt as deeply unpleasant, and an extraordinary variety of coping behavior patterns may be mobilized to restore acceptance, affection, and mutual respect. Perhaps serious threat to a key relationship may be as much emergency in psychophysiological terms as threat of attack by a predator.

Society is not composed of neutral actors but of emotional beings—whether we speak of baboons, chimpanzees, or man, emotion lies at the core of the social process. We fear for ourselves, a few loved ones, and the infants of the species. We are positively bound deeply by a few relations. Threat to these relations is equivalent to an attack on life itself. From the standpoint of the species, these are the critical relations for survival. The physiology of emotion insures the fundamental acts of survival: the desire for sex, the extraordinary interest in the infant, the day-to-day reinforcement of interindividual bonds.

From the standpoint of the individual, the greatest satisfaction and fulfillment come from relations with the biologically essential few. Even if we colonize a planet, the development of an infant there will depend on the presence of another person—a mother, to hold, to love, to give security, to train for the problems ahead. Conquest of the outer world does not free the species from the inner world which made its evolution possible. Social life is rooted in emotion and is basic to survival. A comprehensive human biology must surely take account of one of man's fundamental properties—his social nature.

26

WORLD POPULATION GROWTH: AN INTERNATIONAL DILEMMA

Harold F. Dorn

To control his numbers, man will soon be forced to choose between high mortality and low fertility. At the time the late Harold F. Dorn prepared the article that follows, he was chief of the Biometrics Research Branch, National Heart Institute, affiliated with the National Institute of Health, Bethesda, Maryland.

During all but the most recent years of the centuries of his existence man must have lived, reproduced, and died as other animals do. His increase in number was governed by the three great regulators of the increase of all species of plants and animals—predators, disease, and starvation—or, in terms more applicable to human populations—war, pestilence, and famine. One of the most significant developments for the future of mankind during the first half of the 20th century has been his increasing ability to control pestilence and famine. Although he has not freed himself entirely from the force of these two regulators of population increase, he has gained sufficient control of them so that they no longer effectively govern his increase in number.

Simultaneously he has developed methods of increasing the effectiveness of war as a regulator of population increase, to the extent that he almost certainly could quickly wipe out a large proportion, if not all, of the human race. At the same time he has learned how to separate sexual gratification from reproduction by means of contraception and telegenesis (that is, reproduction by artificial insemination, particularly with spermatozoa preserved for relatively long periods of time), so that he can regulate population increase by voluntary control of fertility. Truly it

(From *Science*, Vol. 135, January 1962, pages 283–290. By permission of the author and the publisher.)

can be said that man has the knowledge and the power to direct, at least in part, the course of his evolution.

This newly gained knowledge and power has not freed man from the inexorable effect of the biological laws that govern all living organisms. The evolutionary process has endowed most species with a reproductive potential that, unchecked, would overpopulate the entire globe within a few generations. It has been estimated that the tapeworm, *Taenia*, may lay 120,000 eggs per day; an adult cod can lay as many as 4 million eggs per year; a frog may produce 10,000 eggs per spawning. Human ovaries are thought to contain approximately 200,000 ova at puberty, while a single ejaculation of human semen may contain 200 million spermatozoa.

This excessive reproductive potential is kept in check for species other than man by interspecies competition in the struggle for existence, by disease, and by limitation of the available food supply. The fact that man has learned how to control, to a large extent, the operation of these biological checks upon unrestrained increase in number has not freed him from the necessity of substituting for them less harsh but equally effective checks. The demonstration of his ability to do this cannot be long delayed.

Only fragmentary data are available to indicate the past rate of growth of the population of the world. Even today, the number of inhabitants is known only approximately. Regular censuses of populations did not exist prior to 1800, although registers were maintained for small population groups prior to that time. As late as a century ago, around 1860, only about one-fifth of the estimated population of the world was covered by a census enumeration once in a 10-year period. The commonly accepted estimates of the population of the world prior to 1800 are only informed guesses. Nevertheless, it is possible to piece together a consistent series of estimates of the world's population during the past two centuries, supplemented by a few rough guesses of the number of persons alive at selected earlier periods. The most generally accepted estimates are presented in Figure 26–1.

These reveal a spectacular spurt during recent decades in the increase of the world's population that must be unparalleled during the preceding millennia of human existence. Furthermore, the rate of increase shows no sign of diminishing (Table 1). The period of time required for the population of the world to double has sharply decreased during the past three centuries and now is about 35 years.

Only a very rough approximation can be made of the length of time required for the population of the world to reach one-quarter of a billion persons, the estimated number at the beginning of the Christian era. The present subgroups of *Homo sapiens* may have existed for as long as 100,000 years. The exact date is not necessary, since for present purposes

TABLE 1

The number of years required to double the population of the world

YEAR (A.D.)	POPULATION (BILLIONS)	NUMBER OF YEARS TO DOUBLE
1	0.25 (?)	1650 (?)
1650	0.50	200
1850	1.1	80
1930	2.0	45
1975	4.0	35
2010	8.0*	?

* A projection of United Nations estimates.

the evidence is sufficient to indicate that probably 50,000 to 100,000 years were required for *Homo sapiens* to increase in number until he reached a global total of one-quarter of a billion persons. This number was reached approximately 2000 years ago.

By 1620, the year the Pilgrims landed on Plymouth Rock, the population of the world had doubled in number. Two hundred years later, shortly before the Civil War, another 500 million persons had been added.

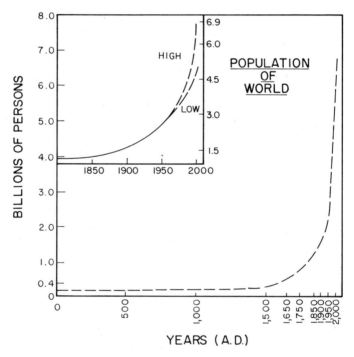

FIGURE 26–1—Estimated population of the world, A.D. 1 to A.D. 2000. (Adapted by Jacquelyn Hetrick.)

Since that time, additional half billions of persons have been added during increasingly shorter intervals of time. The sixth half billion, just added, required slightly less than 11 years, as compared to 200 years for the second half billion. The present rate of growth implies that only 6 to 7 years will be required to add the eighth half billion to the world's population. The change in rate of growth just described has taken place since the first settlers came to New England.

IMPLICATIONS

The accelerating rate of increase in the growth of the population of the world has come about so unobstrusively that most persons are unaware of its implications. There is a small group who are so aroused by this indifference that, like modern Paul Reveres, they attempt to awaken the public with cries of "the population bomb!" or "the population explosion!"

These persons are called alarmists by those who counter with the assertion that similar warnings, such as "standing-room only" and "mankind at the crossroads," have been issued periodically since Malthus wrote his essay on population, about 200 years ago. Nevertheless, says this group, the level of living and the health of the average person has continued to improve, and there is no reason to believe that advances in technology will not be able to make possible a slowly rising level of living for an increasing world population for the indefinite future. Furthermore, the rate of population increase almost certainly will slow down as the standard of education and living rises and as urbanization increases.

A third group of persons has attempted to estimate the maximum population that could be supported by the world's physical resources provided existing technological knowledge is fully utilized. Many of these calculations have been based on estimates of the quantity of food that could be produced and a hypothetical average daily calorie consumption per person.

As might be expected, the range of the various estimates of the maximum world population that could be supported without a lowering of the present level of living is very wide. Once of the lowest, 2.8 billion, made by Pearson and Harper in 1945 on the assumption of an Asiatic standard of consumption, already has been surpassed. Several others, ranging from 5 to 7 billion, almost certainly will be exceeded by the end of this century. Perhaps the most carefully prepared estimate as well as the largest—that of 50 billions, prepared by Harrison Brown—would be reached in about 150 years if the present rate of growth should continue.

I believe it is worth while to prepare estimates of the maximum population that can be supported and to revise these as new information becomes available, even though most of the estimates made in the past already have been, or soon will be, demonstrated to be incorrect (in most instances too small), since this constitutes a rational effort to comprehend the implications of the increase in population. At the same time it should be recognized that estimates of the world's carrying capacity made in this manner are rather unrealistic and are primarily useful only as very general guidelines.

In the first place, these calculations have assumed that the earth's resources and skills are a single reservoir available to all. In reality this is untrue. The U.S. government attempts to restrict production of certain agricultural crops by paying farmers not to grow them. Simultaneously, in Asia and Africa, large numbers of persons are inadequately fed and poorly clothed. Except in a very general sense there is no *world* population problem; there are population problems varying in nature and degree among the several nations of the world. No single solution is applicable to all.

Since the world is not a single political unity, the increases in production actually achieved during any period of time tend to be considerably less than those theoretically possible. Knowledge, technical skill, and capital are concentrated in areas with the highest level of living, whereas the most rapid increase in population is taking place in areas where such skills and capital are relatively scarce or practically nonexistent.

Just as the world is not a single unit from the point of view of needs and the availability of resources, skills and knowledge to meet these needs, so it also is not a single unit with respect to population increase. Due to political barriers that now exist throughout the entire world, overpopulation, however defined, will become a serious problem in specific countries long before it would be a world problem if there were no barriers to population redistribution. I shall return to this point later, after discussing briefly existing forecasts or projections of the total population of the world.

Most demographers believe that, under present conditions, the future population of areas such as countries or continents, or even of the entire world, cannot be predicted for more than a few decades with even a moderate degree of certainty. This represents a marked change from the view held by many only 30 years ago.

In 1930 a prominent demographer wrote, ''The population of the United States ten, twenty, even fifty years hence, can be predicted with a greater degree of assurance than any other economic or social fact, provided the immigration laws are unchanged.'' Nineteen years later, a well-known economist replied that ''it is disheartening to have to assert that the best population forecasts deserve little credence even for 5 years ahead, and none at all for 20–50 years ahead.''

Although both of these statements represent rather extreme views, they do indicate the change that has taken place during the past two decades in the attitude toward the reliability of population forecasts. Some of the reasons for this have been discussed in detail elsewhere and will not be repeated here.

It will be sufficient to point out that knowledge of methods of voluntarily controlling fertility now is so widespread, especially among persons of European ancestry, that sharp changes in the spacing, as well as in the number, of children born during the reproductive period may occur in a relatively short period of time. Furthermore, the birth rate may increase as well as decrease.

FORECASTING POPULATION GROWTH

The two principal methods that have been used in recent years to make population forecasts are (i) the extrapolation of mathematical curves fitted to the past trend of population increase and (ii) the projection of the population by the "component" or "analytical" method, based on specific hypotheses concerning the future trend in fertility, mortality, and migration.

The most frequently used mathematical function has been the logistic curve which was originally suggested by Verhulst in 1838 but which remained unnoticed until it was rediscovered by Pearl and Reed about 40 years ago. At first it was thought by some demographers that the logistic curve represented a rational law of population change. However, it has proved to be as unreliable as other methods of preparing population forecasts and is no longer regarded as having any unique value for estimating future population trends.

A recent illustration of the use of mathematical functions to project the future world population is the forecast prepared by von Foerster, Mora, and Amiot. In view of the comments that subsequently were published, . . . an extensive discussion of this . . . does not seem to be required. It will be sufficient to point out that this forecast probably will set a record, for the entire class of forecasts prepared by the use of mathematical functions, for the short length of time required to demonstrate its unreliability.

The method of projecting or forecasting population growth most frequently used by demographers, whenever the necessary data are available, is the "component" or "analytical" method. Separate estimates are prepared of the future trend of fertility, mortality, and migration. From the total population as distributed by age and sex on a specified date, the future population that would result from the hypothetical combination of fertility, mortality, and migration is computed. Usually, several estimates of the future population are prepared in order to include what the authors believe to be the most likely range of values.

Such estimates generally are claimed by their authors to be not forecasts of the most probable future population but merely indications of the population that would result from the hypothetical assumptions concerning the future trend in fertility, mortality, and migration. However, the projections of fertility, mortality, and migration usually are chosen to include what the authors believe will be the range of likely possibilities. This objective is achieved by making "high," "medium," and "low" assumptions concerning the future trend in population growth. Following the practice of most of the authors of such estimates, I shall refer to these numbers as population projections.

The most authoritative projections of the population of the world are those made by the United Nations (Table 2). Even though the most recent

TABLE 2

Estimated population of the world for A.D. *1900, 1950, 1975, and 2000*

| | ESTIMATED POPULATION (MILLIONS) | | PROJECTED FUTURE POPULATION (MILLIONS) | | | |
| | | | Low Assumptions | | High Assumptions | |
AREA	1900	1950	1975	2000	1975	2000
World	1550	2500	3590	4880	3860	6900
Africa	120	199	295	420	331	663
North America	81	168	232	274	240	326
Latin America	63	163	282	445	304	651
Asia	857	1380	2040	2890	2210	4250
Europe including U.S.S.R.	423	574	724	824	751	987
Oceania	6	13	20	27	21	30

of these projections were published in 1958 . . . it now seems likely that the population of the world will exceed the high projection before the year 2000. By the end of 1961 the world's population at least equaled the high projection for that date.

Although the United Nations' projections appear to be too conservative in that even the highest will be an underestimate of the population only 40 years from now, some of the numerical increases in population implied by these projections will create problems that may be beyond the ability of the nations involved to solve. For example, the estimated increase in the population of Asia from A.D. 1950 to 2000 will be roughly equal to the population of the entire world in 1958! The population of Latin America 40 years hence may very likely be four times that in 1950. The absolute increase in population in Latin America during the last half of the century may equal the total increase in the population of *Homo sapiens* during all the millennia from his origin until about 1650, when the first colonists were settling New England.

Increases in population of this magnitude stagger the imagination. Present trends indicate that they may be succeeded by even larger increases during comparable periods of time. The increase in the rate of growth of the world's population, shown by the data in Table 1, is still continuing. This rate is now estimated to be about 2 percent per year, sufficient to double the world's population every 35 years. It requires only very simple arithmetic to show that a continuation of this rate of growth for even 10 or 15 decades would result in an increase in population that would make the globe resemble an anthill.

But as was pointed out above, the world is not a single unit economically, politically, or demographically. Long before the population of the entire world reaches a size that could not be supported at current levels of living, the increase in population in specific nations and regions will give rise to problems that will affect the health and welfare of the rest of the world. The events of the past few years have graphically demonstrated the rapidity with which the political and economic problems of even a small and weak nation can directly affect the welfare of the largest and most powerful nations. Rather than speculate about the maximum population the world can support and the length of time before this number will be reached, it will be more instructive to examine the demographic changes that are taking place in different regions of the world and to comment briefly on their implications.

DECLINE IN MORTALITY

The major cause of the recent spurt in population increase is a worldwide decline in mortality. Although the birth rate increased in some countries—for example, the United States—during and after World War II, such increases have not been sufficiently widespread to account for more than a small part of the increase in the total population of the world. Moreover, the increase in population prior to World War II occurred in spite of a widespread decline in the birth rate among persons of European origin.

Accurate statistics do not exist, but the best available estimates suggest that the expectation of life at birth in Greece, Rome, Egypt, and the Eastern Mediterranean region probably did not exceed 30 years at the beginning of the Christian era. By 1900 it had increased to about 40 to 50 years in North America and in most countries of northwestern Europe. At present, it has reached 68 to 70 years in many of these countries.

By 1940, only a small minority of the world's population had achieved an expectation of life at birth comparable to that of the population of North America and northwest Europe. Most of the population of the world had an expectation of life no greater than that which prevailed in western Europe during the Middle Ages. Within the past two decades, the possibility of achieving a 20th-century death rate has been opened to these masses of the world's population. An indication of the result can be seen from the data in Figure 26–2.

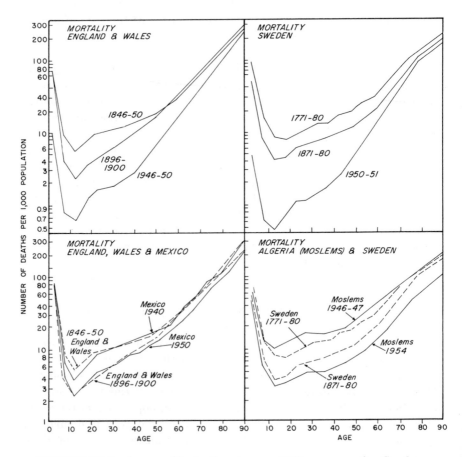

FIGURE 26–2—Age-specific death rates per 1000 per year for Sweden, England and Wales, Mexico, and the Moslem population of Algeria for various time periods from 1771 to 1954. (Adapted by Jacquelyn Hetrick.)

In 1940, the death rate in Mexico was similar to that in England and Wales nearly 100 years earlier. It decreased as much during the following decade as did the death rate in England and Wales during the 50-year period from 1850 to 1900.

In 1946–47 the death rate of the Moslem population of Algeria was higher than that of the population of Sweden in the period 1771–80, the earliest date for which reliable mortality statistics are available for an entire nation. During the following 8 years, the drop in the death rate in Algeria considerably exceeded that in Sweden during the century from 1771 to 1871.

The precipitous decline in mortality in Mexico and in the Moslem population of Algeria is illustrative of what has taken place during the past 15 years in Latin America, Africa, and Asia, where nearly three out of every four persons in the world now live. Throughout most of this area the birth rate has changed very little, remaining near a level of 40 per 1000 per year, as can be seen from Figure 26–3, which shows the birth rate, death rate, and rate of natural increase for selected countries.

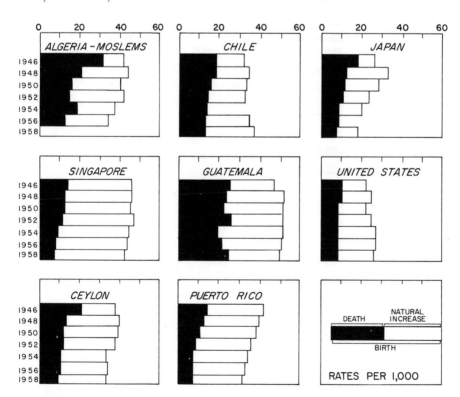

FIGURE 26–3—Birth rate, death rate, and rate of natural increase per 1000 for selected countries for the period 1946–1958. (Adapted by Jacquelyn Hetrick.)

Even in countries such as Puerto Rico and Japan where the birth rate has declined substantially, the rate of natural increase has changed very little, owing to the sharp decrease in mortality. A more typical situation is represented by Singapore, Ceylon, Guatemala, and Chile, where the crude rate of natural increase has risen. There has been a general tendency for death rates to decline universally and for high birth rates to remain high, with the result that those countries with the highest rates of increase are experiencing an acceleration in their rates of growth.

REGIONAL LEVELS

The absolute level of fertility and mortality and the effect of changes in them upon the increase of population in different regions of the world can be only approximately indicated. The United Nations estimates that only about 33 percent of the deaths and 42 percent of the births that

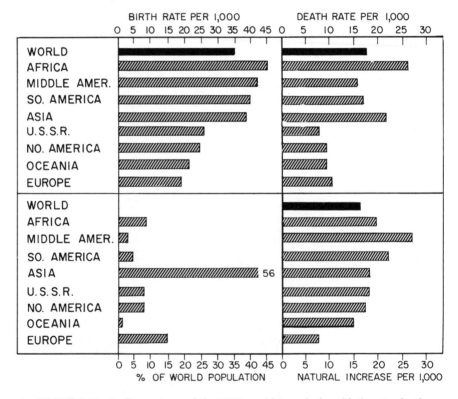

FIGURE 26–4—Percentage of the 1958 world population, birth rate, death rate, and rate of natural increase, per 1000, for the period 1954–1958 for various regions of the world. (Adapted by Jacquelyn Hetrick.)

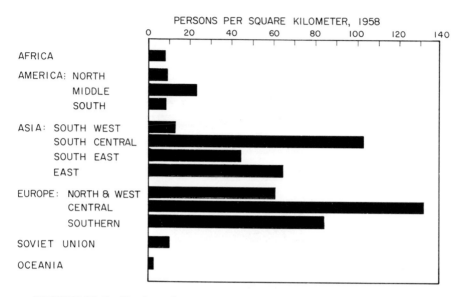

FIGURE 26–5—Number of persons per square kilometer in various regions of the world in 1958. (Adapted by Jacquelyn Hetrick.)

occur in the world are registered. The percentage registered ranges from about 8 to 10 percent in tropical and southern Africa and Eastern Asia to 98 to 100 percent in North America and Europe. Nevertheless, the statistical staff of the United Nations, by a judicious combination of the available fragmentary data, has been able to prepare estimates of fertility and mortality for different regions of the world that are generally accepted as a reasonably correct representation of the actual but unknown figures. The estimated birth rate, death rate, and crude rate of natural increase (the birth rate minus the death rate) for eight regions of the world for the period 1954–58 are shown in Figure 26–4.

The birth rates of the countries of Africa, Asia, Middle America, and South America average nearly 40 per 1000 and probably are as high as they were 500 to 1000 years ago. In the rest of the world—Europe, North America, Oceania, and the Soviet Union—the birth rate is slightly more than half as high, or about 20 to 25 per 1000. The death rate for the former regions, although still definitely higher, is rapidly approaching that for people of European origin, with the result that the highest rates of natural increase are found in the regions with the highest birth rates. The most rapid rate of population growth at present is taking place in Middle and South America, where the population will double about every 26 years if the present rate continues.

These regional differences in fertility and mortality are intensifying

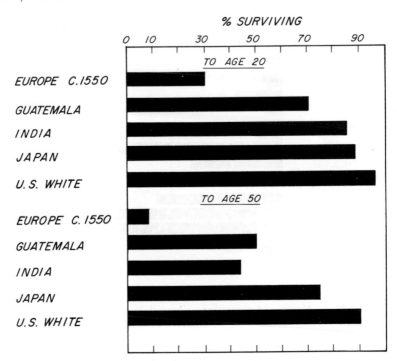

FIGURE 26–6—Percentage of newborn females who would survive to the end of the reproductive period according to mortality rates in Europe around A.D. 1500 and in selected countries around 1950. (Adapted by Jacquelyn Hetrick.)

the existing imbalance of population with land area and natural re-sources. No matter how this imbalance is measured, that it exists is readily apparent. Two rather crude measures are presented in Figures 26–4 and 26–5, which show the percentage distribution of the world's population living in each region and the number of persons per square kilometer.

An important effect of the decline in mortality rates often is overlooked —namely, the increase in effective fertility. An estimated 97 out of every 100 newborn white females subject to the mortality rates prevailing in the United States during 1950 would survive to age 20, slightly past the beginning of the usual childbearing age, and 91 would survive to the end of the childbearing period (Figure 26–6). These estimates are more than 3 and 11 times, respectively, the corresponding estimated proportions for white females that survived to these ages about four centuries ago.

In contrast, about 70 percent of the newborn females in Guatemala would survive to age 20, and only half would live to the end of the childbearing period if subject to the death rates prevailing in that country in 1950. If the death rate in Guatemala should fall to the level of that in

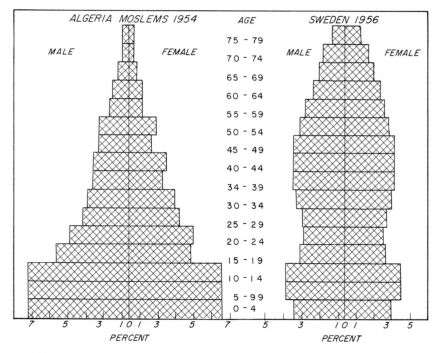

FIGURE 26-7—Percentage distribution by age of the population of Sweden in 1956 and the Moslem population of Algeria in 1954. (Adapted by Jacquelyn Hetrick.)

the United States in 1950—a realistic possibility—the number of new-born females who would survive to the beginning of the childbearing period would increase by 36 percent; the number surviving to the end of the childbearing period would increase by 85 percent. A corresponding decrease in the birth rate would be required to prevent this increase in survivorship from resulting in a rapid acceleration in the existing rate of population growth, which already is excessive. In other words, this decrease in the death rate would require a decrease in the birth rate of more than 40 percent merely to maintain the status quo.

As can be seen from Figure 26-3, the birth rate in countries with high fertility has shown little or no tendency to decrease in recent years. Japan is the exception. There, the birth rate dropped by 46 percent from 1948 to 1958—an amount more than enough to counter-balance the decrease in the death rate, with the result that there was a decrease in the absolute number of births. As yet there is very little evidence that other countries with a correspondingly high birth rate are likely to duplicate this in the near future.

Another effect of a rapid rate of natural increase is demonstrated by Figure 26–7. About 43 percent of the Moslem population of Algeria is under 15 years of age; the corresponding percentage in Sweden is 24, or slightly more than half this number. Percentages in the neighborhood of 40 percent are characteristic of the populations of the countries of Africa, Latin America, and Asia.

This high proportion of young people constitutes a huge fertility potential for 30 years into the future that can be counterbalanced only by a sharp decline in the birth rate, gives rise to serious educational problems, and causes a heavy drain on the capital formation that is necessary to improve the level of living of the entire population. A graphic illustration of this may be found in the recently published 5-year plan for India for 1961–66, which estimates that it will be necessary to provide educational facilities and teachers for 20 million additional children during this 5-year period.

HISTORICAL PATTERN IN WESTERN EUROPE

Some persons, although agreeing that the current rate of increase of the majority of the world's population cannot continue indefinitely without giving rise to grave political, social, and economic problems, point out that a similar situation existed in northwestern and central Europe during the 18th and 19th centuries. Increasing industrialization and urbanization, coupled with a rising standard of living, led to a decline in the birth rate, with a consequent drop in the rate of increase of the population. Why should not the rest of the world follow this pattern?

There is small likelihood that the two-thirds of the world's population which has not yet passed through the demographic revolution from high fertility and mortality rates to low fertility and mortality rates can repeat the history of western European peoples prior to the development of serious political and economic problems. A brief review of the circumstances that led to the virtual domination of the world at the end of the 19th century by persons of European origin will indicate some of the reasons for this opinion.

Around A.D. 1500 the population of Europe probably did not exceed 100 million persons (perhaps 15 to 20 percent of the population of the world) and occupied about 7 percent of the land area of the earth. Four hundred years later, around 1900, the descendants of this population numbered nearly 550 million, constituted about one-third of the world's population, and occupied or controlled five-sixths of the land area of the world. They had seized and peopled two great continents, North and

South America, and one smaller continent, Australia, with its adjacent islands; had partially peopled and entirely controlled a third great continent, Africa; and dominated southern Asia and the neighboring islands.

The English-, French-, and Spanish-speaking peoples were the leaders in this expansion, with lesser roles being played by the Dutch and Portuguese. The Belgians and Germans participated only toward the end of this period of expansion. Among these, the English-speaking people held the dominant position at the end of the era, around 1900.

The number of English-speaking persons around 1500, at the start of this period of expansion, is not known, but it probably did not exceed 4 or 5 million. By 1900 these people numbered about 129 million and occupied and controlled one-third of the land area of the earth and, with the non-English-speaking inhabitants of this territory, made up some 30 percent of the population of the world.

This period was characterized by an unprecedented increase in population, a several-fold expansion of the land base for this population, and a hitherto undreamed of multiplication of capital in the form of precious metals, goods, and commodities. Most important of all, the augmentation in capital and usable land took place more rapidly than the growth in population.

A situation equally favorable for a rapid improvement in the level of living associated with a sharp increase in population does not appear likely to arise for the people who now inhabit Latin America, Africa, and Asia. The last great frontier of the world has been closed. Although there are many thinly populated areas in the world, their existence is testimony to the fact that, until now, these have been regarded as undesirable living places. The expansion of population to the remaining open areas would require large expenditures of capital for irrigation, drainage, transportation facilities, control of insects and parasites, and other purposes—capital that the rapidly increasing populations which will need these areas do not possess.

In addition, this land is not freely available for settlement. The entire land surface of the world is crisscrossed by national boundaries. International migration now is controlled by political considerations; for the majority of the population of the world, migration, both in and out of a country, is restricted.

The horn of plenty, formerly filled with free natural resources, has been emptied. No rapid accumulation of capital in the form of precious metals, goods, and commodities, such as characterized the great 400-year boom enjoyed by the peoples of western-European origin, is possible for the people of Africa, Asia, and Latin America.

Last, but not least, is the sheer arithmetic of the current increase in population. The number of persons in the world is so large that even a small rate of natural increase will result in an almost astronomical increment over a period of time of infinitesimal duration compared to the duration of the past history of the human race. As was pointed out above, continuation of the present rate of increase would result in a population of 50 billion persons in another 150 years. A population of this magnitude is so foreign to our experience that it is difficult to comprehend its implications.

Just as Thomas Malthus, at the end of the 18th century, could not foresee the effect upon the peoples of western Europe of the exploration of the last great frontier of this earth, so we today cannot clearly foresee the final effect of an unprecedented rapid increase of population within closed frontiers. What seems to be least uncertain in a future full of uncertainty is that the demographic history of the next 400 years will not be like that of the past 400 years.

WORLD PROBLEM

The results of human reproduction are no longer solely the concern of the two individuals involved, or of the larger family, or even of the nation of which they are citizens. A stage has been reached in the demographic development of the world when the rate of human reproduction in any part of the globe may directly or indirectly affect the health and welfare of the rest of the human race. It is in this sense that there is a world population problem.

One or two illustrations may make this point more clear. During the past decade, six out of every ten persons added to the population of the world live in Asia; another two out of every ten live in Latin America and Africa. It seems inevitable that the breaking up of the world domination by northwest Europeans and their descendants, which already is well advanced, will continue, and that the center of power and influence will shift toward the demographic center of the world.

The present distribution of population increase enhances the existing imbalance between the distribution of the world's population and the distribution of wealth, available and utilized resources, and the use of nonhuman energy. Probably for the first time in human history there is a universal aspiration for a rapid improvement in the standard of living and a growing impatience with conditions that appear to stand in the way of its attainment. Millions of persons in Asia, Africa, and Latin America now are aware of the standard of living enjoyed by Europeans and North Americans. They are demanding the opportunity to attain the same standard, and they resist the idea that they must be permanently content with less.

A continuation of the present high rate of human multiplication will act as a brake on the already painfully slow improvement in the level of living, thus increasing political unrest and possibly bringing about eventual changes in government. As recent events have graphically demonstrated, such political changes may greatly affect the welfare of even the wealthiest nations.

The capital and technological skills that many of the nations of Africa, Asia, and Latin America require to produce enough food for a rapidly growing population and simultaneously to perceptibly raise per capita income exceed their existing national resources and ability. An immediate supply of capital in the amounts required is available only from the wealthier nations. The principle of public support for social welfare plans is now widely accepted in national affairs. The desirability of extending this principle to the international level for the primary purpose of supporting the economic development of the less advanced nations has not yet been generally accepted by the wealthier and more advanced countries. Even if this principle should be accepted, it is not as yet clear how long the wealthier nations would be willing to support the uncontrolled breeding of the populations receiving this assistance. The general acceptance of a foreign-aid program of the extent required by the countries with a rapidly growing population will only postpone for a few decades the inevitable reckoning with the results of uncontrolled human multiplication.

The future may witness a dramatic increase in man's ability to control his environment, provided he rapidly develops cultural substitutes for those harsh but effective governors of his high reproductive potential—disease and famine—that he has so recently learned to control. Man has been able to modify or control many natural phenomena, but he has not yet discovered how to evade the consequences of biological laws. No species has ever been able to multiply without limit. There are two biological checks upon a rapid increase in number—a high mortality and a low fertility. Unlike other biological organisms, man can choose which of these checks shall be applied, but one of them must be. Whether man can use his scientific knowledge to guide his future evolution more wisely than the blind forces of nature, only the future can reveal. The answer will not be long postponed.

SELECTED READINGS

Darwin, C. G., 1952, *The Next Million Years*. Garden City, N.Y.: Doubleday.

Lederberg, J., 1963, "Molecular Biology, Eugenics, and Euphenics," *Nature*, 198:428–429.

Teilhard de Chardin, P., 1959, *The Phenomenon of Man*. New York: Harper & Row.

Westergaard, Mogens, 1955, "Man's Responsibility to His Genetic Heritage," *Impact*, 6:63–88.

GLOSSARY

ACETABULUM—The socket of the ischium, in the pelvis, which receives the head of the femur, or thigh bone.

ALCHONDROPLASIA—A genetic affliction characterized by dwarfism.

ACTINIANS—Sea anemones.

ADRENALIN—The substance secreted by the adrenal glands when they are activated in a stress situation.

ADRENOCORTICAL—Pertaining to the hormones secreted by the cortical portion of the adrenal glands, which are part of the body's physiological adaptation to stress.

AGONISTIC—Aggressive or competitive.

ALBINISM—A trait determined by a recessive gene in which the individual's system is unable to produce melanin, or pigment.

ALCAPTONURIA—A trait determined by a recessive gene in which the patient's system is unable to oxidize a certain chemical product of metabolism which accordingly shows up in the urine.

ALLELE (ALLELOMORPH)—When a gene occurs in two or more variant chemical forms, the variants are said to be allelic to one another.

ALLELIC GENES—Genes occurring in more than one form.

ALLOMETRIC CHANGES—Changes in the size of a part of the body in accordance with standard proportions to other parts.

ALLOPATRIC—An allopatric population (or species) is one that is geographically distinct from another population (or species).

ANTHROPOID—Pertaining to the suborder Anthropoidea, made up of the monkeys, the apes, and human beings.

ANTHROPOMORPHISM—Ascribing to animals the motives and behavioral drives of humans.

ANTIGEN—A foreign protein that, upon introduction into the body, elicits the production by the body of a specific antibody that will neutralize or destroy it. The antigen-antibody response occurs in transfusions where bloods are incompatible with one or another of the hereditary blood factors.

ARBOREAL—Tree-living.

ARCHANTHROPINE—Collectively, the earliest hominids.

ARCHETYPAL—Original, far removed in time.

ARCUS SUPERCILIARES—Supraorbital ridges or bony growths above the eye sockets.

ARTHROPODS—The phylum of animals possessing jointed external "skeletons," such as insects.

ARTIFACTS—General word for tools and weapons uncovered in archeological excavation.

ATAVISTIC—Possessing characteristics of an earlier form.

BINOMEN—The taxonomic two-part name assigned to every species. The first word denotes the genus, and the second the species, for example, *Homo sapiens.*

BIPEDALISM—Two-legged; erect posture and locomotion characteristic of the hominids.

BOVIDS—Cattle, sheep, and goats, as well as the wild forms from which the domesticated forms are descended.

BRACHIATION—A general term covering the means of arm-over-arm tree-swinging that characterizes the gibbons and the apes.

BRACHYDACTYLY—A genetic affliction characterized by abnormally short fingers or toes.

BRECCHIA-MATES—Fossils found in association in the same deposit.

BUCCAL FACE—The outward aspect of a tooth, that is the surface nearest the cheek.

CALOTTE—"Skull cap"—that is, top of the skull without temporal bones, face, occipit, or jaws.

CALVARIA—A skull without face or lower jaw.

CARNIVOROUS—Meat-eating.

CAROTENOIDS—Yellow to deep red pigment substances found in animal and plant tissues.

CEBOIDEA—Platyrrhine monkeys of the New World.

CENOZOIC ERA—The Age of Mammals; a geologic era lasting from about 75 million years ago to the present.

CERCOPITHECIDAE—The family of monkeys within the Primate order that includes the macaques, the baboons, mandrills, and drills, as well as colobus or leaf-eating monkeys.

CHACMA—A species of large ground-living baboons found in Africa.

CHELIPEDS—Animals with pincer-like legs.

CHELLEO-ACHEULIAN—Pertaining to the transition from Lower to Middle Paleolithic stone-making industries.

CHOUKOUTIEN—Locality near Peking in China where important hominid fossil discoveries have been made of *Homo erectus* and Upper Pleistocene sapiens man.

CHROMATOGRAPHY—Process that permits the physical separation of chemical entities for analysis.

CLACTONIAN—Lower Paleolithic flake industries dating from the Middle Pleistocene.

CLINE—A graded series of gene frequencies in a territory.

COATI—A racoon-like mammal of the New World.

COLOBUS—Leaf-eating monkey with stomach pouches belonging, along with the baboons, macaques, drills, and mandrills, to the family Cercopithecidae.

COMBE-CAPELLE—Upper Pleistocene *Homo sapiens* fossils from Western Europe.

COMMENSALISM—A form of animal social behavior characterized by close association.

CRETACEOUS—The concluding period of the Mesozoic, about 135 million years ago, which saw the climax of the dinosaurs and their extinction.

CYTOLOGY—The scientific study of cell structure and cell activity.

DEME—A Mendelian population; the smallest effective breeding population within a species.

DEMOGRAPHY—Sociological study of a human population and of human population dynamics (changes in death rates, birth rates, and so forth).

DIASTEMA (pl., DIASTEMATA)—A gap between the teeth.

DIMORPHISM—"Two-formed-ness," as in sexual dimorphism, the characteristic of pronounced differences in size between males and females of the same species.

DIPLOID CELL—A cell containing the full number of pairs of chromosomes.

DM_1—First deciduous molar; one of the milk teeth.

DRILL—A species of baboon-like, cheek-pouched cercopithecine monkeys found in Africa.

DYSFUNCTION—Breakdown or interruption of function; poor operation.

ECOLOGY—The study of the interrelationships of animal and plant populations with each other and with their physical environment.

ECOTONES—Areas where two different kinds of population compete for dominance.

ELECTROPHORESIS—Separating different kinds of body protein molecules electrically.

ELEPHAS MERIDIONALIS (or *E. MERIDIONALIS*)—European Pleistocene elephant.

ELEPHAS PLANIFRONS (or *E. PLANIFRONS*)—Asian Pleistocene elephant.

ENCEPHALATED—Controlled by the brain cortex.

ENDOCRINE GLANDS—Ductless glands such as the thyroid, the adrenal, the pituitary, and others that release substances vital for the functioning of the body.

ENZYMATIC POLYMORPHISM—The maintenance of genetic differences among members of a population in regard to enzyme production.

EOCENE—A period of the early Cenozoic era, approximately 50 million years ago.

EOHIPPUS—A small horselike animal of Eocene times, known from fossils. Probably ancestral to modern horses.

ESTRUS—The period of sexual receptivity (coinciding with ovulation) of females in many mammal groups.

ETHOLOGY—The science of animal behavior.

ETIOLOGY—The study of the causes underlying, or the conditions leading to, the appearance of a disease or its symptoms.

EUHOMINID—Pertaining to forms of "true man" such as *Homo erectus* or *Homo sapiens,* as distinguished from protohominids such as the australopithecines.

EXOGAMY—The practice of selecting a mate from a social group different from one's own.

EXTRASOMATIC—Nonbiological.

FAVISM—A genetic enzyme deficiency causing severe reactions to certain chemicals. The gene that causes it may provide some resistance to malaria.

FERAL—Having reverted to the wild state after domestication.

FOVEA—Central depression in the retina with a single layer of cones and lacking blood vessels; the area of greatest visual acuity.

GALLS—Plant growths produced by the attack of parasites or other injury to plants.

GAMETES—Sex cells; male sperm or female ova.

GENOTYPE—Genetic constitution; the heredity of an individual.

GENUS (pl., GENERA)— A taxon that includes a number of related species.

GRIMALDI—Upper Pleistocene *Homo sapiens* fossils from western Europe.

HALLUX—The big toe.

HETEROZYGOTE—Possessing two unlike alleles of a gene.

HOMINOIDEA—The superfamily consisting of the Pongidae (apes) and the Hominidae (man).

HEMOLYTIC ANEMIA— A disease characterized by deficiency of hemoglobin in the blood due to the breakdown of red corpuscles.

HOMO SAPIENS—The species to which all modern human populations, as well as Upper Pleistocene hominid populations, are assigned.

HOMOZYGOUS—Possessing two identical alleles of a gene on a pair of chromosomes.

HUMICOLOUS FAUNAS—Ground- or earth-living animal populations.

HYDROXYCORTICOSTEROIDS—The hormones secreted by the adrenal glands.

HYPOPLASIA—Arrested development; failure to attain full size or growth.

IMMUNOCHEMICAL—Referring to the physiology of immunity and the study of chemical compatibility and incompatibility.

INTERCALARY—Intervening, added, or extra.

INVERTEBRATES—Animals without segmented backbones.

ISCHIUM—The lower margin of the pelvic girdle.

LEMURS—Prosimians or lower nonmonkey-ape-man members of the order of primates.

M^1—First molar.

MACA NEMESTRINA—Large monkey of the cheek-pouched cercopithecine subfamily, related to the baboons.

MACROEVOLUTION—Large-scale, long-term evolution resulting in the differentiation of large taxonomic categories such as genera, families, and orders.

MANDIBLE—Lower jaw.

MANDIBULAR SYMPHYSIS—The thickened area on the outer frontal surface of the mandible, or lower jaw, where the two halves of the jaw join.

MANDRILL—A species of baboon-like, cheek-pouched cercopithecine monkey found in Africa.

MARSUPIALS—The pouched mammals, such as the opossum and the kangaroo, which do not form a placenta.

MASSETER—Muscle that controls jaw movement.

MEDULLATED—Nerve fibers having a myelin sheath.

MEGADONT—"Large-toothed."

MEGANTHROPUS—"Giant man," a fossil jaw fragment recovered in 1940–1941 in Java by von Koenigswald, and assigned variously to the australopithecines, *Homo erectus,* and *Homo habilis.*

METACONID—The rear cusp on the crown of a molar tooth.

MILLENNIUM (pl., MILLENNIA)—Thousand-year period.

MIOCENE—Period of geological time approximately 15 million years ago, characterized by a diversification of primates.

MONOTYPIC—A species characterized by a minimum of genetic diversity among the individuals that compose it.

MORBIDITY—Disease.

MORIBUNDITY—State of dying or being near death.

MORPHOLOGICAL—Pertaining to animal structure and form. A morphological study of a fossil includes the analysis of bones, muscles, and other anatomical features.

MOSAIC EVOLUTION—Asymmetrical evolution, or the evolution of different parts of a system at different rates.

MOUSTERIAN—Upper Paleolithic tools commonly associated with fossils of Neanderthal man.

MULTIALLELIC—Characterized by several alleles of a gene.

MUSTELID—Pertaining to the weasels, skunks, otters, and other members of the Mustelidae.

MUTATION—A term that covers the processes resulting in the appearance of new hereditary characteristics.

MYELIN—The sheath material that surrounds the axillary part of nerve fibers.

NEANDERTHAL—A name used to identify a number of European fossils of the Upper Pleistocene. Generally distinguished from "sapiens man" by larger eye orbits, thicker occipital bone, and lower frontal bone.

NEOPALLIUM—The frontal areas of the cerebral cortex controlling coordination of fine movements of the hands.

NEXUS—Tie, or link.

NUCHAL MUSCLE—One of the muscles attached to the nuchal area at the rear base of the skull.

OCCIPITAL TORUS—The thick bony "bun" at the rear of the skull that characterizes many of the Neanderthal fossil skulls.

OCCIPUT—The rear base bone of the skull.

OLIGOCENE—Geologic epoch of the Middle Tertiary period, about 36 million years ago. This epoch saw the rise of most modern mammal genera.

OMNIVORES—Animals whose diet may consist of both plant and animal materials.

ONTOGENY—The development of the individual from conception to maturity.

ORTHOGENESIS—Apparent evolution toward some climax form.

ORTHOGNATHOUS—Straight-faced, as modern man is, in contrast to the protruding angular faces of the apes.

OSSEOUS ONTOGENY—The development in the individual life cycle of bone and bone formations.

OSTEODONTOKERATIC CULTURE—Assemblages of "tools" consisting of shaped long bones of ungulate animals, as well as other animal bones assigned to the australopithecines, are termed "osteodontokeratic" by some investigators. Not all authorities agree that the bone fragments were actually tools.

OSTEOLOGICAL—Referring to bones or skeleton.

PALEANTHROPUS—Early nonsapiens homonids collectively.

PALEOANTHROPOLOGY—The specialty within anthropology that investigates human evolution through the study of the hominid fossil record.

PALEOCENE—The earliest period of the Cenozoic era, approximately 75 million years ago.

PALEONTOLOGY—The scientific study of fossils.

PAPIO—The genus to which baboons, mandrills, and drills belong.

PARABOLIC—Shaped like a parabola or an arc; bow-shaped.

PASSERINE BIRDS—Songbirds of perching habits.

PEKING MAN.—Chinese fossil of *Homo erectus.*

PEPTIDE—Combination of amino acids.

PHENOTYPE—The structural or behavioral expression of the genotype.

PHYLETIC—Evolutionary transformation of a sequence of populations without extinction.

PHYLOGENESIS—Origin, descent, and evolutionary succession.

PHYLOGENY—Evolutionary history.

PITHECANTHROPUS (also PITHECANTHROPUS ROBUSTUS and PITHE-CANTHROPUS ERECTUS)—Fossils of *Homo erectus,* from Java, approximately half a million years old.

PLACENTAL MAMMALS—Mammals that form a special structure through which the developing embryo receives nutrients and eliminates wastes.

PLASMODIUM ORGANISM OF FALCIPARUM MALARIA—A microorganism that causes malaria.

PLATYPUS—One of the monotremes, or egg-laying mammals.

PLIOCENE—The geologic period immediately preceding the Pleistocene; approximately 2 to 12 million years ago.

POLYGENES—Different multiple genes; genes at different loci that act in concert to determine a trait, any one of which may be shown to make only a small contribution to the phenotype. Human skin pigmentation is an example of a trait determined by polygenes.

POLYMORPHISMS—The maintenance by natural selection of genetic differences with regard to a given trait in a population.

POLYPEPTIDE—Nonprotein combination of amino acids.

POLYTYPIC—A species that is widely distributed in space and is characterized by considerable genetic diversity among the populations that compose it.

PONGIDS—The family of apes including the chimpanzees, gorillas, and orang-utans as well as the subfamily of gibbons.

POPULATIONAL MODEL—The evolutionary concept of variable populations evolving into other populations, rather than of types evolving.

POSTCRANIAL SKELETON—The parts of the skeleton excluding the cranium or skull.

POTTOS—One of the prosimians or lower nonmonkey-ape-man members of the order of primates.

PRECIPITIN—An antibody produced in the blood serum by injection of an antigen.

PREDACEOUS—Living by preying upon other animals.

PREHOMININE—Prehuman.

PRESBYTIS ENTELLUS—Langur monkey of India.

PRIMATOLOGIST—A specialist in the study of primates.

PROSIMIANS—The lower primates outside the suborder Anthropoidea only distantly related to man.

PROTOCONID—The middle cusp on the crown of a molar tooth.

PROTOMEN—Original, earliest hominids.

PTERYGOID—Muscle attached to the lower jaw at the condyle ends.

PTERYGO-PALATINE COMPLEX—The complex of bone formation involving the lower temporal and palatal zones.

QUADRUPEDAL—Four-footed locomotion (in contrast to bipedal or two-footed hominid locomotion).

RAMUS—The side portion of the mandible, or lower jaw.

RHIZOMES—Underground rootlike stems.

RISS-WÜRM INTERGLACIAL—The period between the Riss and the Würm glaciations (lasting approximately 70,000 years) often referred to as the Third Interglacial.

SAGITTAL CREST—Thickened ridge of bone running sagittally, or in the middle, from front to rear on the skull, as in the gorilla.

SALTATIONS—"Leaps," or large-scale genetic mutations.

SAPIENS SAPIENS—The subspecies to which all modern humans and all non-Neanderthal hominids of the Upper Pleistocene are assigned.

SAVANNA—Tropical grasslands with a water supply insufficient to permit forest growth. Grazing animals and predators are characteristic of the fauna in these areas.

SCALA NATURA—The ladder of nature, or chain of being. The arrangement or hierarchy of living things from the simplest to the most complex.

SCAPULA—Shoulder blade.

SEBACEOUS GLANDS—Skin glands secreting a fatty substance, sebum.

SENSORIMOTOR—Pertaining to nervous and muscular responses induced by outer stimuli.

SENSU LATO—In the widest or most general sense (of a term).

SENSU STRICTO—In the narrow or strict sense (of a term).

SEROLOGICAL—Referring to the physiology of the blood. The study of the human blood types is an aspect of serology.

SICKLER—An individual whose blood demonstrates the presence of sickle-shaped red cells.

SIMIAN—Monkey- or ape-like.

SIMIAN SHELF—A thick strap of bone on the inner base of the lower jaw, or mandible. It is found in most pongids and also occasionally in early hominid fossils.

SIMOPITHECUS—Baboon-like fossil cercopithecoid monkey of the Upper Pliocene and Lower Pleistocene.

SOLO MAN—An Upper Pleistocene fossil from Indonesia, known from fragmentary skull material.

STADIAL—A period of maximum extension of glacial ice.

SUPRAORBITAL TORUS—A thick bar of bone projecting visor-like over the eye orbits. Found in hominid fossils (compare Broken Hill, Peking, as well as pongids, such as the gorilla).

SYMPATRIC—Populations inhabiting different ecological niches in the same zone or territory.

SYMPHYSIAL—Referring to a symphysis or thickened area where two bony structures join in the course of development.

SYNCHRONOUS—Occurring at the same time.

TARSIERS—Prosimians or lower nonmonkey-ape-man members of the order of primates.

TARSUS—The bony heel.

TAXON (pl., TAXA)—Any · zoological or botanical category, such as genus, family, and order.

TEMPORALIS—Muscle sheet running across the temporal bone area of the skull.

TERTIARY—The subdivision of geologic time that includes the Cenozoic, or Age of Mammals, up to Pleistocene (approximately 2 to 75 million years ago).

THALASSEMIA—A kind of anemia found primarily among populations of the Mediterranean region.

TRANSFERRINS—Blood proteins that may be significant in maintaining body resistance against infection.

TREE SHREWS—The prosimians or lower nonmonkey-ape-man members of the order of primates.

TRICONID CREST—A thickening on the chewing surface of a molar between cusps.

TYPOLOGICAL MODELS—An obsolescent point of view that regards evolution as dependent on the concept of *types* of organisms evolving from one to another. (See population model.)

ULNA (adj., ULNAR)—The inner of the two bones comprising the forearm.

UNGULATES—Herbivorous mammals such as deer, sheep, and goats.

VERVET—Small African monkey.

VITILIGINOUS—Pertaining to leukoderma, a skin disease characterized by irregular patchy pigmentation.

WÜRM—The fourth or final glacial phase of the Pleistocene lasting from approximately 20,000 to 120,000 years ago.

ZYGOMATIC PROCESS OF THE MAXILLA—The area where the cheekbone fuses with the upper jaw.

ZYGOTE—An ovum that has been fertilized by a sperm.

INDEX

457